KAMCHATKA

AIGA

STANOVOY MTS.

Lake Baykal

Amur R.

MTS.

GOBI DESERT

Peking

Huang (Yellow) R.

JAPAN

Tokyo

TROPIC OF CANCER

PACIFIC OCEAN

Yangtze R.

OF TIBET

TAIWAN

YAS

ges R.

Calcutta

Irrawaddy R.

HAINAN

SOUTH CHINA SEA

Manila

PHILIPPINE

ISLANDS

Mekong R.

Bangkok

Saigon

BAY OF BENGAL

Singapore

BORNEO

CELEBES

SUMATRA

EYLON

EQUATOR

JAVA

ASIA

Photographs by

Emil Schulthess

E. P. Gee

Walter Ferguson

F. G. H. Allen

E. Hanumantha Rao

J. Allan Cash

Michael Fogden

Tokumitsu Iwago

A. G. Bannikov

Max Hemple

M. Krishnan

and others

Maps drawn by Kenneth Thompson

A Chanticleer Press Edition

The Continents We Live On

ASIA

A NATURAL HISTORY

Pierre Pfeffer

Random House · New York

To my friend Ou Kim San,

devoted ornithologist and great conservationist,

I dedicate this book in fond recollection

of our tours through the forests of Cambodia.

Planned and produced by Chanticleer Press, New York

Manufactured by Conzett & Huber in Zurich, Switzerland

Library of Congress Catalog Card Number 68–28330

Contents

Foreword

I write the last lines of this book—since one almost always writes a preface last—from the veranda of a hut in Tuk Sap, in southwestern Cambodia. The hut is in the midst of a forest which is still beautiful although the woodcutters have begun to make inroads into it. Large hornbills, their big beaks topped with grotesque casques, fly noisily overhead, trumpeting nasally. A small lizard, a flying dragon, in a patch of sunlight on a nearby tree trunk, opens and closes its wings in a nuptial dance in front of its mate. At sunrise and sunset, the forest echoes with the wailing of gibbons and the resonant calls of a host of birds—bulbuls, barbets, titmice. Morning and evening, a small red squirrel circles around the clearing, always following exactly the same track among the branches.

This blessed corner is one of the last peaceful havens of southeast Asia. I can talk about it and other regions that I have been fortunate enought to visit; but who can boast that he has seen all of Asia with his own eyes? A single lifetime would not be long enough for that, especially since man has everywhere added barriers to the countless natural obstacles. From this point of view, it is no exaggeration to say that Asia is the most secret continent, more impenetrable today than it was seven centuries ago in the time of Marco Polo. Then, in spite of many dangers, caravans circulated freely from Persia to northern China. The slow, months-long crossing of the continent at camel's gait gave travelers a chance to observe the land and its inhabitants, plants and animals. The accounts of some of the Chinese, Persian and European merchant-explorers that have filtered down to us form a documentary treasure. Today, most of Asia is crisscrossed by hermetically sealed frontiers and the rest, the most beautiful part, is ravaged by devastating wars or shaken by violent political upheavals that hinder the movement of innocent naturalists.

Moreover, one talks well only of what one knows well. The ideal preparation for this book would have been to cross all Asia in zigzag journeys. But Asia's immense size and the obstacles cited above made such a journey unrealizable. I consider myself lucky to have been able to devote the last twelve years to long stays in India, Indochina, Malaysia and Indonesia. A trip to the Soviet Union enabled me to cross Central Asia as far as the Chinese Tien Shan frontier.

Finally, for the purposes of this book, and with the help of Chanticleer Press, I visited northern and southern China. For regions I have been unable to visit personally, I have had recourse to the writings of other travelers, some of them invaluable.

It is, moreover, a pleasant task to express my gratitude to friends and colleagues who have assisted me and to officials who welcomed me in foreign lands and facilitated my travels. I am especially indebted to Professors A. G. Bannikov, A. N. Formozov, and A. G. Démentiev, Doctors I. I. Sokolov and I. S. Kirikov in the Soviet Union; His Excellency M. L. Paye, Messrs. J. Richard, Christian Amalric, and the directors of the Academia Sinica in Peking; Mr. G. Munro of Calcutta and the officers of the Forestry Department in Assam, Bengal and Madya Pradesh; Messrs. Tan Kim Huon, Director of Forests and Waterways, Ou Kim San, Hunting Director and Cabinet Chief in the Ministry of Agriculture, Chnong Saudi, Governor of Kirirum Province, and all my forester friends in Cambodia; Dr. Ivan Polunin of the University of Malaya, Singapore; Dr. Sampurno Kadarsan, Director of the Zoological Museum of Bogor; Messrs. Hassan Basjaroedin, Made Taman and Walman Sinaga of the Natural Conservation Service, as well as the staffs of the French Embassy and the French Cultural Center and the many experts in the French Public Works in Indonesia. Although it is doubtful that these lines will ever be seen by them, I cannot neglect mentioning all the villagers, hunters and trappers who, from the Himalayan hills to the Sunda Islands, received me into their communities and initiated me into the life of the forest and its animals.

I also cannot forget the assistance given me in France by Prof. F. Bourlière, who read the manuscript of this book and offered suggestions, and by my colleagues and friends at the Muséum d'Histoire Naturelle de Paris, particularly Dr. F. Petter, Assistant Director, and Madame H. Genest, Assistant, who undertook countless tasks that would have normally been mine had I not been away. Dr. H. Saint-Girons, Research Director of the C.N.R.S. and my delightful companion on the trip to Cambodia, has made useful suggestions for the introduction to this book.

I am, finally, happy to express all my thanks to Chanticleer Press, especially to the publisher, Mr. Paul Steiner, and the editors, Mr. Milton Rugoff and Miss Dori Watson. I want also to thank Mrs. Matila Simon for her faithful translation from the French.

As for the book itself, readers may perhaps be surprised that I have given as much space to the area north of the Himalayas as to tropical Asia, which represents only a small portion of the continent. The reason for this is that the first is a succession of vast natural zones that are homogeneous throughout and require no detailed regional descriptions. In addition, these zones continue into Europe and North America and are thus relatively familiar to many readers. On the other hand, tropical Asia is the strangest and least-known section of the continent. Its natural environments are also richest in both plants and animals.

It should be added that the Latin name of an animal or plant is given when the species is first mentioned. It is sometimes repeated further on in the text to indicate that the same species is being cited.

PIERRE PFEFFER

7

Asia: The Immeasurable Land

Although we learned in school that Asia is one of the five continents, this terminology is merely a convenient label since there is no separate Asiatic continent. What we call Asia is separated from Europe only by the low barrier of the Ural Mountains, from America by the narrow and geologically recent Bering Strait, and was joined to Africa until the mid-nineteenth century by a narrow strip of land, now cut by the Suez Canal.

But Asia is actually more than a continent. It is a separate world where everything is proportionate to its immense size. Stretching from the shore of the icy Arctic Ocean to the warm waters of the Indian Ocean, from the Mediterranean to the Pacific, the earth's largest landmass—16,900,000 square miles in contrast to 15,240,000 for North and South America together and 11,500,000 for Africa—possesses the highest mountains, the vastest deserts, the widest stretches of forests and steppes, the most desolate tundras, the deepest lakes and several of the longest rivers in the world. If geographers and naturalists consider this mosaic of natural regions an entity, it is because it has such unusual characteristics in its topography, its climate, and its botanical and zoological elements, and its human inhabitants. One might apply to the whole of Asia the motto of Indonesia, itself made up of very diverse geographic elements: *Bhinneka tunggal ika,* "Unity in diversity." For the tundra strewn with stunted bushes, the coniferous taiga, the grassy steppe, the bamboo thickets and the tropical jungle are typically Asiatic formations whose vernacular names have been universally adopted and extended to more or less similar plant combinations on the other continents. Among animals, the tiger, the orangutan, the gibbon, the giant panda, the yak, the water buffalo, the one-horned rhinoceros and the saiga antelope, to name only the best-known, are strictly Asiatic

With fourteen peaks soaring higher than 26,000 feet, the Himalayas, Pamirs and Karakorams (right) constitute the greatest geographic and climatic barrier in the world. (George I. Bell)

8

forms. Even the human species subdivides into a special Asiatic type.

There is thus a certain unity among the apparently different elements that compose Asia. This unity stems less from physical geography than from biogeography, that is, the botanical and zoological relationships among various areas of the globe. The naturalist who wishes to discuss Asia must approach the continent from this point of view, although the task is not simple that way either.

While Africa, the Americas, Europe and Australia present well-defined natural zones in more or less regular succession from north to south, Asia, because of its irregular topography and many climatic influences, is more like a patchwork quilt made up of deserts, forests and mountains. The center is an immense expanse of mountains and high plateaus dominating the continent from a mean height of nearly ten thousand feet. From Lake Baykal to the plains of the Ganges and the Brahmaputra Rivers, from the Pamirs to the Great Khingan, this giant causeway covers five million square miles with peaks lost in the clouds. It well merits its name: The Roof of the World.

To the north and east of this formidable center stretch the tundras and forests of Siberia and Manchuria, to the west lie the endless steppes of Central Asia and the dry plateaus of Asia Minor, while the south is covered by the rich alluvial plains of China and the luxuriant forests of Indo-Malaysia. Some sizeable fragments form Sakhalin Island, the Japanese Archipelago and Formosa on the east, the Philippines, the Celebes, the Moluccas, and the Sunda Islands on the south.

It is more than four thousand miles from Cape Chelyuskin in the Arctic to the southernmost tip of India and more than seven thousand from the Red Sea in the west to Bering Strait in the east. Before the advent of air travel, a traveler had to cross the Arctic wastes by dog sledge, the tundra by reindeer sledge, the taiga and the steppe on horseback, the deserts on camelback, use yaks in the central mountains, and ride an elephant across the swampy plains and through the tropical jungles in the south.

Such a journey in a straight line would have given him only a faint idea of the infinite variety of the landscape of Asia. To know more, he would have to go the longest way, crisscrossing the continent region by region. Unfortunately, as we have noted, Asia's natural regions do not follow one another in an orderly pattern. There are vast expanses containing only one type of landscape and other areas that are almost a mosaic of many kinds of landscape.

The climate is just as diversified. Both the cold pole of the world, Verkhoyansk in Siberia, where the thermometer descends to –60° F in winter, and the hot pole, Jacobabad in Pakistan, where the mean temperature in June reaches 125° F, are in Asia. Asia also holds the record for wetness: Cherrapunji in Assam gets more than 400 inches of rain a year; and it ties the record for dryness: the Gobi, Sind and Kara Kumy deserts are as arid as the heart of the Sahara.

If we consider only temperature, we can fairly easily divide the Eurasian continent into two masses, one cold or temperate, located to the north of the Himalayas, and the other distinctly tropical and south of these mountains. In the first, the transition from summer to winter and from winter to summer is noticeable, whereas in the second it is usually barely perceptible and often nonexistent. On the same latitude, the difference between summer and winter temperatures is more accentuated the farther one moves from the coast because

rainfall then attenuates or augments the effects of temperature.

A certain amount of humidity is indispensable to life, but when the temperature drops too low in temperate regions living organisms cannot utilize the water in the atmosphere. Thus, regions located on the same latitudes but without the same amount of rainfall will be different from the biogeographical point of view. Summer and winter temperatures in the Mediterranean countries are similar to those of southern China. But around the Mediterranean almost all the rain falls in winter when low temperatures inhibit the growth of plants and reproduction in animals, while in southern and eastern China, summer rains permit plants and animals to profit from the combined effect of warmth and humidity. Hence, vegetation and animal life around the Mediterranean are of the palearctic type, while those in southern China, Formosa and southern Japan are distinctly subtropical.

In the northern and central parts of Asia, most of the rains fall in spring or at the beginning of summer. In the western part, rains fall principally in winter. Throughout tropical Asia north of the equator, summer monsoon winds, which we shall study later, bring rain. Equatorial Asia enjoys more or less constant rainfall throughout the year. Yet in many regions these general conditions are altered by such obstacles as mountain barriers. Such barriers intercept winds laden with humidity and deprive certain adjacent regions of the rains they normally would get, so that some humid zones may contain great arid expanses.

Another important factor is the distribution of light. The total number of hours of light and of darkness is about the same on the entire surface of the globe. At the equator the length of a day equals that of a night throughout the year, while polar regions have six months of light followed by six months of constant darkness. Between these two extremes, there is a complete gamut of variations. It is easy to imagine the influence such differences in light rhythms may exert on plants that in one case may bloom all year long, while in another they must rest several months each year. In transitional zones, photoperiodism, or the relative length of days and nights, plays an important role. Many plants cannot flower or fruit unless they have, at least for a brief period of the year, a succession of long or, in some instances, short days. This holds true for many species even among the large mammals, where molting or reproductive cycles occur only according to the rhythm of light.

Considering these factors, we can divide the continent of Asia into a number of climatic zones, with plants and animals varying locally according to the nature of the soil. The Arctic coast and the tundra are characterized by a cold climate, slight rainfall, and a prolonged polar night followed by a six-month period of light. Perpetually frozen in depth and thawing on the surface only in the summer months, the soil, lacking light for half the year, permits only stunted vegetation and imposes on plants and animals all kinds of special adaptations.

To the south, the number of days increases progressively, even though the total number of hours of light annually is

Dense tropical growth borders such streams as this in the jungles of Pahang, West Malaysia. In the heart of the jungle where trees cut out the sunlight, lower plants are sparse. (Ivan Polunin)

not much greater. Summers are longer and hotter, but the rainfall diminishes, allowing only the less demanding species, such as the conifers, birches and alders of the taiga, to survive. In regions such as Manchuria, where the influence of the sea leads to increased rainfall, the true coniferous taiga gives way to a mixed coniferous and variegated leafy forest.

Since rainfall diminishes toward the south, trees can live only in certain valleys, and the steppe or prairie, then the semidesert, and finally the true desert succeeds the forest. Although all deserts are arid, conditions on them vary with mean temperature and with the season when the slight rain falls. To simplify, we have divided the deserts into two basic types: the hot deserts of Arabia, southern Iran and northern India, and the cold deserts of Central Asia and Mongolia, which have rigorous winters although their summer temperatures are as high as those of the hot deserts.

The high plateaus of Tibet and Mongolia, in the heart of Asia, also have an arid climate, since winds from the north have lost most of their humidity and those of the southern monsoon are intercepted by the towering barrier of the Himalayas. These plateaus are covered with vegetation similar to that found in semideserts and in cold deserts of low regions. Contrarily, the southern slopes of the Himalayas are among the best-watered in the world. Since all their humidity falls during the hottest months of the year, those of the summer monsoons, the slopes sprout a vegetation no less luxuriant than that in tropical forests. Yet very high up, where the mean temperature drops sharply, there are only dwarf plants similar to those on the Arctic tundra. Regions south of the Himalayan barrier—India, Indochina and southern China— also benefit from summer monsoon rains, more abundant on the mountains than in the low regions. More or less luxuriant vegetation grows there, too, at least during the humid season, and according to the quality of the soil.

We end our journey through Asia's equatorial zone in the Malay Archipelago. On all such islands located right on the equator, constant rainfall and high temperatures all year round assure conditions most favorable to plant life and great forests. North and south of the equator, the alternation of dry and wet seasons makes itself felt, and the plant cover approximates that of the tropics.

These zones, with their characteristic plants and animals, will constitute the chapter titles of our book. We must not, however, lose sight of the basic division of the continent into two large masses corresponding to cold and temperate Asia on the one hand and tropical Asia on the other hand: the Palearctic Region, north of the Himalayas, and the Yangtse River and the Oriental Region or Indo-Malaysia, south of these frontiers.

The Palearctic Region includes Europe and has often been linked to North America by biogeographers to form the Holarctic Region. This is not an arbitrary link, for paleontology proves that the Bering Strait dates only from the end of the Tertiary Period and until its appearance, the two continents were one. The same natural zones exist in North America as in Eurasia: Arctic shore, tundra, taiga, steppes and deserts. The same or very closely related species of animals inhabit these zones: white and brown bears, lynxes, wolves, foxes, reindeer, elks, red deer, mountain sheep, squirrels, chipmunks, susliks or prairie dogs and so on.

The Oriental Region differs sharply from the Palearctic and is much closer in plant and animal life to Africa and especially to Africa's forest regions. Those who know African wildlife are usually surprised to find in Asia a host of familiar birds and mammals: sunbirds, bulbuls, barbets, pangolins, jackals, panthers, hyenas.

Despite these similarities, tropical Asia has more than enough plants and animals of its own to hold the interest of naturalists. It is also a part of the world in which much remains to be done in the study of plant and animal life. A simple inventory of plants and animals of the Oriental Region has yet to be made and a study of species already described has only just begun. Flowers and fruits of many plants have never been observed. Many mammals, birds and reptiles—and we refer only to sizeable animals—are known only through a small number of museum specimens; and nothing at all is known about their biology.

Asia is an extraordinarily rich research area for naturalists and biogeographers, for it is situated at the crossroads of all the other continents, and American, African and Australian flora and fauna have contributed to its stock throughout the history of our planet. We shall have achieved our goal if this book succeeds in conveying at least a superficial idea of this immense continent and its astonishing diversity.

Right above: At the northernmost border of Asia is a vast floating island of pack-ice which moves around the polar basin with the winds and currents of the Arctic Ocean. (Novosti) Right: At Asia's southwest corner lies the Arabian Peninsula, nearly a million square miles of desert. (Aramco)

Bleak Shores
and Barren
Lands

The Arctic Coast and Tundra Zone

1 From Scandinavia to Korea, nearly 16,000 miles of the northern and eastern Asiatic coast are washed by cold or temperate waters. Great peninsulas and archipelagos are created by such bodies of water as—going from west to east—the Barents Sea and the White Sea, the Kara Sea, the Laptev Sea, the East Siberian Sea, the Chukchi Sea, the Bering Strait and Bering Sea, the Sea of Okhotsk, and the Sea of Japan. Most of this coast is rocky, and in the many places where the mountains extend into the sea, it is steep. Some shores, however, particularly in the bays, descend gently and are covered with pebbles or coarse sand.

In this latitude, the western waters are distinctly more temperate than the eastern ones, for an interaction of hot and cold ocean currents causes a movement of cold water toward the east. A branch of the Gulf Stream reaches nearly to Novaya Zemlya and warms the Barents Sea, while the Oya-Shivo, a branch of the icy Arctic current, cools the Bering and Okhotsk seas.

Free of ice for a large part of the year, the waters of the Barents Sea shelter a relatively rich and varied animal life. The coastal rocks are covered with a host of mussels and periwinkles, sea acorns, sponges and ascidians. Many crabs, shrimps, sea urchins, and starfish dwell amidst the seaweed, and nearly 150 species of fish, mainly cod, herring and flat-fish, live in the open sea. This diversity of coastal and sea-dwelling animals guarantees food for a great many aquatic or amphibious mammals such as whales, dolphins and seals, and for a huge number of sea birds: divers, guillemots, puffins, petrels, shearwaters, gulls, skuas and ducks.

East of Novaya Zemlya, an area not reached by the benefi-cent influence of warm currents, ice covers the sea most of

The polar bear haunts the northern Arctic coasts and may range hundreds of miles, sometimes carried on drifting ice floes. (Sven Gillsater)

14

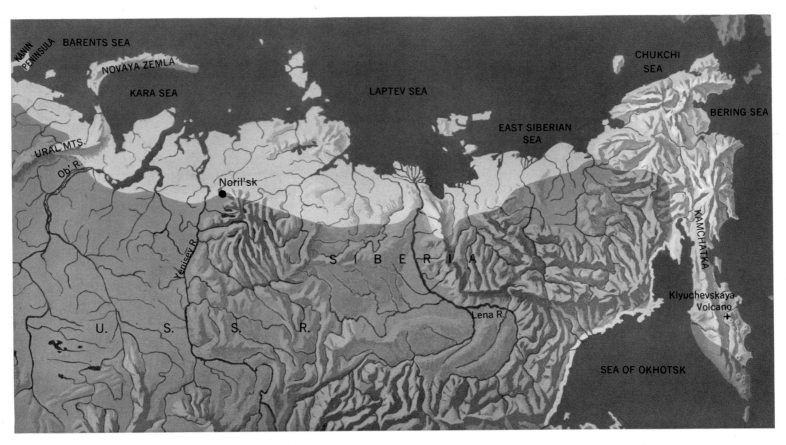

Below the Arctic coast lies more than a million square miles of desolate tundra, extending from the Urals to Kamchatka.

the year, sometimes not melting even in summer. The waters freeze more easily and deeply because they are not particularly saline, the result both of a lack of evaporation and a massive flow of fresh water from the great Siberian rivers. The scraping of the ice against the shore makes all coastal life impossible and only pelagic organisms can flourish. Continual sunlight in the summer months favors the growth of phytoplankton and consequently of the crustaceans of the Euphausiacea family and of mollusks of the genus *Clione* that form the vast banks of "krill" eaten by whales. Only thirty species of fish live in the Laptev Sea and only sixty in the Chukchi Sea. Mammals and sea birds are also less numerous than in the comparatively temperate waters of the Barents Sea, for a layer of ice throughout most of the year makes any fishing impossible.

The waters of the Bering and Okhotsk seas, although distinctly colder than those of the Barents Sea, are relatively warmer than those of the Arctic shores, for the cooling influence of the Oya-Shivo is partly counteracted by the warm Kouro-Shivo current of the Pacific. The animal life of the deep sea and the coastal waters is much richer and more varied there, including not only several local forms but many animals commonly found in European waters.

THE GREGARIOUS SEALS

One of the interesting characteristics of many animals of the Arctic is their gregariousness. Most seals, fur-seals and walruses gather in great numbers on the shore at breeding time and as late as the nineteenth century even whales were found in huge shoals as they followed the migrations of krill and the fish that fed on it. Only the polar bear, one of the best adapted to shore life of typically forest-dwelling flesh-eaters, leads a family life. Widespread along Asiatic and American Arctic coasts, it moves about on ice floes, eating seal and fish, especially salmon, which it deftly harpoons with its claws as the fish swim up the estuaries of the rivers.

Among the so-called fin-footed mammals, only the walrus *(Odobaenus rosmarus),* the ringed seal *(Phoca hispida)* and the bearded seal *(Erignathus barbatus)* are spread over as vast an area as the polar bear. Other pinnipeds are more or less limited to the west or east of the Arctic coast. They have all been so hunted for their skins or their oil that they have disappeared from many places where they formed seemingly inexhaustible colonies at the beginning of the nineteenth century.

The walrus, with males that may be fourteen feet long and weigh nearly three thousand pounds, is the giant of the group. The female walrus is smaller and has not the characteristic tusks of the species. Walruses live in herds, sometimes quite large, and seek shallow coastal waters to gather bivalves or crustaceans, whose shells they crush with their incisors and molars. In winter, when most Arctic seas are covered with ice, they migrate into the warmer Barents Sea or Bering Sea. In spring, the female goes ashore or to an ice floe to give birth to one offspring, which she nurses for two years.

The Pribilof seal (Callorhinus ursinus), *hunted for its fur and almost annihilated, now thrives in immense protected colonies such as this one on Robben Island. (V. B. Scheffer)*

The walrus leads a highly social life and great numbers congregate along parts of the Siberian coast, feeding chiefly on mollusks. Only the males have tusks. (Novosti)

The ringed seal is a small animal, no more than five feet long when fully grown. It is usually dark, with the back ringed and veined in white or light gray. Unlike the walrus, it is a hunter and pursues fish in the open sea. To give birth in April, at the beginning of the polar spring, the female seal hollows out a niche in hard snow amid the ice. The young animal has thick white fur, much prized by furriers, so that the ringed seal is economically important to the peoples dwelling on Arctic and Far Eastern shores.

The bearded seal (so called because of the long hair on its chin and its mustaches) is a larger animal, the male attaining a length of almost ten feet and weighing seven or eight hundred pounds. The females are about one-third smaller. Truly a circumpolar animal, it descends in the Atlantic as far as the English coast and in the Pacific to Japan and Canada. The least sociable of all seals, it often leads a solitary existence near the coast or in estuaries. Although it is generally rare and not too well known, we do know that it eats mainly crustaceans, mollusks and sea urchins gathered from the bottom of the sea.

Other pinnipeds prefer temperate waters. The harp seal *(Phoca groenlandica)*, the gray seal *(Halichoerus grypus)*, the hooded seal *(Cystophora cristata)* and the common seal *(Phoca vitulina)* are found in Barents Sea, but live mainly on European coasts. The last species also frequents eastern waters, from the Bering Strait to Japan, biogeographers describing it as an amphiboreal form because it lives in temperate waters

The ringed seal (Phoca hispida) *feeds on fish and lives in families along the Arctic coast and on ice floes. (Tass from Sovfoto)*

of both the Atlantic and the Pacific but is completely absent from Arctic seas. The common porpoise *(Phocoena phocoena)* and many fish and invertebrates fall into the same category. Thus, our herring *(Clupea harengus)* and cod *(Gadus morhua)* are found west and east of Eurasia, but not north and south of it. And countless mollusks, echinoderms, worms and marine crustaceans are represented in the Atlantic by species identical or closely related to those in the North Pacific.

The presence of the same life forms on both sides of a continent and their absence from its northern and southern coasts may be explained, according to some biogeographers, by the fact that at the end of the Tertiary Era and the beginning of the Quaternary, the climate in Arctic regions was more moderate than it is now; thus an exchange of temperate forms of life was then possible.

The most favorable waters for Arctic pinnipeds are those along the eastern coasts of Asia, south of the Bering Strait. Beside walruses and most of the seals already mentioned, we find the ribbon seal *(Phoca fasciata)* and two fur-seals, the California sea lion *(Eumetopias jubatus)* and the Pribilof fur-seal *(Callorhinus ursinus),* both much prized for their fur. Irrational exploitation at the beginning of this century nearly exterminated the second of these species, but wise protective measures have brought their number back up to three million. Fur-seals, which differ from other seals in that they have external ears, are gregarious and make long annual migrations, those from the Pribilof Islands, for example, going to Japan each autumn, a trek of 3,000 to 3,500 miles.

However, the most unusual animals of this region are, or at least were, the sea otter *(Enhydra lutris)* and the rhytina or Steller's sea cow *(Hydrodamalis stelleri).* The sea otter is the only musteline that has almost entirely adapted to a marine

The only seagoing member of a land-dwelling forest family, the polar bear has adapted to the stringent conditions in the North, hibernating only during the harshest winter months. (Sven Gillsater)

existence, seeking refuge on land only during the worst storms or when giving birth. Soon after its birth, the young animal is led into the water. There it lies on its mother's belly while the mother sleeps on her back after having rolled some seaweed around herself to prevent the offspring from being dragged off by the current.

Compared to fresh-water otters the adult is a large animal, reaching a length of six feet and weighing from sixty-five to ninety pounds. Its brown or silvery black fur is so highly prized that this once abundant animal was very nearly wiped out. Only a complete ban on hunting it saved the species from extinction. Its population now numbers about four thousand; these are distributed around a few islands in the Bering Sea and along the California coast. There one may still see several hundred sea otters playing on the surface of the water or diving for shellfish.

THE MYSTERY OF STELLER'S SEA COW

One of the most extraordinary animals ever discovered by man, Steller's sea cow, was not so fortunate and disappeared from the zoological scene exactly twenty-seven years after it was discovered.

In 1741, one of the vessels in the navy of Peter the Great, commanded by the Danish captain Vitus Bering, was shipwrecked on what were later called the Commander Islands. It is easy to imagine the crew's astonishment at the sight of hundreds of huge unknown animals gamboling on the shore and browsing seaweed and sea cabbage. The spindle-shaped, sausage-like form, over thirty feet long, ended in front in a small head with a mustache and at the rear in a walrus tail. It had two finlike paws, which were absolutely useless for movement on solid ground.

The surgeon and naturalist of the expedition, the Germano-Russian Georg Steller, had the brilliant idea of relating these strange monsters to two inhabitants of tropical waters of the Old and New Worlds, the manatee and the dugong, and classing them among the Sirenians. These sea cows, weighing nearly four tons, seemed like a heavenly gift to the unfortunate castaways. The meat tasted like veal and the fat like breast of pork. Unable to escape and unafraid of the men, the sea cows let themselves be slaughtered with no other reactions than violent jerks and a powerful flapping of the tail.

News of this discovery spread rapidly among whalers when Bering's expedition, its leader having meanwhile died of scurvy, returned home after having repaired the boat. Since large colonies of sea otters also lived on the Commander Islands, the area soon became a favorite hunting ground for sealers, who where guaranteed a rich source of food by the constant presence of the herds of sea cows. These herds, however, were not very large, their population probably total-

ing no more than a few thousand at the time of Bering's shipwreck. By 1768 the last of Steller's sea cows had been killed—before anything more had been learned about the habits of this singular animal.

And then, on a morning in July, 1962, the crew of a Soviet whaler cruising south of the Gulf of Anadyr sighted six huge, strange-looking beasts a hundred yards from the ship. From twenty to twenty-six feet long, dark in color, with small heads and a distinctly split upper lip, and with tails like dolphins, they swam slowly along, diving for a moment from time to time, and then rising vigorously above the water. A similar animal was seen the next day at the same spot and, according to the crew of veteran sailors and whalers, bore no resemblance to any known walrus or seal. These animals were found at the mouth of a river where the shallow waters, which never freeze, are rich in seaweed and sea cabbage—the typical habitat of Steller's sea cow. Some Soviet scientists therefore wonder whether the sea cow, believed extinct for two centuries, could have survived in small numbers far from areas frequented by seal and whale hunters. Nothing has so far either confirmed or contradicted this hypothesis, and hope for a startling rediscovery of Steller's sea cow has not been abandoned.

ISLANDS OF THE BIRDS

When April arrives, millions of birds gather in certain places on the coast or on countless rocky islets. The clownlike silhouettes of puffins, the black and white suits of divers and guillemots, the snowy or silvery plumage of gulls brighten the somber cliffs, while the flapping of wings and deafening clamor of kittiwakes, terns and skuas shatter the Arctic silence.

Nesting in colonies is for these birds the most efficient method of survival. Each bird defends the small space it occupies and together the birds form a mass of wings and beaks discouraging to the most resolute enemy, from the Arctic fox to the polar bear. Since the safest areas are in the center of a colony, these are bitterly disputed and in April and May the days and nights are filled with the sound of endless battles among the colonists. A similar rivalry goes on among different species. As always, the strongest species claim the best places and push the weakest outwards toward the edge. The distinguished Russian zoologist A. G. Bannikov noted that on some islands of the Barents Sea, the widest rocky platforms are occupied by large guillemots *(Uria aalge)* while Brunnich's guillemots *(U. lomvia),* black guillemots *(U. grylle)* and razorbilled auks *(Alca torda)* must make do with narrow and barely accessible ledges. The kittiwakes *(Rissa tridactyla)* take what is left, the steepest crevices, for their turf and dry grass nests.

The puffins hollow out tunnels several yards long in the turfy ground, often joining them in a subterranean network. Each tunnel ends in a nesting chamber where the puffin lays its one egg on the ground.

One finds the eider's nest carefully hidden away in places covered with stunted vegetation. Of the three species of eiders

that live on the Arctic coast, the best-known is the eider *(Somateria mollissima)* of Northeastern Europe, the Barents Sea and the White Sea. The two others, the king eider *(S. spectabilis)* and Fisher's eider *(S. fisheri),* dwell in eastern Arctic seas as far as Bering Strait. The celebrated eiderdown comes from the bird's breast. The female plucks it from herself to line the interior of her nest and cover the eggs while she flies out to sea for her food. Young eiders leave the nest permanently a few hours after they are hatched and the down may then be gathered without harm to the birds.

Guillemots lay their single egg on bare rock. The female uses her beak to roll the egg onto her webbed feet and then squats upon it. The most delicate moment comes when the young bird must launch onto the water for the first time. Encouraged by its parents who call to it from the sea or flutter around it, the baby moves to the edge of the cliff but recoils in fear. This scene is repeated several times until the young bird gathers courage and suddenly launches out from the top of the rocks. Sometimes, however, when it cannot make up its mind, an adult must brutally push it off. As soon as the bird strikes the water, its cries of fright redouble. Then its parents surround it, leading it rapidly out to sea where its education will be completed.

Guillemots feed in the open sea and dive to a depth of several yards to capture small fish and shellfish. Puffins and divers are also remarkable for their underwater exploits. Using their wings, they literally "fly" beneath the water in pursuit of their prey. Terns and gulls merely catch fish on the surface, while eiders dive to considerable depths. Such different methods of seeking food serve to prevent competition among these species.

This concentration of all sorts of birds attracts many four-legged or winged predators. The most fearsome of the first kind, aside from occasional raiding polar bears or Arctic foxes, are the weasels from the tundra. But their depredations are insignificant compared to those of gulls, skuas and the occasional gyrfalcon.

Several species of gulls nest on the Arctic coasts. Most typical is the ivory gull *(Pagophila eburnea),* which is all white except for its black legs. The two other species, the herring gull *(Larus argentatus)* and the great black-backed gull *(L. marinus),* are also found off the coasts of Europe. Ivory and herring gulls concentrate on fish, crustaceans and mollusks, but the great black-backed gull also has a taste for nesting birds. Constantly wheeling above the colonies, it takes advantage of the slightest parental inattention to snatch an egg or a fledgling. Very strong, it even attacks adult puffins, signing its aggressions by leaving along the shores their skins turned inside out like gloves.

Skuas, especially the great skua *(Stercorarius skua),* the Arctic skua *(S. parasiticus)* and the pomarine skua *(S. pomarinus),* also steal eggs and fledglings at the edge of colonies, and they are especially adept at piracy. When they see a bird returning from fishing, they pounce on it with a shrill cry and pursue it, renewing their attacks until it disgorges the contents of its stomach.

Like many birds of the Arctic coast, these thick-billed guillemots (Uria lomvia) *nest on rocks in great colonies. Massed together, they can fend off the fiercest predators. (Soviet Life from Sovfoto)*

The gyrfalcon, with pale, sometimes almost white, plumage, the only falcon nesting regularly on the Arctic coast, is a hunter of sea birds. Much prized by falconers, it has become rare almost everywhere and has even disappeared from some islets of the Barents Sea that were set up as preserves by eighteenth-century Russian czars who alone had the right to take these birds for their hunting stables.

OLD WORLD TUNDRAS

Below the Arctic coasts lies a region of tundras covering nearly 1,150,000 square miles of Asia from Scandinavia to Kamchatka. Although the name *tundra* comes from the Finnish *tunturi,* signifying a treeless and flat plain, in some places it is strewn with rocks or tumuli of earth or turf left by thawing glaciers. But it is generally true that the tundra's relief features are insignificant and the view of the horizon is not interrupted by the slightest hill.

The prevailing landscape here is the "spotted tundra," covered with flat, plate-sized circles of clay entirely without vegetation. Strangely enough, these patches have never within the memory of man borne the smallest plant, and no trace of plant humus can be found in them no matter how deep one excavates.

In other places, vast expanses are covered with turfy soil, one to two feet deep and studded with convex cushions of moss *(Polytrichum)* and tufts of fescue-grass *(Festuca ovina).* The turf is especially thick in hollows carpeted with densely growing mosses *(Hypnum, Aulacomnium)* and scattered lichens. Most of these lichens, belonging to the genus *Cladonia,* flourish on sandy soil and give the tundra a bluish color that is particularly striking in spring. They are extremely important to the animal life of the region for they are the principal food of reindeer. They grow very slowly, a tiny fraction of an inch a year, and in places that serve as pasturage for reindeer they may be completely destroyed. It has been estimated that in such pastures it would take fifteen to twenty years for the lichens to recover their normal density.

In some regions, and particularly on the Kanin peninsula, turfy hillocks from six to nine feet high give the tundra an undulating appearance. The depressions between these hillocks are filled with water during the melting of the snows in summer. In winter, the landscape looks like a chessboard for the hillocks are swept clean by the winds and snow covers the hollows.

The conditions of life on the tundra are harsh. Winters are long, cold and dark since the maximum light during nine months of the year is a dim twilight at midday. For eight to nine months, the temperature never rises above the freezing point, and even in July, the hottest month of the year, it does not reach 50° F during the day and often falls below freezing at night. Unbelievably violent winds, ranging from ten miles an hour in summer to eighty miles an hour in winter, constantly sweep across the open spaces, so that the snow remains only in depressions where it can pack down and form a crust. The snowfall is, however, not great in the tundra, the total annual precipitation often amounting to little more than that of arid regions. Precipitation diminishes toward the east, ranging from sixteen inches on the shores of the Barents Sea to less than four inches at the mouth of the Lena.

Unprotected by the snow, the ground freezes deeply in

winter and thaws only slightly on the surface during the two or two and a half months of summer. The perpetually frozen ground or permafrost is almost everywhere a few score and sometimes several hundred yards deep. This prevents animals from burrowing and hence keeps out such invertebrates as earthworms as well as the moles and shrews that feed on these invertebrates.

DWARF TREES AND MULTICOLORED FLOWERS

Such extreme conditions prevent a normal plant development on the tundra. Thus there is a striking absence of annuals, the brief summers preventing the maturation of seeds within the space of a year. The only plants are perennials and in the most northerly regions even these reproduce only by vegetative processes. In the southern tundra, perennials usually bear fruit every two years, flowering one year and forming seeds the next. Often buds form but do not have time to open before the winter. Then, in the spring, flowers burst into bloom a day or two after the snow melts.

But the growth of even perennial and woody plants is very slow. The polar willow *(Salix polaris)* grows little more than a sixteenth of an inch each season and sprouts only two or three leaves on a branch. Slow growth and violent winds explain the dwarf size of most tundra plants. Dwarf birches and willows *(Betula nana, Salix herbacea, S. glauca, S. lanata)* grow no more than a foot high. The trunk of a juniper that was cut down on the Kola peninsula, and had 577 annual rings, indi-

Right: The black-tailed gull (Larus crassirostris), *common on the Asian Arctic coast, is very popular in Japan, where its mewing cry has earned it the name "sea-cat." (T. Iwago) Below: After endless quarrels over nesting sites, thick-billed murres lay their eggs on the bare rocks. (V. B. Scheffer)*

cating that it was nearly six centuries old, measured only three and a half inches in diameter.

Most shrubs on the tundra scarcely rise above the ground, behaving much like creepers in order to withstand the wind and make the most of the earth's summer warmth. Nevertheless, they form the uppermost layer of the tundra's plant life. Below them grow sedges (*Carex rigida*), fescues (*Festuca supina, F. ovina*), whortleberries and myrtles (*Vaccinium vitis, V. myrtillus*), knotgrass (*Polygonum viviparum*) and, in spring, myriads of such brightly colored flowers as forget-me-nots (*Myosotis alpestris*), geraniums (*Geranium silvaticum*), veronica (*Veronica longifolia*), golden rod (*Solidago virgaurea*), yarrow (*Achillea millefolium*), catch-fly (*Silene acaulis*), willow-herb (*Epilobium angustifolium*), and lady's mantle (*Alchemilla* sp.). Finally at ground level, mosses and lichens grow as they do on the open tundra.

Bulbous or tuberous plants are rare on the tundra because their underground parts get no chance to form during the uninterrupted light of the summer months. Moreover, most plants remain beneath the snow all winter, their fruits ready to free their seeds and their buds waiting to burst into bloom at the first sign of spring. All these plants are rich in vitamins and insure fresh food for tundra animals during the most rigorous period of the year.

Other natural factors are equally favorable to the development of animal life. The almost constant summer light lets diurnal species remain active nearly twenty-four hours each day and thus make up for time lost during the winter. An atmosphere rich in ultra-violet rays, probably because of an almost complete absence of dust in the air, stimulates the growth of animal organisms. Finally, the rarity of infectious diseases and the sparsity of the human population can only prove favorable for animal life in these regions.

LIFE ON THE TUNDRA

The tundra, therefore, shelters a much richer animal life, at least in number of individuals, than we might believe. Relatively few animals have been able to adapt to the extreme conditions, but their adaptation has been so distinct that a large proportion of them are considered not only separate species but even separate genera. Some of the species that are also found in the "barren lands" of North America include the Arctic fox (*Alopex lagopus*), the collared lemming (*Dicrostonyx torquatus*) and, among the birds, the snowy owl (*Nyctea scandiaca*), the Lapland longspur (*Calcarius lapponicus*) and the snow bunting (*Plectrophenax nivalis*). Among the species that are characteristic of the tundras but also penetrate other natural environments are the Arctic hare (*Lepus timidus*), the common or Norway lemming (*Lemmus lemmus*), the Obi lemming (*L. obensis*), the Siberian lemming (*L. sibiricus*), the reindeer (*Rangifer tarandus*), the willow grouse (*Lagopus lagopus*), the rough-legged buzzard (*Buteo lagopus*), the white-fronted goose (*Anser albifrons*), the bean goose (*Anser arvensis*), the snow goose (*A. hyperboreus*), the brant goose (*Branta bernicla*), the whooper swan, Bewick's swan, and several species of sandpipers and a considerable variety of other waders. All these birds are associated with permanent or temporary lakes and swamps, which are as frequent in forest zones as in tundras.

Some animals are common to the tundra and to mountains in the interior where climate and vegetation are often strikingly similar to those in Arctic regions. The classic examples of this are the snow sheep or bighorn (*Ovis canadensis*), the ptarmigan (*Lagopus mutus*), and the horned lark (*Eremophila alpestris*). Other species, remarkably adaptable to almost every environment, are found in all the cold and temperate regions of the Eurasian landmass. These are the wolf, the red fox (*Vulpes vulpes*), the weasel (*Mustela nivalis*), the stoat (*M. erminea*), and several species of voles and field mice.

On the other hand, we have seen that the tundra's deep-frozen soil is poor in burrowing invertebrates, so that almost none of the generally prevalent insect-eaters, such as hedgehogs, moles and shrews are found here. The scarcity of insects, except for mosquitos, which are the plague of the summer months, and the almost total absence of grasses also explain the dearth of small passerines here.

The intensity of animal life varies greatly from one season to the next. In winter, when the tundra is a desert swept by snow storms and with little light except from the stars, everything seems dead. The reindeer herds take shelter at the forest edge, where the winds are less violent and the snows are lighter. Arctic hares, grouse, and most of the predators—foxes, wolves and wolverines—follow them. The great mass of birds has long since migrated toward the temperate or warm regions of Europe, Asia and Africa.

Yet despite appearances, life continues actively beneath the snow. None of the tundra's sedentary mammals hibernates, evidently because of the impossibility of digging deep enough tunnels and because the brief summer does not allow enough time for reproduction and the accumulation of reserves of fat for the winter. However, most of them are perfectly adapted to this disproportion in the seasons. Mammals that continue to reproduce during the summer—as do several species of voles found in the tundra and elsewhere—show a reduction in frequency of litters but a distinct increase in the number born in each litter.

THE MIGRATIONS OF THE LEMMINGS

The lemmings have solved the problem of survival on the tundra by living in burrows dug under the snow. There they find both shelter against cold and an abundance of rich food in frozen plants. If the winter is abnormally long, these resources dwindle and many lemmings die before the snow melts. But if the winter is comparatively short and follows an exceptionally long and favorable summer, food abounds, the rodents reproduce unrestrainedly and finally swarm in great numbers.

These swarming peaks, recurring every two, three or four years, have always struck man's imagination and given rise to a belief in suicidal migrations by lemmings, waves of frenzy that lead millions of rampaging animals to plunge into the sea. The work of Russian, Swedish, and Finnish scholars has now reduced that wild legend to the proportions of a natural phenomenon. As the Swedish zoologist Kai Curry-Lindahl explained in the volume on Europe in this series, in some years

Typical tundra, as on Kotelni Island in western Siberia, is a wasteland where only lichens (Cladonia), *mosses* (Polytrichum), *fescue-grass* (Festuca ovina) *and occasional dwarf birches and willows grow. (Novosti)*

all the conditions unite to produce a superabundance of lemmings. The rodents then find themselves without living space become frantic, and rush off to find less densely populated areas.

But these are random movements, a far cry from the tale of hordes of lemmings marching implacably in a specific direction as if moved by some demonic force. In fact, it is only on the European tundras, in the Scandinavian and Ural mountains, that the swarming of the lemmings, superimposed on their seasonal migrations, channels their disorderly flight into certain valleys and sometimes into the sea. Farther east, on the flat Siberian tundra, the rodents move individually in every direction and never in spectacular groups.

These peaks of swarming are a boon to predators. Arctic foxes, stoats, weasels, snowy owls and rough-legged buzzards feed heartily on the rodents and in turn reproduce exceptionally. Then, in ensuing years, when the rodent population has returned to normal, a great many of these predators perish, or, like the snowy owl, set out on aimless migrations that also end in death. Some Arctic coast birds, such as the skuas, specializing in the capture of lemmings, nest in the interior of the tundra. It is a most interesting fact that some skuas reproduce only during the rodents' swarming peaks and lay no eggs in other years.

The economic importance of lemmings is considerable since they contribute to the feeding of many fur-bearing animals, especially of the Arctic fox, a typical tundra inhabitant although it sometimes descends into the taiga. Anatomically different

Left: Wild reindeer, mostly gone from European tundras, still range in Siberia, but their numbers are dwindling as domestic herds take over their pasture areas. (Camera Press: Pix) Below: Arctic poppies herald the spring thaw. Because of the short northern summers many tundra plants have a two-year cycle, flowering one year and forming seeds the next. (Novosti)

29

from other foxes, the Arctic fox can be distinguished by small rounded ears, and shorter tail. Its tawny summer coat turns white in winter, but in some individuals remains a constant year-round bluish smoke-gray. This is the "blue fox" sought by furriers.

ADAPTING TO A TUNDRA ENVIRONMENT

Lemmings are not the only animals adapted to life beneath the snow. Stoats spend most of their time there, tracking the rodents in their galleries. Some non-migratory birds, the willow grouse, for example, have also adopted this way of life and seek nest sites beneath the ground cover of snow. Still another adaptation to this environment is the white fur or plumage donned by most tundra animals in winter. This phenomenon, like all moults, is primarily triggered by variations in the duration of daylight, which is especially important in these regions. This winter mimicry occurs in the Arctic fox, the Arctic hare, the collared lemming, the stoat, the snowy owl, and the two species of grouse.

Moving about on soft snow also poses problems and gives rise to adaptations similar to those of animals living in sandy deserts. All these involve an increase in the bearing surface and consequently a greater distribution of pressure on the snow. The Arctic hare's paws grow hair profusely and the willow grouse's legs sprout abundant feathers, forming veritable snowshoes. The collared lemming's claws grow larger in winter and join to form a sort of hoof that not only aids walking on the snow but also makes burrowing easier. And the exceptionally broad hoofs of the reindeer are as well adapted to movement on soft snow in winter as across marshy land in summer. It has been calculated that the pressure on the snow of a reindeer is only about two pounds per square inch, as against twice as much for a Eurasian stag. This, together with the reindeer's adaptable feeding habits explains its reputation as the best beast of burden in Siberia, for although the dog is faster, it requires provisions of dried fish. During the winter, the reindeer eats only lichens of the genus *Cladonia*, uncovering them by scraping in the snow with its hoofs. In spring, it eats berries, mushrooms, sedge and the leaves of birch and willow, and has been known to take lemmings and the eggs of birds. Reindeer meat is the basic food of the Samoyedes, Ostiaks, Iakoutes and other inhabitants of the tundra, who also use the animals' skins to make clothing and huts.

During the last few years a disturbing phenomenon that may have some effect on animal life in this area has been observed by Swedish scientists. Radioactive elements from atomic detonations in the air are selectively collected by the lichens browsed by reindeer. The level of radioactivity of reindeer meat is consequently nearly 250 times that of cattle raised in the same latitude. The Lapps who eat this meat have also been affected, the cesium concentrations in their tissues being thirty to forty times greater than in Swedes of the southern area.

Wild reindeer have almost vanished from the tundras of Europe but they are still numerous in Siberia and, like the North American subspecies called caribou, make long seasonal

Left: Spongy, waterlogged tundra soil buckles when it freezes. Elsewhere, snow collecting in hollows hardens into an icy crust. (Jorgen Bisch)

Such rodents as red-backed voles (Clethrionomys rufocanus) *are adapted to tundra life. Although short summers restrict their breeding period, they have far more young in a litter than their relatives in temperate regions. (Novosti)*

The terek sandpiper (Tringa terek), *found around the rivers and lakes of Siberia, is a wader whose incessant movement and melodic calls enliven the gloomy landscape. (Novosti)*

Klyuchevskaya volcano (15,584 feet) is the highest peak on Kamchatka Peninsula. One of many active volcanoes on the peninsula, its eruptions illuminate the long polar night. (Novosti)

migrations. In winter, they live on the edge or even in the interior of the taiga; but with the spring and the hatching of clouds of mosquitos that drive the beasts mad, they return to the open spaces, where strong winds sweep away the stinging insects.

THE POLAR SPRING

Late in May or early in June, when the snow melts, the tundra is covered with countless lakes, ponds and marshes. Great expanses are covered with multicolored flowers and in a few days, the dwarf willows and birches unfurl their leaves and all plants grow at an accelerated rate. Life goes on intensely day and night. A pale but strong sun burns the entire twenty-four hours of the day, and if the wind falls, the temperature at midnight may be several degrees higher than that at noon.

The few non-migratory birds, grouse and snowy owls, can scarcely make a dent in the sudden surfeit of food offered by plants, fresh-water fish and mosquito larvae. Flocks of migrants fly in from southern regions to profit from these ephemeral riches. The first arrival is always the snow bunting, who turns up on the first days of May when the temperature is still below freezing. A month later come the little waders whose fluted or sharp cries are the tundra's sound effects: the purple sandpipers *(Calidris maritima)*, knots *(C. canutus)*, sanderlings *(Crocethia alba)*, turnstones *(Arenaria interpres)*,

red phalaropes *(Phalaropus fulicarius)*, bar-tailed godwits *(Limosa lapponica)* and gray plovers *(Charadrius squatarola)*.

As numerous and varied, but more noisy and spectacular, are the swans, geese and ducks, who often nest in huge groups on the grassy islands in the lakes or amid brush on the tundra. They all offer the local populations a convenient supply of meat, eggs, and down. Their capture is easy since some of them, especially the geese, undergo accelerated moults and, losing all their large feathers at once, are totally unable to fly.

In mid-June appear woodcocks, snipe, curlews and divers *(Gavia arctica, G. stellata)*, endemic here and on the Arctic coasts, where they spend the winter. They have plenty of food since the streams and rivers are rich in fish of all kinds and especially salmonids: Atlantic salmon *(Salmo)*, whitefish *(Coregonus)* and lake trout *(Salvelinus)*, which are probably the fresh-water fish that go farthest north. In eastern Siberia, typical salmon are replaced by those of the genus *Oncorhynchus* or Pacific salmon.

Thus, for two or two and a half months the tundra seethes with life. Then, at the end of August, the migrators depart as they came, leaving behind the silence and darkness of the long polar night.

Part of the Pacific "ring of fire," the Kamchatka Peninsula has more than forty volcanoes, some of them, like Dzenzur, covered with hardened lava. (Novosti)

Sea of Conifers

The Siberian Taiga

2 The Siberian taiga, the largest forest in the world, extends over nearly 4,600,000 square miles, an area about a third larger than the United States. The word taiga, which in Russian conjures up a dark, mysterious forest, is a plant community primitively composed of a few species of coniferous trees, mainly firs *(Abies sibirica)*, larches *(Larix sibirica)*, a type of pines *(Picea excelsa)*, Siberian pines or "cedars" *(Pinus cembra)*, and in some places, Scotch pines *(Pinus sylvestris)* and Daurian larches *(Larix daurica)*. Found with the conifers and predominant on the southern edge of the taiga are some broadleafed trees such as birches, aspens and alders. On the other hand, the oaks characteristic of European or Far Eastern forests are totally absent from the true taiga. Birches *(Betula pubescens, B. verrucosa)*, fond of light and not too particular about soil or humidity, grow in sandy areas like the peaty bogs found from the Arctic coast to the Black Sea.

Birch or aspen *(Populus tremula)* forests are in fact temporary formations that always give way to conifers, for the taiga is the equivalent in the cold or temperate zone of the primary forest of equatorial regions. With the exception of the sylvan pine, often found growing with the larch, the taiga is formed of species that normally grow only in shade. Thus, if the taiga is cleared or is destroyed by fire, its trees cannot spring up spontaneously in the new clearings. Birches and aspens, whose seeds germinate readily in bright light, grow rapidly in such clearings and form a secondary growth. This growth, however, bears within it the germs of its own destruction, for young birches cannot grow in the shade of their elders whereas this shade is favorable to the growth of seeds of conifers from the surrounding taiga. Once grown, the conifers smother the light-loving trees and in about a century the forest returns to its original composition.

In winter, reindeer move from the tundra to the edge of the taiga where the snow is softer and can be probed for the lichens beneath. (Novosti)

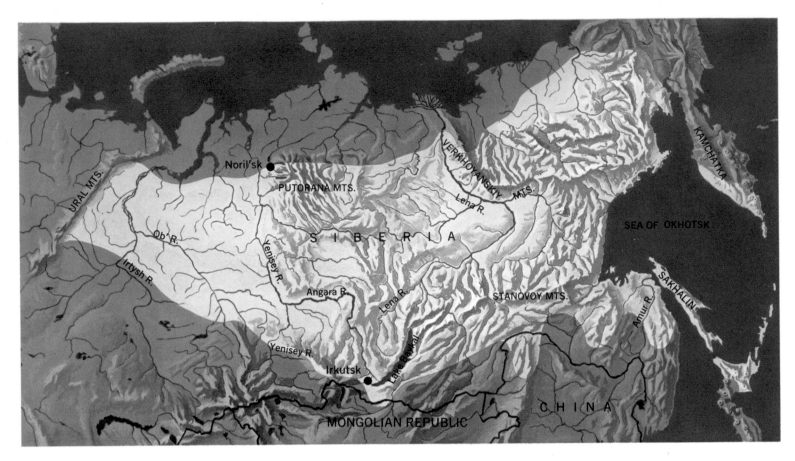

The Siberian taiga, a vast coniferous forest, covering more than four and a half million square miles, is divided into two fauna zones by the Yenisey River.

The undergrowth in the taiga is comparatively poor. In some places it is made up of Siberian junipers *(Juniperus sibirica),* dwarf willows *(Salix depressa),* and wild rosebushes *(Rosa acicularis),* all often thickly entwined with bindweed *(Atragene sibirica).* Elsewhere, there are almost pure stretches of whortleberries *(Vaccinium)* or sedge *(Carex schmidti)* that grow in small clumps. Most typically, the taiga is made up of scattered larches, growing no taller than sixty to seventy feet high and with trunks no more than twelve inches in diameter when they are 175 to 225 years old. The undergrowth consists of wild rosemary *(Ledum palustre),* whortleberries, sparse clumps of sedge, bushy cinquefoil *(Potentilla fruticosa)* and meadowsweet *(Spirea media).* Selaginellas *(Selaginella),* mosses *(Polytrichum)* and lichens *(Cladonia)* carpet the open spaces.

The monotony of the undergrowth in the taiga results not so much from lack of light, since the trees are often scattered, as from the inferior quality of the soil and a perpetually frozen layer not far beneath the surface. The poverty of the soil is a direct consequence of the climate in the Siberian forest zone. Rainfall is scarce, varying between twelve inches annually at the tundra's edge and twenty inches at the border of the steppe, but rains are usually violent, because concentrated almost entirely during July and August. As for the temperature, although it often falls below –60° F in winter, reaching –75° F and even –90° F, it is quite common for it to go over 100° F in summer.

The combined action of rain and heat literally leaches the surface soil and forces basic mineral salts deep into the earth. The absence of minerals and particularly of calcium causes great instability in the humus, whose components, remaining soluble, are carried away as rapidly as they form. Only insoluble particles of silica resist this washing process, which ends in the progressive increase of sand in the top soil.

The resultant soil, called *podzol* in Russian, is rich in silica and poor in lime and organic compounds. It is usually gray. Moreover, pure sand covers vast areas in the forest zone. In such places, the taiga is often formed of Scotch pines, which demand less of the soil than do other conifers. In some places, and especially in the basin of the Vilyuy River, dunes stretch across dozens and even hundreds of miles. Were it not for occasional knotty-trunked Siberian pines or cedars, we might believe we were in the heart of the Sahara Desert.

THE YENISEY FRONTIER

There is, nevertheless, a great difference between the landscapes of western Siberia and those of central and eastern Siberia. To the west of the Yenisey River, nature differs little from that in European Russia. The taiga is flat, swampy and monotonous. Its slope is so slight that the Ob' River drops only 308 feet in its 2,000-mile course.

The change in the landscape becomes perceptible only east

The taiga is composed mainly of firs, larches and pines, but along the edges of the many rivers and lakes are also found birches and aspens. (Novosti)

of the Yenisey; this was noted in 1730 by I. G. Gmelin, noted naturalist and traveler: "I had no feeling that I was in Asia until I reached the Yenisey. I had seen no animal, plant or stone that could not be seen in Europe or at least on the steppes of the Lower Volga. Even the earth seemed European to me, but to the east, south and north of the Yenisey, the land was entirely different, as if it had received fresh strength."

To the east of the Yenisey the taiga is furrowed with steep valleys dug out by the great Siberian rivers, including the 2,680-mile Lena, one of the longest rivers in the world. The Lena flows between cliffs nearly a thousand feet high and is swelled by several large tributaries that descend from the central Siberian plateaus. The most remarkable of these plateaus is the Noril'sk Plateau, also called the Putorana Mountains, dominating the surrounding plain from a mean height of almost two thousand feet and reaching a high point of 6,683 feet. Frequent moraines and many lakes bear witness to massive Quaternary glaciations. The lakes, mainly around the edges of the plateau, are long, narrow and very deep. Lake Lama, on the upper stream of the Pyasina River, is 682 feet deep and 51 miles long, but measures less than 5 miles at its widest point.

East and southeast of Noril'sk Plateau stretch the flat Vilyuyskiye Mountains, source of the Vilyuy, Olenek and Khatanga Rivers. The Vilyuyskiye Mountains rise no higher than two thousand feet and are also the result of a succession of glacial and river erosions. The streams carry down alluvium rich in gold and platinum. Between the Vilyuy and the Aldan, both tributaries of the Lena, the taiga is covered with innumerable natural amphitheaters and depressions, often filled with fresh or salt water. The natives of this region, the Iakuts, say that there are as many lakes in their land as stars in the sky. These bodies of water gradually become overgrown with plants and form small prairies in the midst of the forest.

East of the Lena, the topographical features are more marked and several ranges dominate the coastal plain from a height of nearly ten thousand feet. These are the Stanovoy Mountains, the Verkhoyanskiy Range, the Kolymskiy Range, and the Central Range of Kamchatka, which includes a number of active volcanoes, the most famous being the Klyuchevskaya (15,584 feet) and the Kronotskaya (11,575 feet).

LIFE ON THE TAIGA

It is interesting that the Yenisey is also the frontier for a certain number of animals of the taiga. For some it is the eastern and for others it is the western limit. A few, such as the European hedgehog, the common shrew (Sorex araneus), and Daubenton's bat (Myotis daubentoni) reappear in the composite taiga of Manchuria beyond a gap of several thousand miles. But the great majority, such as the European mole, marten and Eurasian wild sheep, are not found east of the Yenisey and its tributary, the Angara. Sometimes they are replaced eastwards by a closely related species: for example, the Altai mole. In other instances, a species lives on both sides of the Yenisey but is represented by a different race to the east. Thus the oriental reindeer differs from that of central Siberia but resembles the American caribou. Even more curious is the fact that some birds, like the great snipe, are found only on the west side of the river or on the east, like the Asiatic snipe, the Pacific swift and the pine grosbeak. The case of the crow (Corvus corone) is especially strange. The black crow lives only in Western Europe and east of the Yenisey. The hooded crow, whose plumage is partly gray, replaces it in Central Europe and in Siberia west of the river. Proof that these two forms are only geographical subspecies lies in the fact that in both western and eastern contact zones there are hybrids with intermediate plumage.

Whatever the biogeographical significance of the Yenisey may be, the animal population is comparatively homogeneous from the Urals to Kamchatka. Only the density of distribution of species varies with the plant life. The animal population is fairly small because living conditions are comparatively rigorous. But it is less difficult than on the tundra since here, too, certain favorable factors make life possible for animals.

Although the winters are long and severe, with temperatures normally descending to below −60° F, the lack of wind leaves

Left: The Eurasian boar increases in size as one moves east, and some specimens in eastern Siberia weigh more than four hundred pounds. (Zdzislaw Wdowinski)

Right: One of more than three hundred tributaries of Lake Baykal, this river follows its course along glacier-carved slopes. (Robert Frederick)

the snow, which is more abundant than on the tundra, rather loosely packed. Even if the ground is perpetually frozen in some regions, it is protected from the external cold by the snowy cover. The soil thus does not freeze at the surface except for a brief period of the year, so that insect-eaters can survive, and burrowing animals can dig tunnels in which to spend the winter comfortably

The presence of trees is also a factor favorable to animal life. They furnish a rather monotonous diet of seeds, buds. twigs and bark, but since the trees are coniferous they are available throughout the year. So the animals peculiar to the taiga—unlike those living in open spaces like the tundra or the steppe—generally lead settled lives, moving only enough to reach the most promising sectors of the forest.

The trees also furnish shelter for animals that, like the red squirrel (Sciurus vulgaris) and many birds, nest in branches, or, like the flying squirrel (Pteromys volans), the striped ground-squirrel (Eutamias sibiricus), woodpeckers, and nocturnal birds of prey, seek out holes in tree trunks. Even the brown bear often settles down between the roots or in the hollow trunk of a giant tree.

The availability of a variety of hiding places in the ground or in trees and an abundance of food during relatively brief periods of the year encourage many species to store up provisions for the winter. The root vole (Microtus oeconomus) and the ground-squirrel pile up seeds of fir or Norwegian pine in their burrows. The red squirrel hides cedar nuts in tree hollows or impales mushrooms on the ends of branches. The Siberian pica (Ochotona hyperborea) piles up hay in its burrow under a fallen trunk or a flat stone. And the Siberian jay (Cractes infaustus) buries cedar cones in the forest floor. This noisy, restless bird seems to have a mysterious sixth sense that enables it to bury seeds where the snow will be less thick. However, the jay forgets a good many of the buried seeds and these germinate the following spring. The bird thus plays a major role in the replacement of cedar forests, which are currently receding in most of Siberia.

Animals that store up provisions do not ordinarily hibernate, but the ground-squirrel, that striped tightrope-walker of the taiga, accumulates very little fatty reserve. It therefore awakens very early at the end of the winter and remains in its shelter eating the seeds and nuts it has collected there. True hibernators, such as the brown bear and the badger, develop a thick layer of fat at the beginning of winter and can maintain themselves for several months on an extremely reduced rate of metabolism.

THE CYCLE OF THE CONIFERS

Except for some migrating birds, most non-hibernating animals remain in the taiga and normally move only to the forest areas richest in seeds of coniferous trees. These seeds are the basic food of species peculiar to the taiga and these species are all specialists in opening cones and extracting the seeds of firs, Norwegian pines and cedars. Among the native birds, those best adapted to such feeding are the pine crossbill (Loxia curvirostra) and the white-winged crossbill (L. leucoptera), whose mandibles form a good pair of pincers. Others, such as the pine grosbeak (Pinicola enucleator), the spotted nutcracker (Nucifraga caryocatactes) and the great spotted woodpecker (Dendrocopos major) use their powerful beaks

to break the pine cones and cedar nuts. Most other species, such as the hazel grouse (Tetrastes bonasia), capercaillie (Tetrao urogallus), and Bohemian waxwings (Bombycilla garrulus) pick up seeds lying on the ground and add buds and berries to their diet.

These birds are thus less dependent on the ripening of conifers than birds that are strictly seed-eaters. The fruiting of these trees occurs in a comparatively regular cycle, varying only according to region. In eastern Siberia, on the borders of the Altai and east of Lake Baykal, only three truly poor harvests are expected in any ten-year period and there is abundant fruiting every two or three years. In western Siberia, good years for conifers and especially for firs are rarer and there is an average of nearly five poor harvests in every ten-year period. But larches and Norwegian pines that often fruit in years when the firs are unproductive serve to insure the subsistence of seed-eating species.

When seeds of conifers are abundant, the nesting of birds who feed on the seeds is early and prolonged. Fertility is also increased. As a result, at the end of the year, one may see within a day's time a hundred flights of crossbills, each consisting of forty-five to sixty-five birds, in forests where normally one may not see one bird a day. When lean years follow these fat periods, the excess populations must go off to find more favorable territory. This explains the periodic invasions of Central and Western Europe by Siberian crossbills, great spotted woodpeckers and nutcrackers.

SQUIRREL MIGRATIONS

Mammals that feed on the seeds of conifers—voles (Clethrionomys rutilus, C. rufocanus), forest lemmings (Myopus schisticolor), ground-squirrels, flying squirrels and red squirrels—show the same cyclical fluctuations in population numbers. Russian hunters have known for years that their collections of "Russian squirrel" skins, a variety of red squirrel whose fur becomes bluish-gray in winter, correspond closely to the fruiting of the conifers. During favorable years, those following an autumn rich in seeds, the squirrels reproduce early and bear between seven and ten young in a litter. Abundant food permits as many as three litters a summer and greatly reduces the mortality rate of both young and adult animals. As a result, each pair may raise eight or nine baby squirrels in a year, increasing the population nearly 400 percent. On the other hand, if the seed crop has been low, reproduction of the animals is late, fertility is reduced, and juvenile mortality is very high. The number of young in each litter falls to no more than from two to five, and only one or two reach adulthood. The population increase falls to 75 percent, barely compensating for the yearly mortality of squirrels.

Since the fruiting of conifers varies from region to region, the squirrels abandon less favorable areas for those where they hope to find more abundant food. It is unsound to speak of these as true migrations, although they may cover several hundred miles and include most of the population. Such movements are particularly frequent in the northern regions of the taiga, where vegetation is uniformly distributed and consequently large areas are involved whenever there is an alternation of scarcity and abundance.

During these movements, the squirrels generally travel as individuals but all go forward in the same direction, forming

The Siberian weasel (Mustela sibirica), *with magnificent orange-colored fur, is found throughout most of the taiga. (Novosti)*

what the Russian zoologist N. A. Bobrinsky describes as a front line that may be almost two hundred miles wide. The rate of progress of this rodent army is about two miles an hour and it sometimes takes as much as two months for them to pass a point. No obstacle stops these hordes, and squirrels have been seen swimming across rivers such as the Yenisey, the Amur, and the Dvina at points nearly four miles wide.

The flying squirrel does not seem to undertake even limited migrations. Of course, it is a nocturnal animal and is not so numerous anywhere. Its preferred habitat is the undisturbed taiga where trees with immense trunks offer the shelter it needs, for it uses either a natural hole or one bored by a northern titmouse *(Parus atricapillus),* a great spotted woodpecker, a black woodpecker *(Dryocopus martius)* or a three-toed woodpecker *(Picoides tridactylus).* The flying squirrel looks like a small gray squirrel with big black eyes, but is easily recognized by a fur-covered fold of skin that stretches between the body and the ends of the four paws. When the animal soars from a treetop, it spreads this membrane like a

parachute and descends, gliding for as much as several dozen yards.

The great enemy of the three species of squirrels in the taiga west of the Yenisey is the marten *(Martes martes),* which follows them into their refuges in trees or in the ground. Although the brown bear will also take a squirrel when the opportunity presents itself, it devotes more of its attention, especially in the spring, to a search for the provisions hoarded by the ground-squirrel, thus condemning the rodent to death from hunger.

THE RESURRECTION OF THE SABLE

The sable *(Martes zibellina),* whose habitat once coincided everywhere with the limits of the taiga east of the Yenisey, is also an active hunter of the striped squirrel and other small ground rodents, particularly voles. Unlike its cousin the marten, the sable dislikes climbing trees. Harried for its precious

41

fur, the sable itself would have disappeared without the protective measures undertaken at the beginning of World War I. Efforts to breed the animal in captivity had been useless until a biological peculiarity was noted. When a male and a female sable were placed together at what was believed to be a favorable time, February and March, breeders saw a nuptial parade during which the male brought food to its companion but never went so far as to mate. Yet, in the wild, the young were born thirty-five to forty days after the time of this "false rut." Patient investigation finally showed that mating really took place during the months of June and July, but that development of the embryo was delayed for seven or eight months, during the harshest period of the year, and began again in the spring. The male's interest in the female at that moment, but with no attempt to fertilize her, indicated that he knew she was already gestating. Bringing food at a time of year when it is scarce seems to be, according to Professor A. G. Bannikov, a kind of manifestation of the paternal instinct. In any case, it was not until the true length of the sable's gestation period was discovered to be not thirty-five to forty days, but nine months, and that genuine rut occurred in summer, that breeding in captivity and restoration of the wild population became possible.

The principal role in this resurrection was played by the Barguzin reserve, on the eastern shore of Lake Baykal. The splendid primeval taiga of cedars, larches and firs bordering the lake is ideal for this precious animal, and its fur takes on a deep chocolate hue and a particularly desirable silken quality here. So when the imperial government sent out an expedition in 1914 to find a favorable spot for setting up a reserve for sables, experts selected the region of Barguzin without hesitation. The project was resumed after the revolution at a time when barely twenty animals remained in the reserve. In 1934, the population of that area had reached about two hundred, and nearly a hundred and fifty sables spilled over onto the neighboring taiga each year. Today, seven to eight hundred sables live in the reserve, a number that cannot be increased since each animal requires a hunting area of one or two square miles. In 1957, 12,600 sables were set free at various places in Siberia and, according to Soviet experts, the population has reached its level of two centuries ago.

Intolerant of competition, the sable eliminates its close relatives, the ermine *(Mustela erminea)* and the Siberian weasel *(M. sibirica),* from its own home range. These two carnivorous animals abound in other regions, as does the common weasel *(M. nivalis),* but the golden-yellow Altai weasel *(M. altaica)* lives only on the high taiga of southern Siberia.

Left above: The well-known red fox (Vulpes vulpes) *is found all through the palearctic region. It feeds on seeds, berries and small animals and has adapted to man's presence.   Left: The wolf, ancient enemy of shepherds, is relatively common throughout Eurasia, sometimes penetrating the forests but generally preferring open tundra and steppes. (Both, Zdzislaw Wdowinski)*

Right: The brown bear (Ursus arctos), *an omnivorous forest-dweller, is found north of the Himalayas from the Pyrenees to Japan. (Zdzislaw Wdowinski)*

The lynx *(Lynx lynx)* is widely distributed throughout the coniferous belt and in the broad-leafed forests. Although it occasionally hunts all kinds of animals, birds as well as mammals, its basic food is the varying hare. Its search for this prey is so specialized that here, as in Canada, lynx populations fluctuate with those of the hare. For more than a century, Siberian trappers have noted that swarming peaks of hares, occurring about every ten years, are followed by unusually good lynx hunting.

The wolverine *(Gulo gulo),* which is frequently found making summer raids on the tundra, is in general native to the taiga, although not abundant there. Comparatively clumsy but exceptionally strong, it seeks prey of any size up to that of the fawn of the reindeer or stag. Since it eats anything, feasting as readily on plants as on carrion or wounded animals, it is hated by trappers, from whom it steals both bait and trapped animals.

Among other carnivores are the badger and the fox, the latter wearing an especially thick red fur coat in the taiga. The wolf usually remains at the edge of the forest, entering it only through clearings or river valleys. There it hunts reindeer and elk, which are found all over the taiga, roebucks and marals, a variety of red European stag, which frequents only those sections of forest with a mixture of broad-leafed trees, and the musk-deer that appear east of the Yenisey.

Rodents and birds of the taiga are also subject to many other marauders: the golden eagle *(Aquila chrysaetos),* the common buzzard *(Buteo buteo),* the hawk *(Accipter nisus),* the goshawk *(A. gentilis),* the peregrine falcon *(Falco peregrinus),* the eagle owl *(Bubo bubo),* the great gray owl *(Strix nebulosa),* the hawk owl *(Surnia ulula)* and the Tengmalm's owl *(Aegolius funereus).* Along streams and above the taiga's countless lakes one may see the white-tailed eagle *(Haliaeetus albicilla)* or the fish-hawk *(Pandion haliaetus).* An abundance of fish, including carp, pike, perch and various salmonids also attract the otter *(Lutra lutra),* as common in the rivers and lakes of the taiga as in those of the tundra. Among species dependent upon water but indifferent to the forest are the water vole *(Arvicola terrestris),* the aquatic shrewmouse *(Neomys fodiens)* and a host of web-footed, shore-dwelling birds that live in wooded regions as well as on the tundra or the steppe. Still other animals are equally bound to water but not found outside the forest belt because trees are essential to their existence. These include the beaver, whose basic food is bark and branches, and such diving birds as the goldeneye *(Bucephala clangula)* and the little smew *(Mergus albellus),* which nests almost exclusively in hollow trees.

THE OLDEST LAKE IN THE WORLD

The most famous of the many lakes on the Siberian taiga is Lake Baykal. Situated at the edge of the highlands of Central Asia, it is surrounded by strikingly sculptured mountains with bare summits, but with slopes covered with green pastures

Red deer (Cervus elaphus), *found in Europe and palearctic Asia, seek mountain pastures in summer and descend to forested valleys in winter. (Novosti)*

painted in the spring with poppies, iris and wild anemones. Lower down are vast forests of cedar, larch and fir strewn with stands of birches, ash and aspens. Steep valleys, cirques covered with eternal snows, and the slashed sides of numerous fjords are relics of great glacial activity.

The entire region is a huge collecting basin whence nearly three hundred streams and rivers flow toward Lake Baykal. The most important is the Selenga River, almost a thousand miles long, rising in the Khangai Range in the heart of Mongolia and carrying nearly half the water that flows into the lake. The overflow runs toward the Yenisey by means of the Angara, a turbulent river cut by many gorges. Although it is not the largest lake in the world, Baykal is the deepest, 5,314 feet. It is also the largest fresh-water reservoir in the world: 5,520 cubic miles, or a fifth of earth's total reserves. Astonishingly clear and rich in oxygen, the water makes it possible for plants to grow as far down as 220 feet and for animal life to flourish near the bottom of the lake.

The purity of the waters of Baykal was dramatically pointed out recently by Dr. Grigory Galazy, head of the Soviet Institute of Limnology. According to Dr. Galazy, victims of drowning in the lake vanish without a trace. Their flesh is quickly consumed by crustaceans and their bones dissolve in the almost mineral-free water.

But the most extraordinary fact about Lake Baykal is its antiquity. Even though geologists do not agree on its age, the most conservative estimates date its appearance back to the Miocene Period, twenty-five million years ago, making it by far the oldest lake in the world. This antiquity makes Baykal zoologically interesting, for residual animals from Asiatic and North American fresh waters, which were still connected at the time of the lake's birth, have been able to survive and evolve amidst almost unaltered conditions. It even appears that the waters of the lake are colder today than at the beginning of the Tertiary Era, but since this temperature change has taken place very gradually, living organisms have been able to adapt to it.

The result of this long evolutionary process is that out of nearly six hundred species of algae and more than twelve hundred species of animals, three-quarters are endemic, truly peculiar to Lake Baykal. This endemism is not limited to species, but includes entire genera and even families—the best evidence of the antiquity of the lake's animals. Thus the lake has a family of sponges with three genera and six distinct species; forty endemic species of turbellarian or planarian worms; two families, six genera, and forty-six species of gastropod mollusks; nearly forty orders and two hundred and sixty original species of crustaceans, including asellids and gammarids with astonishing shapes; two families, with seven

Left: The white-tailed eagle (Haliaeetus albicilla), *one of a few species of fishing-eagles found in Russia, haunts lakes and rivers and catches fish with its powerful talons. (Novosti)*

Right above: The Ural owl (Strix uralensis), *a nocturnal predator of Siberian forests, hunts voles, striped squirrels and other rodents.   Right: The Siberian squirrel, famous for its blue-gray winter coat, is a close relative of the common red squirrel. (Both, Novosti)*

The beaver of Northern Asia, like its near relative in North America, survives only due to strict protection. The sight of one of them building its dam is rare in Siberia now. (Novosti)

genera and twenty-three endemic species of fish; and a unique mammal, the Baykal seal *(Phoca sibirica)*.

The greedy Baykal crustaceans are eager to gobble up any fish eggs that appear, and the fish have had to develop curious spawning habits. Some travel up the rivers to breed; others lay eggs that are poisonous or foul-smelling to predators. One species, *Cottus inermis,* places its eggs under stones that the male then guards; and to increase his effectiveness he has evolved enormous side fins which he spreads over the stones.

The most extraordinary fish in the lake are the Comephoridae. The size of a pencil, they have transparent bodies without scales and an extremely pure fat that accounts for 26 percent of their weight. If one takes this little fish out of the water and leaves it in the sun, it literally melts away.

The other endemic family of fish is that of the Cottocomephoridae. These live on the stony bottom and, with their short bodies and large triangular heads, resemble bullheads. In May, when they spawn near the shores and in the mouths of

Lake Baykal, the deepest and oldest lake in the world, is rich in endemic species. Its waters are so pure that the slightest pollution would threaten its unique animal life. (Harrison Forman)

the streams of the taiga, all the bears in the neighborhood gather on the lake shore to turn over the stones and spear the fish with their long claws. The noise the bears make is like that of a gang of ditch-diggers. Not until they are satiated, late at night, do they rest for a few hours.

The Cottocomephoridae are also the basic food of the Baykal seal, which zoologists agree is closely related to the species dwelling on the Arctic coast. Many theories have been put forward as to how these seals could have been isolated in the heart of Asia. The most persuasive is that they reached Lake Baykal at the time of the melting of the big glaciers by swimming up the Lena River.

The Baykal seal came very close to being annihilated by fur hunters, but conservation measures have fortunately been taken by the Soviet Union and the seal population has been brought up to 30,000 individuals. Concern is now focused on preserving the lake itself and all of the unique and remarkable species it harbors. A typical threat is a huge new pulp mill which is reportedly discharging its wastes into the lake and will alter or destroy the life that has evolved in it over the ages. The volume of Baykal is so great that a bucketful of water—or pollutants—flowing into it will remain there for about four hundred years before flowing out again.

Mixed Forests and a Belt of Fire

Manchuria, Korea and Japan

3 Life on the taiga of Central Asia, made up of species fairly indifferent to the available water, is restricted by the scant rainfall of the area. Near the sea, in both Europe and the Far East, more abundant rain fosters the growth of broad-leafed trees, and the true coniferous taiga is succeeded first by the composite or mixed taiga and then by completely deciduous forests.

In the Far East, the influence of the sea reaches far inland as a result of summer monsoon winds that sweep the entire

Right: Much richer in plant species than the taiga, the mixed forest turns red and gold in autumn. The Japanese forest, shown here near Aomori, has 168 species of trees as against Europe's 85. (Orion Press)   Below: The white-cheeked flying squirrel (Petaurista leucogenys) of Japan and Korea is related to the large flying squirrels of tropical Asia. (T. Iwago)

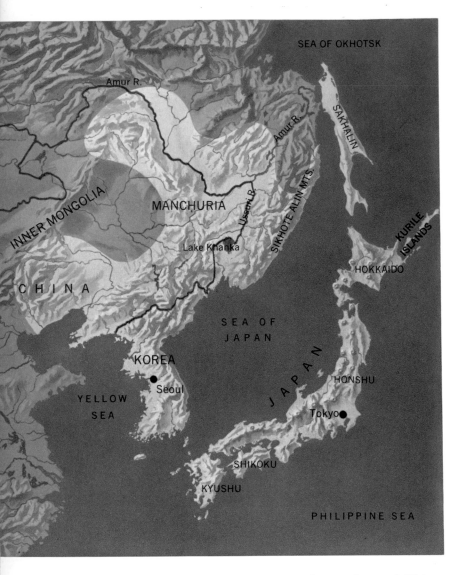

SEA OF OKHOTSK

Amur R.

MANCHURIA

SAKHALIN

Amur R.

INNER MONGOLIA

SIKHOTE ALIN MTS.

Ussuri R.

Lake Khanka

KURILE ISLANDS

HOKKAIDO

CHINA

SEA OF JAPAN

KOREA

JAPAN

HONSHU

Seoul

YELLOW SEA

Tokyo

SHIKOKU

KYUSHU

PHILIPPINE SEA

The Amur and Ussuri river regions, the northeast of China, Korea and Japan are covered with a mixed forest where coniferous trees of the taiga mingle with leafy trees characteristic of temperate and sub-tropical areas.

region of the Ussuri and Amur Rivers, Manchuria and part of Japan and Korea. These great river basins and Manchuria, now called the Northeast Provinces by the Chinese, form a unit of more than 400,000 square miles, twice the area of France. Low forests alternate with alluvial prairies and two great mountain ranges, the Great Khingan and the Sikhote Alin, climbing as high as eleven thousand feet, mark the region from southwest to northwest. Prolonging the massifs of Central Asia, these ranges have permitted the extension northward of some Himalayan animals and plants, rhododendrons, the Tibetan black bear and a small mountain goat-antelope, the goral *(Nemorhaedus goral)*.

Rivers, often wide and swift, flow either toward the interior, emptying into the Amur, or toward the sea. They are rich in fish: carp, catfish, Chinese perch *(Sinaperca chuatsi)*, and all sorts of salmonids, especially the giant Far Eastern salmon or taimen *(Hucho taimen)* and the "lenok" *(Brachymystax lenok)*.

The Korean peninsula, 560 miles long and 140 miles wide, bristles with mountains that reach to the sea, forming steep, indented coasts bordered with countless islands. Although located in the same latitude as Naples and Sicily, Korea has a

climate as severe as that of Manchuria, and the late eigtheenth-century French explorer La Pérouse was much surprised to find snow in the valleys during the month of May. In summer, by contrast, regions influenced by the monsoons are so hot and humid that the air is as saturated with moisture as in the tropics. Plant life, dormant for months, bursts into frenzied growth. The annual and perennial plants, bushes, ferns and creeping and climbing vines become so dense as to be almost impenetrable.

Unlike the taiga, where the undergrowth is scarce, the composite forests of the Far East are characterized by three plant levels: a canopy of tall trees, an intermediate stratum of smaller trees, and thick undergrowth. Among the tallest trees are many conifers: Korean pines *(Pinus coraiensis)*, black firs *(Abies holophylla)*, the spruce *(Picea koyamai)* and larches *(Larix olgensis)*. However, except in mountainous areas, leafy trees predominate. The oak reappears after an eclipse of several thousand miles and is represented by a species *(Quercus mongolica)* different from those found in Europe and North America. This is also true, of the Amur linden *(Tilia amurensis)*, recognizable by its small leaves. Many other European forest trees are found in species peculiar to the Far East: birches *(Betula costata, B. dahurica)*, Manchurian maples, lindens, and walnuts *(Acer mandshuricum, Tilia mandshurica, Juglans mandshurica)*, and small-leafed elms *(Ulmus pumila)*.

The middle level is composed mainly of small species of maples, hornbeans, ash, wild apple and wild pear trees, hawthorn, and cork *(Phellodendron amurense)*. They are interspersed with bushy plants, spindle-trees, hazelnut trees, dogwoods, elders, lilacs, wild roses, bramble bushes and such climbers as honeysuckle, clematis and wild vine *(Vitis amurensis)*, rising to ten or fifteen feet above the ground. Sometimes huge ferns *(Dryopteris crassirhizoma)*, spread out over large areas, and all the open ground is covered by a thick carpet of mosses, with sphagnum predominant.

The swampy or semiswamp depression between the Amur and the Ussuri is a series of vast grassy prairies; some of the grasses *(Calamagrostis langsdorfii)* grow as tall as a man. Curiously, these boggy stretches have been colonized by plant and animal species typical of the arid steppes of Central Asia. One finds here such combinations of plants as the grass *Stipa capillata*, the lily *Hemerocallis minor*, and the composite *Tanacetum sibiricum*, all considered strictly steppe plants by botanists. One may also see susliks or ground-squirrels, bustards and sand-grouse belonging to species that we shall meet on the steppes and semideserts of the center of the continent. It is very possible that these large Far Eastern prairies are of secondary origin, the result, as in tropical regions, of man's immemorial habit of cutting down forests and preventing their growing back by regularly burning off the grassland.

On the heights above the timber line, there is natural pasture, and above 6,500 feet this gives way to alpine tundra formed of a mixture of such typical mountain plants as the rhododendron, here found in pygmy forms *(Rhodendendrum aureum, R. redowskianum)*, and such characteristic species of Arctic

The red deer (Cervus elaphus), *here photographed in the Sary-Telchek reserve in Kirghizia, is a typical denizen of the mixed temperate forests of Eurasia where it is represented by several local races. One of them, the* maral, *lives between the Caucasus and Altai Mountains. (Novosti)*

Handsome in its winter coat, the tiger of Manchuria and Korea is the rarest and largest of its species on the continent, often growing to nearly twelve feet long. Russian experts estimate that no more than 120 remain. (Soviet Life from Sovfoto)

tundra as dwarf birches and willows, bushes of *Dryas octopetala* with tiny toothed leaves and velvety white flowers.

A FABLED ROOT

The most singular plant of the Far East's composite taigas is the ginseng, meaning, in Chinese, man-root, or root with human qualities. A member of the family of the Araliaceae, the ginseng *(Panax ginseng)* is a modest herbaceous perennial with a long, slim stem ending in three or four slender leaflets, resembling a hand with outspread fingers. The plant bears small pink or white umbellate flowers in August and its fruits are light red berries containing flat white seeds.

Certainly no other plant in the world has such a reputation or is so shrouded in mystery. Ginseng root has been used for ages in Chinese and Tibetan medicine as a specific for many serious diseases, notably tuberculosis, and especially against the general aging of the human organism, whence comes the name often applied to it, the "root of life." The miraculous root is not, however, extraordinary in appearance. It is pale yellow, thick, about two and a half inches in diameter, with a blackish, forked end.

The root undoubtedly contains alkaloids with medical prop-

erties and for some years now scientists have been studying its possible uses. With such uses in mind, the plant has been successfully cultivated in Korea and in America, but oriental medicine doubts the curative powers of cultivated ginseng. Orientals appreciate only roots of the wild plant; and these bring fabulous prices.

Thus, each year, when summer begins, ginseng hunters plunge deep into the taiga, spurred by hope of the fortune that an exceptionally large root will bring. According to legend, however, a greedy or wicked man may pass by the ginseng ten times without seeing it, for at his approach, the root sinks deep into the ground, the mountains tremble, and "Big Van" comes out of its lair to devour him. "Big Van," lord of the forest, is the giant Manchurian tiger. These are the largest of all extant felines, hunters having killed some that measure nearly thirteen feet long and weigh 715 pounds. The forest basins between the Amur and the Ussuri as far as Korea, suit this cat perfectly, contrary to general opinion, which thinks of it as a typical tropical animal. It is remarkable that in proportion to its remoteness from cold countries, the tiger diminishes in size. Indian tigers rarely reach ten feet in total length; Indochinese, nine feet; Javanese, eight feet, eight inches. As for Balinese tigers, they are no longer than eight feet, five inches, the size of Manchurian leopards.

These huge animals find plenty of prey in the composite forests of the Far East. The tiger attacks wild boars, also enormous here, and stags, elks and roe deer. The leopard, like the lynx, tracks down musk-deer, short-eared hares *(Lepus brachyurus)*, ring-necked pheasants, black grouse, the large capercaillies and hazel-grouse. On the heights, leopards attack gorals, Himalayan animals that, like Tibetan bears, reached Manchuria across the mountain ranges of interior China.

Animals of the composite taigas seem to be a mixture of Siberian, tropical and Himalayan forms to which are added animals from the steppes, species common in European and American forests, and those characteristic of this region. The Himalayan animals are the goral and the Tibetan black bear. Tropical mammals and birds are the tiger, the leopard, and the Bengal cat *(Felis bengalensis)*, the black-headed oriole *(Oriolus xanthornus)*, the long-tailed broadbill *(Psarisomus dalhousiae)*, the Indian goatsucker *(Caprimulgus indicus)* and the black drongo *(Dicrurus hottentottus)*.

Representing Siberian fauna are the Siberian weasel, the striped ground-squirrel, the flying squirrel, the black woodpecker, the great spotted woodpecker, the three-toed woodpecker, the hazel-grouse and the capercaillie. Steppe animals include susliks, marmots, bustards and sand-grouse. Common to Far Eastern, European and American composite forests are the brown bear, lynx, fox, badger, weasel, ermine, elk, red stag, roe deer, red squirrel, field-mouse *(Apodemus agrarius)*, common shrew *(Sorex araneus)*, and the common hedgehog.

Peculiar to the region are the musk-deer *(Moschus moschiferus)*, the sika deer *(Cervus nippon)*, the short-eared Manchurian hare, moles of the genus *Mogera*, the taloned shrew *(Sorex unguiculatus)*, a dwarf hamster *(Cricetulus triton)*, a lemming *(Lemmus amurensis)*, and, among the birds, the Manchurian pheasant, the mandarin duck *(Aix galericulata)*, the Manchurian crane *(Grus japonensis)*, the spotted harrier *(Circus melanoleucos)*, and a white-eye *(Zosterops erythropleura)*, the most northern representative of a very widely diffused tropical genus.

A CURIOUS LITTLE DOG

The most extraordinary indigenous inhabitant of the Far East's composite taigas is a small animal that looks at first glance like a cross between a Pekinese and a raccoon. It has the raccoon's pointed muzzle and bright eyes encircled with black rings that form a pair of eyeglasses under a white forehead. It has the long, thick hair, short legs and clumsy walk of the Pekinese. This curious beast, zoologically a member of the canine family, is the raccoon dog, *Nyctereutes procyonides*.

Its original habitat is the damp taiga of northeastern China

Right above: An ermine (Mustela erminea) *in its summer coat on the Chukchi Peninsula where it feeds on lemmings. Common in Europe and Northern Asia, it is best known for its white winter fur. (Novosti)   Center: Despite its name, the raccoon dog* (Nyctereutes procyonides) *is a member of the canine family. A native of the Ussuri region, it has spread, often with man's help, as far as Central Europe. (A. G. Bannikov)   Right: This species,* Sorex caecutiens, *is the most common of the shrewmice in the taiga of western Siberia, where it finds an abundance of worms and insects. (Novosti)*

where the alternation of severe winters and hot, rainy summers is favorable to the many bushy plants swarming with the small animals and insects it eats. The raccoon dog avoids purely coniferous forests without undergrowth and is found in such areas only along streams or in thickly tangled shrubbery. It is also found on mountains, along the seacoast or in swampy areas beside lakes and rivers. A good swimmer, it crosses large bodies of water and settles on small islands. It can set up its den, usually carpeted with grass and hair, in the abandoned burrow of a fox or in one it digs itself, usually in a rock crevice or in the hollow of a dead tree. Some yards from its lair, it makes little holes where it leaves its excrement. When its home no longer suits it, the raccoon dog moves. Animals that nest in reeds at the edges of rivers or lakes move to higher ground when the water begins to rise in the spring. Natives of these regions have sometimes noted the movement of several hundred raccoon dogs over a period of several days, and some biologists have mistakenly concluded from this that these animals make regular seasonal migrations.

In the coldest habitats, raccoon dogs sleep away a large part of the winter in their dens. This false hibernation, unlike the hibernation of marmots, which is accompanied by an abrupt fall in the metabolic rate and body temperature, is merely a deep winter sleep that may be broken if the weather becomes mild. Nevertheless, a drop of 25 percent in the breathing and temperature of the sleeping animals has been noted.

At the beginning of their pseudo-hibernation, a mean 18 or 23 percent of the total weight of the raccoon dogs is subcutaneous fat and 3 to 5 percent is internal fat. Animals that have less than these quantities must interrupt their sleep to seek food; they rarely survive the winter. However, in many regions or when the winter is not very severe, a large percentage of the animals remain active all winter long and have been captured out of their shelters at –5° F or –10° F.

The raccoon dog is as flexible in its choice of food as in its selection of living quarters. Professor Bannikov reported that in its natural habitat, 35 percent of its food was rodents and insect-eaters such as voles, field-mice, striped squirrels, moles, and hedgehogs. Insects accounted for another 30 percent, and fruit, nestling birds, small reptiles, and fish made up the rest.

The raccoon dog has many natural enemies, chiefly wolves, but also foxes, roving dogs, lynxes, and birds of prey, especially golden eagles and great horned owls. Its greatest enemy, however, is man, who hunts it for its rather rough but thick, long and durable fur, and for its meat, which peoples of the Far East enjoy. The usual method of hunting is nocturnal tracking with "laika" dogs, whose baying locates the game.

Left above: The sika (Cervus nippon), *or Japanese deer, has been introduced into Europe and New Zealand. Medium-sized, white-spotted in summer, it wears antlers with three or four prongs. Left: The serow* (Capricornus crispus), *a long-haired, small-horned goat-antelope of the mountain forests of Japan and Formosa, has a close relative in the Himalayas, Szechwan, Indochina and Sumatra. (Both, T. Iwago)*

Right: The Japanese macaque (Macaca fuscata) *lives farthest north of all the monkeys. At home in forests and along the sea coasts, it eats fruits, leaves, crabs and crustaceans (T. Iwago)*

The alpine ptarmigan (Lagopus mutus), *found in almost all western Eurasian mountains, is called* raicho *or "thunderbird," in Japan. Once venerated for its reputed power to raise storms, it has become quite rare. (Japan National Tourist Organization)*

Many raccoon dogs are also captured in traps, a sport which was, in the nineteenth century, a favorite of exiles and deportees in Siberia.

Nearly 70,000 raccoon dog pelts are taken in the Soviet Union alone each year, but the species continues to flourish because of its extreme fertility. It can begin to reproduce when it is eight or ten months old, and females bear a mean of six to seven pups a year but often reaching twelve or, more rarely, fifteen. Taking into account the mortality of young animals, the annual increase in raccoon dog populations varies between 54 and 60 percent according to regions, a tremendously high rate for an animal of its size.

Consequently, unlike other wild carnivores, the raccoon dog has so adapted to the advances of civilization that it has spread widely over Eurasia. After the clearing of the coniferous taiga, which did not suit it, it has colonized almost all of Siberia. Introduced into European Russia as a fur-bearing animal, it has spread westward into Poland and Central Europe as far as Western Germany. In addition to its remarkable fertility, two factors have enabled this clumsy animal to conquer the continent. One is the decline of its natural enemies and rivals, the wolf and the fox, and the other is its astonishing adaptability to different places and diets.

The history of the raccoon dog resembles that of the American armadillo, which is also clumsy-looking, but which continues to extend its living space despite the encroachment of civilization. Like the raccoon dog, the armadillo has profited from the battle waged against its enemies, especially the coyote, and has also shown a remarkable capacity to adapt to different environments. It is interesting to note that both animals live and reproduce in burrows that shelter them from man and his helper, the dog.

FIRE BELT OF THE PACIFIC

Stretching from the mouth of the Amur River to La Pérouse Strait, the long narrow island of Sakhalin separates the Sea of Okhotsk from the Sea of Japan. Sakhalin was considered a peninsula by La Pérouse and other navigators who sailed in those waters during the end of the eighteenth and the begin-

The "Japanese Alps" are the most famous of the high mountains of central Honshu. This variegated leafy forest at 4,875 feet in the subalpine zone of Kamikochi shelters many birds. (Orion)

ning of the nineteenth centuries. Their error was understandable, for Sakhalin is divided from the continent only by a four-mile strip of water that is covered with ice for most of the year. Not until 1849, when a Russian voyager G. I. Nevelsky managed to navigate the narrow strait, was Sakhalin discovered to be an island.

On either side of Sakhalin, the seas of Okhotsk and of Japan form almost closed basins separated from the Pacific by a garland that includes the thirty Kurile Islands and the thirty-three hundred islands and islets of the Japanese archipelago. This chaplet of islands on the edge of the great Pacific abyss —which is often more than 30,000 feet deep—is part of the long volcanic belt linking the Sunda Islands to Alaska by way of the Philippines, Kamchatka and the Aleutians. Most of the volcanoes in this chain are extinct, but many are still active. The turbulent history of these islands explains their form and their very irregular topography. During the Tertiary Era, powerful upheavals lifted huge underwater ridges and divided them into a series of distinct arcs: the Aleutians, the arc of Kamchatka and the Kuriles, the Japanese arc, and, further south, the arcs of the Ryukyus and of Taiwan, and of the Philippine and Sunda islands.

Sakhalin is really a part of the Japanese arc. Two parallel mountain chains, running from north to south and rising as high as 5,000 feet, cover the island almost entirely. Although the island is very narrow, its six-hundred-mile length and its mountains combine to give it twice the surface area of Switzerland and very steep relief effects. The Kuriles, forming a string nearly 625 miles long, are almost purely volcanic and comprise more than a hundred volcanoes, thirty-five of them still active. The tallest one, Mount Alaid (7,568 feet), with a cone as perfect as that of Fuji-yama, forms the chain's most northerly island. Alaid has not been active since 1821, but other Kurile volcanoes have begun to erupt more recently. In 1946, Sarychev, on Matoua Island, began to cough up bursts of incandescent lava and clouds of ashes. The presence of many craters overrun

by the sea and of rivers whose valleys empty out several hundred feet above sea level bear witness to the tumultuous geological history of the islands and their continuing upheavals.

The same movements carved out the Japanese archipelago whose shores are probably among the most irregular in the world. The geographer Pierre Gourou calculated that Japan has five-eighths of a mile of coastline for every six and a half square miles of territory, whereas the British Isles have five-eighths of a mile of coastline for every thirteen and a half square miles of surface. The total coastline of the Japanese islands is 17,875 miles, more than all the coasts of the United States, whose total surface is nearly twenty times greater than of Japan. The settling of the Japanese islands and the consequent encroachment by the sea have given rise to the huge bays of Tokyo and Osaka and the lacy shoreline of the west coast of Kyushu at Nagasaki or the Bay of Wasaka, north of Kyoto. The famous Interior Sea, called the Japanese Mediterranean, is the result of a water invasion of a vast trench studded with granite peaks. Nowhere more than 160 feet deep, the sea has a calm blue surface strewn with about six hundred small islands. These islets are often covered with forests or terraced fields and present an idyllic landscape.

The upheavals that formed Japan continue to this day in the form of frequent earthquakes. The frequency record is held by Gifu, in the northwest of Nagoya, where each year there are more than five hundred seismic vibrations strong enough to be felt by man. These quakes, sometimes quite strong, constantly alter the topography, for horizontal movements following the vertical ones cause fissures that cut across roads and fields. It was in this locality that the large Buddhist temple of Ogaki collapsed during the earthquake of 1891, killing four hundred worshippers. In the past thousand years Japan has had more than 227 major earthquakes; one of the most disastrous of these struck Tokyo and Yokohama in 1923, killing more than one hundred thousand people and raising the shores of the Bay of Sagami by more than twenty-three feet. Even more destructive than earthquakes are seaquakes or tidal waves, called *tsunami,* terrifying liquid walls that may be a hundred feet high and drown everything in their path.

As a result of this turbulent history, more than three-quarters of the 237,500 square miles of Japan's landmass slopes more than fifteen percent and less than a fifth of its surface is truly level ground. Formations of volcanic origin occupy a third of the country and it has 165 volcanoes, fifty-four of them still active, of every shape and size. The most famous is Fuji-yama, the tallest mountain in Japan, 12,395 feet high. Taller volcanoes are found at other points of the globe, especially in the Andes, but none is more majestic than the snowy, solitary cone of Fuji rising above the sea. Worshipped by the Japanese from time immemorial, it has become the national symbol, a decoration found on every type of object from Hokusai's

Left: Hunting the large oriental white egret (Egretta alba) *was once reserved for Japanese noblemen. It now lives in vast colonies like that of Noda-Sagiyama, a National Park near Tokyo. (T. Iwago)*

Right: Japanese forests such as this one on the lower slopes of the mountains near Kyoto are among the most beautiful in the world, plants of temperate and hot regions intermingling remarkably. (Fosco Maraini)

paintings to souvenir ashtrays. All Japanese volcanoes that resemble Fuji-yama in having a more or less perfect cone are named *fuji:* thus Ezo-fuji, Iwa-fuji, Izumo-fuji, Sanuki-fuji, and so on.

Other Japanese volcanoes are of the caldera or cauldron type. Mount Akan, on Hokkaido, is composed of two calderas side by side; one of these, Kutcharo, is the widest in the world, measuring sixteen by twelve and a half miles and containing an active volcano and an astonishingly clear crater lake. The other caldera encloses two volcanoes, O-Akan or the male Akan, and Me-Akan, the female Akan. It is at Kyushu, however, that one may see one of the most magnificent calderas in the world, Mount Aso, almost as wide as Kutcharo and containing five volcanoes. One of these, Naka-Daka, is always fully active, belching huge columns of black or white smoke mixed with gaseous sulphuric acid, sulphuric hydrogen, and a large quantity of ash. As in every country that is as heavily populated and as lacking in flat land as Japan, all the space between these volcanoes is inhabited and is covered with carefully cultivated fields.

FOG AND BAMBOO

Since the northernmost of the Kuriles reaches as far as Kamchatka, while southernmost Japan lies on the same latitude as Korea, it is not surprising that there are a variety of climates and forms of plant life along the island chain. All the islands show the influence of the large bodies of water around them and of the monsoon winds blowing from the sea in summer and from the land in winter. The winter monsoon winds from the northwest are generally more violent than the summer winds from the southwest. The climate of each island depends, therefore, on its distance from the Asiatic mainland and its relation to both prevailing winds and important Pacific Ocean currents.

Theoretically, only the summer winds from the sea bring rain, but even winter winds rising on the continent can become laden with humidity as they pass above the Sea of Okhotsk and the Sea of Japan and before reaching islands located very far out to sea. Precipitation, whether rain or snow, is therefore almost as abundant in winter as in summer. On the other hand, Sakhalin, very close to the continent, receives very little water in winter when it is swept by cold dry air originating in the heart of Siberia. The humidity is heavy everywhere on the archipelago and in the northern islands causes persistent fogs that have always been the terror of seafaring men. In the Kuriles, there is normally not a single clear day between November and February. During the other months of the year the average of clear days is no more than two a month. The fog layer is often so low that a sailor can get above it by climbing a mast, but this does not make navigation easier since the sailor is then in the position of an aviator above the clouds. Around Sakhalin, fogs are more frequent in summer, whereas winter days are quite often clear. Summer fogs arise because the cold Kurile ocean current condenses the humidity from warm sea breezes.

While the most northerly islands, the Kuriles and Sakhalin, have generally very low temperatures, with chilly summers and almost Siberian winters, the Japanese archipelago, swept by tropical monsoons in summer, shows great seasonal differences. Although Tokyo is on the same latitude as Sicily or southern Greece, air currents originating on the continent generate sixty-seven days of frost a year, and the mean January temperature is barely higher than that of Paris. The mean for the hottest summer month is close to 79° Fahrenheit, ten degrees higher than the mean in San Francisco. Rains are abundant and give the air a tropical moisture. Finally, two important ocean currents, the warm Kuro Shivo that runs along the southern coasts of Honshu and the cold Oya Shivo that bathes the northern shoreline, heighten Japan's climatic peculiarities.

Located on the same latitude as the great Siberian forests, but subjected to the alternation of monsoons, the northern islands, the Kuriles and Sakhalin, are covered with a vegetation that is sometimes almost pure taiga and sometimes like that of the mixed forest of Manchuria. Plant life on these islands is much impoverished in comparison to that on the continent and numbers only about a thousand species. As one moves south, the leafy trees increasingly dominate over the conifers, except on the heights where the latter sometimes form almost pure stands. The northern Kuriles are covered with forests of Kamchatka alders and dwarf pines *(Pinus pumila).* Further south another typical species appears, the Kuriles bamboo *(Sasa kurilensis)* as well as an entire group of plants common to the Manchurian forests: maples, cork trees, Amur lindens, Manchurian ash and oak, several species of aspens and birches, magnolias, and various wild vines. Sakhalin firs *(Abies sachalinensis)* and Hokkaido spruce *(Picea jezoensis)* cover the mountains.

On Sakhalin, the forests of firs and pines are predominant on the hills and the mountains. Mixed with the Sakhalin firs and Hokkaido spruce is another spruce, *Picea glehni,* which is peculiar to this island, the southern Kuriles and northern Japan. On the Pacific slopes, more favored by humidity, appear aspens, birches, oaks, willows, poplars and maples. In the south of the island is the typical mixed forest, containing, besides the species mentioned, cork oaks, walnuts and all sorts of lianas and wild vines. The large coniferous or leafy-treed forests do not grow more than 2,000 or 2,500 hundred feet above sea level. Above that are sparse low forests of dwarf cedars, rock birches *(Betula ernani),* holly *(Ilex rugosa),* spindle-trees *(Euonymus macroptera)* and Kuriles bamboos. The underbrush is covered with myrtle, golden rhododendron and sweet-smelling honeysuckle.

The Japanese climate, warmer and damper, favors plant life. Since Japan did not experience the quaternary glacial epoch that pushed all tropical plants of the Asiatic continent much further south, it contains a remarkable mixture of the vegetation of cold, temperate and hot regions—nearly 2,750 species as against the thousand found on Sakhalin. Among these are 168 species of trees, compared to eighty-five species in all of Europe. A unique phenomenon in a modern, densely populated country, is the forest that still covers sixty percent of the land. This miracle is not explained merely by the fact that agriculture developed only on the plains; it is proof rather of the respect that Japanese peasants have for nature in general and for trees in particular. While the Chinese have completely destroyed the vast forests that covered the most

About sixty thousand Japanese macaques live in bands of twenty to two hundred, each band commanded by a large male and occupying a specific territory. (T. Iwago)

densely inhabited parts of their country, the Japanese have made great efforts to conserve theirs by planting a tree each time they cut one down. The Japanese have of course often planted conifers because those are more useful, so that the beautiful forests of Japan, as of Germany, are not exactly what they were originally. A few shreds of residual forest still stand in the most isolated regions or around temples, and these give us some idea of Japan's primitive vegetation. A temperate forest of oaks, beeches, ash-trees, hornbeams, maples, poplars, elms, alders, magnolias, aralias, and Japanese cherry trees, covered the lowlands from southwest Hokkaido to northern Honshu as well as all of the medium-to-high altitude regions of southern Honshu. The mountains were covered with thick pine and fir forests, similar to those on Sakhalin. A subtropical forest of live oaks, camphor trees, giant cedars, bamboos, azaleas, tall ferns, lianas and orchids covered the entire southern part of the archipelago up to the thirty-eighth parallel. In its composition, this forest resembled the forests of Formosa and of China south of the Yangtze River.

About twenty national parks, which rival those in the United States, keep this rich plant cover intact. Annually, millions of Japanese, never missing an opportunity to admire their country's natural beauties, visit the parks. Pilgrimages take place to see the flowering of the plum trees in February, that of the cherry trees in March, of the azaleas in May and the iris in June. Impatient crowds cluster around the edges of pools in August, waiting for the moment when the sun's first rays strike the lotus blossoms, and cause them to open abruptly. A few trees are celebrated throughout the country: the camphor tree of the Kano Temple in Kagoshima, whose trunk measures seventy-one feet in circumference at breast height, the cherry tree of Kariyado at Shizuoka, which is twenty-seven feet around, and, among the conifers, the cedar of Kiyosumi Temple in Chiba, which stands 160 feet high on a trunk measuring thirty-nine feet around.

HIMALAYAN BEARS AND JAPANESE MACAQUES

Like all islands, the northern Pacific archipelagos are distinctly poorer in animal life than the neighboring continent. The islands, however, are not uninteresting to naturalists for, beside a host of sea birds and mammals, there is a strange mixture of animals from different plant zones. In a comparatively limited area one can observe representatives of the taiga and the mixed forest and species typical of the tropical or mountainous regions of Central Asia. Generally, however, with the exception of the most northerly Kuriles and the extreme south of Japan, mixed forest animals like those of Manchuria and the Amur basin are predominant.

The raccoon dog is common in Sakhalin and northern Japan, but the Manchurian tiger is restricted to Sakhalin. It is not even certain that the tigers inhabiting that island live there permanently, for it is easy for them to cross to the continent and back on the thick layer of ice that covers the Strait of Nevelsky in winter. Other large animals such as lynx, wolves, wolverines and reindeer, and such small carnivores of

Volcanic formations occupy one-third of Japan's landmass. Azo-san, 5,961 feet high, is still active. (Japan National Tourist Association)

the taiga as the fox, the sable and the weasel surely use this ice bridge. The otter also lives on Sakhalin, as does the brown bear; and the latter's habitat extends as far as Hokkaido where it is represented by a special race called the Japanese bear. Wolves and wild boars found in Japan are only local varieties of continental forms although some zoologists raise the Japanese or white-cheeked boar (Sus leucomystax) to the rank of a separate species. Another representative of Siberian forests, the striped ground-squirrel (Eutamias sibiricus), Asiatic equivalent of the American chipmunk, lives in Sakhalin and northern Japan. The small flying-squirrel of the taiga is replaced on the Japanese archipelago by the white-cheeked flying-squirrel (Petaurista leucogenys), a relative of the species inhabiting Southeastern Asia. It is a comparatively giant form, growing to a length of forty inches, including a long tail. Smoky-gray above and white underneath, it has, as its name indicates, two whitish patches between the eye and the ear on either side of the head. Another tree-dwelling rodent, the Japanese dormouse (Glirulus japonicus) is the only oriental representative of a group widespread in Southwestern Europe and Asia, but completely absent from the center of the continent. The Japanese dormouse has a bushy tail and resembles a tiny squirrel slightly more than an inch long but with a two-inch tail. Its ears hide in its light brown fur and its back is ornamented with a black band. Peculiar to Japan, this species seems either very rare or very prudent, for it is known only through a small number of specimens.

Marmots and susliks, abundant on the continent, have not migrated to any of the northern Pacific islands. One species of Asiatic pika (Ochotona hyperborea) has managed to reach Sakhalin and Hokkaido. Called the "whistling hare" because of the sound it utters in alarm, the Japanese pika is found as high up as 8,000 feet. Resembling a guinea-pig with large rounded ears, this pika, like its relatives in the mountains of continental Asia, piles up provisions for the winter. In this "hay," botanists have counted sixteen species of Japanese alpine plants. The hare is also common in the Japanese mountains. Its tail and very short ears make clear its relationship to the hare (Lepus timidus) of Eurasia.

In the mountains of Hondo there are two large animals that we met while crossing the southern ranges of Upper Asia: the Himalayan bear (Selenarctos thibetanus) and the serow (Capricornis crispus). Recognizable by its long-haired shining black coat and the large white crescent on its breast, the Himalayan bear grows to a length of nearly five and a half feet and weighs 250 pounds. The Japanese race is smaller, apparently growing no larger than four feet. As for the Japanese serow, although zoologists give it a different name from the continental animal, Capricornis sumatraensis, it undoubtedly belongs to the same species, but is, as often happens, a smaller island race.

One of the Japanese ungulates most familiar to western naturalists and hunters is the sika deer (Cervus nippon), introduced into France, England and New Zealand as an ornamental or game animal. Medium-sized, with antlers ordinarily branching into four points, its coat characteristically white-spotted in summer, the Japanese sika is the only deer found in western forests. Other races, often larger in size, occur from Formosa and southern China to Manchuria and in Korea.

The most popular found animal in Japan is probably the Japanese macaque (Macaca fuscata), which is the most

When alarmed, the Japanese pika (Ochotona hyperborea) *utters a shrill cry that has earned it the name of* naki-usagi, *"whistling hare." It stores provisions of hay under rocks for the winter. (T. Iwago)*

northerly of all monkeys. These animals are very timid in the wild, but their quick monkey intelligence soon tells them when no harm is intended and they then seek human contacts. At the western end of the Interior Sea is a hill called Takasaki-yama inhabited by about 450 macaques that come down at regular hours to be fed by the local population and visitors.

Between forty and sixty thousand macaques live in Japan and their very interesting social life has been studied for fifteen years by a team of Japanese scholars led by Professor Denzabura Miyadi of the University of Tokyo. These monkeys ordinarily dwell in the forest in bands of from thirty to two hundred, each group possessing a living space two to three miles square where they gather leaves and fruit and find the small animals that form their basic diet. They communicate among themselves through a genuine language made up of various mimicries and about thirty different sounds. Certain very precise cries indicate arrival at or departure from their feeding grounds. Other sounds signal danger or express threats toward other members of the band. Among the warning sounds, the one that approximates the sound "kuan" seems especially important. It is uttered by the strongest monkey and when it is heard all the others stop whatever they are doing and prepare to take flight. The one who uttered the cry remains behind and keeps an eye on the danger.

The macaque band has a distinct hierarchy. Each individual knows his own rank and his parental ties and expresses his submission to the one who holds a superior position. Thus, in the presence of a dominant male, animals lower in the hierarchy carry their tails downward, while the dominant male holds his erect. Even more interesting in the study of the evolution of higher animal societies, the Japanese scholars

have discovered that the monkeys can learn new actions and transmit them to the entire group and even to neighboring groups. In 1953, they noted a young female who habitually used sea water to wash the sweet potatoes that their human neighbors put out as lures to attract the monkeys. She was soon imitated by members of her own family and then by all the other animals with the exception of the oldest males. This habit became, at least within a limited area, a new cultural characteristic of the species.

CROSSROADS OF THE BIRDS

Although poor in comparison to the ensemble of the Asiatic continent, the birdlife of the northern Pacific archipelagos is definitely more varied than the mammalian life there. The Kuriles and Sakhalin are inhabited only by birds native to the Arctic coast or the Siberian forests, but the Japanese islands, with their variety of climates and natural surroundings, are favorable to both northern and tropical species. Considering its small surface, Japan is relatively rich in birds: 415 resident or migratory species have been counted so far, whereas all of North America has no more than 691.

Since a mixed forest of leafy and coniferous trees covers the greater part of Japan, no naturalist from the continent is surprised to find the most common birds of the temperate regions of Eurasia: crows, jays, titmice, buntings, goldfinches, greenfinches, bullfinches, thrushes, warblers, flycatchers, nuthatches and even familiar sparrows. Many of them are identical with those of the continent, while others are represented by other races or species.

The pure coniferous forests, predominant on the heights, are inhabited principally by birds characteristic of the taiga: various species of crossbills, grosbeaks, waxwings, hazel grouse and black woodpeckers. The alpine ptarmigan *(Lagopus mutus),* which we have met at the very limit of the Siberian taiga, lives on the mountains above the forest zone. Called *raicho,* that is, thunderbird, in Japan, the ptarmigan was long considered the messenger of the gods and was believed to have the power to control storms. This ancient veneration protected the bird from hunters, but the waning of old beliefs allowed the animal to become fair game and, although declared a protected bird in 1922, it is becoming rare.

Birds of tropical affinities are more numerous in southern Japan, although some species have moved quite far up on Honshu Island. One of the most beautiful of these birds is the Indian pitta *(Pitta brachyura),* an inhabitant of Southern Asian forests. All the colors of the rainbow blend in its plumage, but it is a timid bird that hides in low thickets and betrays its presence only by melodious whistling. It is easier to catch a glimpse of the broad-billed roller *(Eurystomus orientalis).* Called the dollar bird because of its bluish-gray plumage, it ordinarily perches on the giant cedars surrounding temples. It watches for insects that it can capture in full flight while performing the most astonishing aerial acrobatics. Despite its diurnal habits, the Japanese believe that it is this bird that utters the night cry that they hear as *bupposo:* the three treasures of Buddhism. Their veneration for this bird is unmerited, for the cry is uttered by a small owl *(Otus scops);* the dollar bird's cry is a guttural "kya-kya."

Among the birds of tropical Asia that are represented in Japan by identical or closely related species are the Japanese or jungle nightjar *(Caprimulgus indicus)*; the small cuckoo *(Cuculus poliocephalus)*, whose call is more raucuous than that of its European cousin; the Japanese white-eye *(Zosterops japonica)*; the rosy minivet *(Pericrocotus roseus)*, the black paradise flycatcher *(Terpsiphone atrocaudata)*, and the white-bellied black woodpecker of the island of Tsushima *(Dryocopus javensis)*. The latter bird, a very large woodpecker with a scarlet crest above its black feathers, is considered extinct at present. Probably it was never abundant in the forests of this small island, but it was always respected by the local population because of certain religious powers attributed to it. Bird collectors were, unfortunately, not so respectful, and the bird has not been seen since 1920. Luckily, the species still lives in Korea and it is hoped that, protected by the government, it will return to the Tsushima forests.

Other birds are considered specifically Japanese, although some of them are only local races of continental species. Among these is the jungle crow *(Corvus levaillanti)*, which swarms in the ports and fishing villages, everywhere displaying extraordinary impudence. It is abundant and so familiar undoubtedly because, in a country where all birds are hunted for food, a blind prejudice exists against crow's flesh even though it is better than that of the seafowl that is a part of the regular Japanese diet. The Japanese also believe that when young crows become adult, they in turn feed their parents; the bird has thus become a symbol of filial devotion.

The Japanese or green pheasant *(Phasianus versicolor)* and the copper pheasant *(Syrmaticus sommeringi)* are peculiar to the Japanese archipelago. Both of these splendid birds are pursued by hunters who flush them with the assistance of small dogs working in packs. Both species are still abundant today chiefly because such hunting is difficult on uneven ground. Unhappily, this is not true of the Japanese crane *(Grus japonensis)*, immortalized by Japanese artists and once considered royal game and protected by imperial decree. Barely 180 of these majestic birds have managed to remain alive in a very inaccessible swamp on Hokkaido. The Siberian white crane *(Grus leucogeranus)* that once lived in Japan has been even more unlucky since it now seems extinct on the archipelago and quite rare on the continent. Other species *(Grus monacha, G. vipio)* visit Japan in the winter and large flocks of them may be seen there.

Large birds are clearly more vulnerable than small ones, but small size does not protect birds from human greediness. The Japanese bunting *(Emberiza yessoensis)* and the Japanese reed warbler *(Megalurus pryeri)* have been at the brink of extinction ever since skewers of small broiled birds became specialties in certain Tokyo restaurants. To meet the constantly increasing demand, bands of hunters work with nets in the swamps near the capital. They thus capture not only a great many winter migrants, but also local species with a restricted area of distribution and reduced numbers.

Windswept Plains and Wandering Herds

Steppes and Semideserts from Iran to Mongolia

4

As one moves southward and approaches the center of Asia, the influence of the sea gradually diminishes, drought increases, and first prairie and then desert replace the forest. A vast grassy belt, stretching almost without interruption from Iran through Tibet to Mongolia, marks the heart of the continent.

The true steppe is an ocean of grass billowing in a wind that often blows violently. The grass is usually a combination of plants, mainly fescues *(Festuca sulcata, F. ovina)*, feathergrass *(Stipa lessingiana, S. capillata)*, couch grass *(Agropyrum cristatum)*, koeleria *(Koeleria cristata)*, and, at summer's end, steppe sedge *(Carex stenophylla)*. In some places, daisies *(Leucanthemum millefoliatum)* and creeping goosefoot *(Kochia prostrata)* grow thick amid the grasses. Unlike the relatively damp prairies throughout the forest region, the steppe is characterized by scattered tufts of grass with black soil, rich in humus, visible between them.

In June, when summer begins and almost all the rain of the year falls, this sea of grass is pale green and then deepens in color. The steppe is covered with myriads of multicolored flowers; red and yellow tulips *(Tulipa schrenki)*, yellow, purple or blue iris *(Iris pumila)*, magenta peonies *(Paeonia tenuifolia)*, blue sage *(Salvia nutans)*, several species of adonis in every shade of red, and purple, white or pink anemones. In the southernmost regions, from February on, the steppe is sown with meadow-saffron *(Colchicum biebersteini)*, crocus *(Crocus reticulatus)*, grape hyacinths *(Muscari racemosum)* and two-leafed squill *(Scilla bifolia)*. In July and August, when often not a drop of rain falls, the grass becomes the color of straw, crumples under the force of the wind, and only the countless red balls of steppe thistle *(Carduus uncinatus)* stand out on the endless plain.

In some places, especially where the terrain undulates slightly, low bushes appear. These are dwarf almonds *(Amygdalus nana)*, laburnums *(Cytisus ruthenicus)* and spireas *(Spiraea crenifolia, S. hypericifolia)*. These shrubs are important in the evolution of steppe landscapes for they hold the snow in

winter and thus increase the humidity of the soil. This permits the forest to conquer the steppe by progressive colonization of such areas. The first trees to appear are the wild apples and pears, then the birches, and last, the oaks.

In this manner, forest islands, prolonging the wooded steppe and creating an intermediate zone between forest and prairie, are formed. This zone is almost evenly divided between grass-covered and tree-covered areas. The dominant element in Asia is the birch, while west of the Urals it is the oak. In western Siberia, the birch woods form circular clumps that alternate with prairies of the same size to give the land, as seen from an airplane, the appearance of a checkerboard. The wooded steppe is in every sense a transition zone: the forest mingles with the prairie, podzol with black earth, and animals of the taiga with those of the open spaces. The same interpenetration occurs at the boundary between the steppe and the desert regions. The grassy carpet becomes more and more scant, and marly, sandy or stony soil more and more evident between the scattered tufts.

The black earth becomes poorer and poorer and gives way to the brown soil characteristic of semidesert regions. The vegetation is characterized by an abundance of wormwood or absinth *(Artemisia)*, whose strong odor always marks these landscapes. The two dominant species are white absinth *(Artemisia maritima)*, which grows on sandy soil with little salt, and black absinth *(A. pauciflora)*, which prefers marly, salty soil and is better adapted to arid zones. To reduce the loss of water, it folds its leaves entirely and with its black, burned-looking branches seems dead. But let the rains fall and the plant spreads out its leaves instantly, thrusting skyward long stalks tipped with grayish flower clusters.

Occupying considerable space are perennial grasses; among them are fescues, koelerias, and stipas. In some places, bushy orachs *(Atriplex cana)* characteristic of semideserts replace the absinths. During the rains, many ephemeral plants bloom and then soon disappear: tulips, ranunculas *(Ranunculus polyrhizus)* and a plant relished by camels, *Rheum tataricum.*

A characteristic of steppes and especially of semideserts is an abundance of temporary ponds caused by the appearance of impermeable layers about five inches below the surface. These ponds dry up in summer, and blackish flakes and bundles of stiff horsehair-like filaments appear on the cracked bottom of them. With the slightest rain, the flakes spread and reveal a lichen of the genus *Aspicilia*, while the filaments swell, turn green, and form colonies of algae *(Stratonostoc commune)*.

Animal life on Asiatic semideserts is a mixture of the life of the steppes with that of the true deserts. The mixture varies seasonally, animals normally associated with the prairie belt sometimes moving deeply into desert or subdesert zones. This is particularly true in spring when ephemeral plants cover the desert and in winter when heavy snowfalls force the animals southward.

The steppe zone has a climate that is generally dry and hot in summer with a sharp contrast between day and night temperatures, and very cold in winter with usually tempestu-

The hemione or wild ass (Equus hemionus) *lives on low or high steppes and semideserts from Iran to Mongolia. Seen at an altitude of more than sixteen thousand feet in western Tibet, these belong to the race called* kiang. *(Salim Ali)*

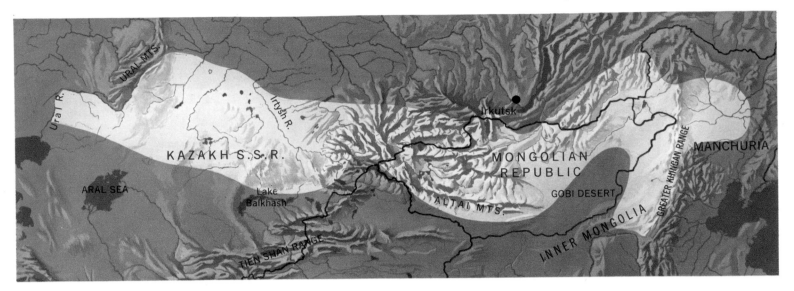

As rainfall diminishes from the periphery to the center of the continent, the forest gives way to the steppes and to cold or temperate semideserts. The band of dry pasture land stretching from Iraq to northern China is the equivalent of American prairie.

ous winds. The mercury ordinarily rises to over 100° F in summer, but in winter on the steppes of Kazakh and Mongolia may go down just as readily to –60° F.

THE SCULPTORS OF THE STEPPES

Animals adapt in many ways to the special conditions of the steppe. The absence of trees or rocks, for instance, compels the great majority of them to go underground for shelter from extreme temperatures and natural enemies. With the exception of the hare, all rodents and ground insect-eating and small carnivorous animals dig burrows or occupy those of their prey. Even some birds, like the ruddy sheldrake *(Tadorna ferruginea),* the common sheldrake *(Tadorna tadorna)* and wheatears *(Oenanthe* sp.) nest in abandoned burrows and take refuge in them from the sun during the day. This is also true of snakes, lizards and frogs. A few rodents, primarily those of the genera *Ellobius, Myospalax* and *Spalax,* are completely subterranean and look like moles. The Russian popular name for these is "the blind," for the first two genera have very tiny eyes and the last has eyes completely covered with a fold of skin. These extraordinarily modified rodents dig their tunnels as deep as sixteen feet underground. They eat only bulbs and bulbous roots, plentiful on the steppes, and store large stocks of food for the winter in special chambers off their tunnels.

The burrows of other rodents, although often vast and branching, are mere shelters, places for reproduction and hibernation, and "granaries" for reserves. During fine weather, they feed above ground, eating the green parts and seeds of grasses or digging up their roots. Among these rodents, there are marmots *(Marmota bobac),* several species of susliks or gophers, related to American prairie dogs, numerous voles, common hamsters, dwarf hamsters *(Cricetulus),* field mice *(Apodemus),* steppe mice *(Sicista subtilis),* jerboas, gerbils, pikas *(Ochotona)* and steppe lemmings *(Lagurus lagurus).*

There are a large number of individual animals as well as species, for, unlike animals of the forest, steppe animals often live in colonies of several thousand individuals. We can get some idea of the density of their populations by considering that as many as 325,000 have been counted in about four square miles. It has been estimated that this voracious horde destroyed nearly two tons of greens, bulbs and tubers in twenty-four hours. Such hosts of rodent must have a profound influence on the vegetation and soil of the steppe.

The role of the marmots and susliks is partly indirect, for they feed principally on young shoots and begin to hibernate in the middle of the summer when the plants are seared by the sun. But their digging activity does eventually alter the microrelief and the structure of the soil, and leads to important changes in the grassy layer. To appreciate the extent of their activity, it must be remembered that each marmot brings from three and a half to seven cubic feet of subsoil to the surface each year. At the same time, he carries organic matter and grasses used as bedding down into the depths and leaves excrement in blind alleys set up for the purpose. All this rapidly becomes humus. According to Professor A. N. Formozov, long an observer of these rodents, the exceptional depth of black earth—humus layers reaching ten feet thick—the true wealth of these regions, come from the burrowing of rodents.

Susliks play an equally important role in some regions. Mounds of earth thrown up from their burrows stand so close together that the steppe, according to observers, "resembles a harvested prairie with haystacks stretching as far as the eye can see." Each of these tumuli is made of two and a half to four cubic yards of earth and since there are five to ten on an area of 380 square yards, it would seem that at least 40,000 cubic yards of earth per square mile are brought to the surface in a few years by these tireless excavators. And since colonies of susliks occupy thousands of square miles of steppe, it is not exaggerating to attribute to them an important role in soil formation.

The Bactrian camel (Camelus bactrianus), *age-old pack animal, is as resistant to thirst as its one-humped relative. When vegetation is not yet burned by the sun, as in this Mongolian steppe, it can do without water for several weeks. (Ralph Herrmanns)*

70

The large-eared hedgehog (Hemiechinus auritus), *here seen on the steppes of the Altai, lives on crickets and lizards in all the dry regions from Egypt to India. (Novosti)*

In brown earth with salty subsoil, the susliks help to "salt" the upper layers and so aid in the replacement of steppe grasses by such salt-loving species as the black absinth. Conversely, in regions where the soil is brackish, they help "desalt" the soil by bringing up salt-free earth from the lower layer, opening the way for such useful grasses as meadowgrass, which normally grows in virgin soil.

The voles play a more direct part by digging up roots or by constantly razing plants. They thus create many bare spots which almost cover the steppe in years when the rodents swarm. On these spots grow only weeds, disdained by voles and hoofed animals, and not until the rodents have disappeared does the original vegetation begin to return.

ENEMIES OF THE RODENTS

The explosion in rodent populations is fortunately checked by several predators, including both mammals and birds. Among the four-footed killers, besides the wolf and some widely distributed species such as the common fox, the weasel, the ermine, and the badger, are a few that may be considered natives of the Eurasian steppes and semideserts. These are the desert fox *(Vulpes corsac)*, the steppe polecat *(Mustela eversmanni)*, the marbled polecat *(Vormela peregusna)*, and a feline called Pallas' cat *(Felis manul)*. Another feline also

widespread throughout Asia is the common African wild cat *(Felis libyca)*, found also in Africa and on certain Mediterranean islands. The leopard and the cheetah were once found in all southern subdesert parts of the palearctic region, but the former has become very rare and the latter disappeared early in the twentieth century.

The most specialized of these animals is indubitably the steppe polecat, which feeds almost exclusively on susliks, hunting them right into their tunnels, just as the European polecat hunts rabbits. Very numerous in some places, it does much to limit rodent populations.

The most characteristic birds of prey of the great open steppe spaces are the steppe eagle *(Aquila nipalensis)*, the golden eagle *(A. chrysaetos)*, often used in hunting wolves or antelopes, the imperial eagle *(A. heliaca)*, the long-tailed harrier *(Circus macrourus)*, the common buzzard *(Buteo buteo)*, the kestrel *(Falco tinnunculus)*, the pigmy kestrel *(F.*

Right above: The bobac marmot (Marmota bobac) *a characteristic steppe species, lives in small colonies in the vast plains watered by the Don, the middle central Volga and the Ural. (Robert Frederick)   Right: The suslik* (Citellus citellus) *is the equivalent of the New World's prairie dog. Like the marmot, its burrowing has altered the steppe by changing the chemical structure of the surface soil. (Gerard Grandjean)*

naumanni), the hobby (F. subbuteo), the saker falcon (F. cherrug), and, among the nocturnal birds, the great horned owl (Bubo bubo), which is very common on the wooded steppe.

Small rodents and insects (mainly locusts or crickets and the bees that gather honey from the flowers) are hunted by many birds typical of the open spaces: the great bustard (Otis tarda), the little bustard (O. tetrax), the common crane (Grus grus), the Numidian crane (Anthropoides virgo), the roller (Coracias garrulus), European and Persian bee-eaters, the common shrike, and the roseate starling, a beautiful pink bird that often gathers in flocks of several thousands.

Seed-eating birds are just as numerous, including partridges, quail, sand-grouse (Syrrhaptes paradoxus), various larks, pipits, and all sorts of finches. There are also swarms of ravens and, according to whether one is west or east of the Yenisey, black or hooded crows.

Although reptiles are not numerous in these arid zones, four species are common: Orsini's viper (Vipera ursini), the yellow-bellied rat snake (Boiga sp.), the scheltopusik (Ophisaurus apodus), a huge legless lizard whose powerful jaws can crush a small rodent as well as the shell of a mollusk, and a small multicolored lizard of the Agamid family, the Phrynocephalus, whose abundance has always surprised travelers.

The long winters and excessively hot summers of the steppe are hardly favorable to the spread of amphibians. Only common toads are truly abundant, and these often live with the rodents, whose deep tunnels retain a certain amount of humidity even at the height of the dry season. Russet frogs, moor frogs (Rana arvalis), Siberian frogs (R. chensinensis), and salamanders (Hynobius keyserlingii) live on wooded islands or in the forests along streams.

WINTER ON THE STEPPE

Another form of adaptation to life on the steppes is the capacity of many animals to move rapidly and far when conditions become unfavorable. Such movements have not been studied for such small animals as hares or for birds. They have, however, been observed since ancient times among the numerous ungulates to whom these vast pastures offered a particularly

Left above: The scheltopusik (Ophisaurus apodus) *is a large legless lizard. Unlike snakes, which never chew their prey, it crushes the shells of snails and the skeletons of small rodents in its powerful jaws. (Ludwig Trutnau)   Left: Cobras, widespread in Africa and tropical Asia, seek humidity, extending along river valleys far northward in the subdesert regions of Central Asia. (Novosti)*

Right above: The flowering steppe, so dear to Russians, is covered with countless iris, anemones and poppies in the spring. In June only the red globes of steppe thistles rise above the scorched grass. (Harrison Forman)   Right: The short-toed harrier eagle (Circaëtus gallicus) *is found in mountain and plains regions from Africa to India and Mongolia. It may often be seen hovering overhead, ready to swoop down on a snake, lizard or frog.   Far right: The crested lark* (Galerida cristata) *is a very familiar bird seeking seeds and insects on open ground from Northern Africa as far as Manchuria. (Both, Livna Yigael)*

The wild ass (Equus hemionus) *of Central Asia was found in immense herds up to 1900. Today there are only a few hundred in a reserve in Turkmen S.S.R. and on the Aral island of Barsa-Kelmes. (A. G. Bannikov)*

attractive environment. Travelers in earlier periods were astonished to see large herds of horses and wild asses, gazelles and antelopes, all peacefully wandering over the steppes.

All this has changed greatly. The aurochs and the bison were wiped out between the fifteenth and seventeenth centuries. Przewalski's horse, still reported by the French naturalist Chaffanjon, as abundant on the Irtysh steppes at the close of the nineteenth century, probably disappeared about ten years ago. A Russo-Mongolian expedition led by Professor Bannikov in 1954 did not see one specimen even in the most remote corners of Mongolia. This stocky little horse, with thick light hair and a short erect mane, has luckily escaped extinc-

tion because a few survive in zoos. About a hundred remain, most of them in Prague, and they seem able to reproduce perfectly in captivity.

The wild ass *(Equus hemionus)* has been totally eliminated from the steppes of Kazakh and Mongolia. However, protective measures have preserved it in the southern semideserts and notably Turkmen, where nearly seven hundred survive. From there it has been reintroduced into other regions and especially certain reserves such as that on the island of Barsa Kel'mes in the Aral Sea, where it has become completely acclimated. Like Przewalski's horse, the wild ass suffered as much from competition by tame herds that took over its watering places as from direct hunting. Faster than the horse, which cannot do better than thirty miles an hour, the wild ass can make long runs at forty to forty-five miles an hour and can easily outdistance its pursuers. It can do nothing, however, to protect itself from the automobile and the firearms that have managed to destroy most of the large animals of the open ranges.

The two-humped Bactrian camel *(Camelus bactrianus)* was also once widespread. There is no assurance that any of these are still holding out in the more remote steppes and semideserts of Mongolia. Two gazelles, the goitered gazelle *(Gazella subgutturosa),* so called because of its long dewlap, and the zeren *(G. gutturosa)* have been decimated, but are still found in some places, the first on the western steppes and the other on the steppes of Mongolia.

Other ungulates, chiefly those that ordinarily live on the wooded steppe but frequently raid the true steppe during the summer, are still relatively abundant. The most common is the elk, which has benefited from recent protective measures. Roe deer, represented in Siberia by a large-sized race, are also plentiful, but the maral deer, a Siberian variety of the European red deer, has suffered from hunters. The wild boar abounds in Kazakh where thick vegetation along the rivers offers it a haven. A purely steppe ungulate, the saiga *(Saiga tatarica),* has managed, as we shall see, to escape extinction because of vigorous measures taken to protect it and its extraordinary adaptability to life in open areas. The saiga's huge nose, forming a kind of grotesque trunk, distinguishes it from all other animals except the Tibetan chiru. It is believed that the nose either filters the dust raised by the animal's constant trot or warms cold air before it reaches the lungs. More developed in the male than in the female, the strange appendage is also a secondary sexual characteristic. The male has finely twisted horns.

All the ungulates, sometimes joined by species like the mouflon that normally dwell on the high steppes, undertake migrations that may exceed several hundred miles. Although they migrate to avoid cold and snow, most of the animals can withstand very low temperatures. The wild ass, Przewalski's horse and the saiga have winter coats with hair two or three times longer and thicker than in summer. The wild boar develops a thick layer of fat and huddles in families in nests of grass or brush. The gazelle, less fortunate in the development of a winter coat or subcutaneous fat, finds shelter in the

Until recently herds of gazelles, saiga antelopes, wild horses and camels (right) roamed the vast Central Asian steppes. Today, most of them have been evicted by domestic herds. (Ralph Herrmanns)

Allactaga saltator, *locally called "earth hare," is one of some twenty species of jerboas of the dry regions of Central Asia. Like miniature kangaroos, they hop along on their hind legs. (Novosti)*

rare bushes and hollows. All the animals seek protection from the icy winds of winter. In very severe winters, saigas, gazelles and wild asses take shelter among dunes or in forests and groves that they normally avoid. In 1950–1951, in Kazakh, saigas huddled together and died by the dozen behind railroad embankments, in drainage canals, and behind telegraph poles. Often the animals let themselves be buried by the snow wherever they had taken refuge against the gales, and saigas, gazelles and even horses were found literally frozen on their feet.

In years of great cold but not too much snow, the animals move northward. This paradoxical habit may be explained in two ways. It seems that the pastures of the south, made up mainly of plants with bulbs or bulbous roots, afford the animals much poorer food than do northern grass pastures, because the grasses remain even when dry. The freezing of watering places in southern areas also forces the animals to move north in search of snow to quench their thirst.

Thus the determining factor in these migrations is not cold but snow, which hinders the search for food and, when it is deeper than the animal's hind legs, impedes movement. The chances of survival depend on relative size: the critical thickness of snow is thirty-five inches for the elk, from twenty-four to twenty-eight inches for the wild ass, wild horse and stag, and sixteen inches for the saiga and the gazelle.

The weight of the animal and the bearing surface of its hoofs must also be taken into account. The pressure on the snow amounts to fourteen pounds per square inch for the wild ass, a little less for Przewalski's horse, about six pounds for the gazelle, adult wild boar, and the elk. By comparison, the

reindeer exerts, as we said, two pounds of pressure and with its wide hoofs is perfectly adapted to walking on snow. Since the adult wolf exerts a pressure of only two pounds, usually three to four times less than that of its prey, it can run easily across fairly well-packed snow or snow covered with an icy crust that would collapse under the weight of any of the steppe ungulates. During snowy winters wolves commit almost unbelievable carnage, wiping out almost all roe deer, most of the saigas and practically all the baby boars. Russian experts estimate that one wolf kills between fifty and ninety saigas each year. Until recently, wolves were prodigiously abundant on the steppes and semideserts, where the wealth of herbivorous animals and the flat terrain made hunting at sight easy. In Kazakh alone, 208,000 wolves have been officially destroyed in the past twenty years with the aid of helicopters or vehicles with caterpillar tires.

THE "DJOUT"

The cold and violent winds that dominate the heart of Asia cause the snow to pack rapidly and last for months, making the search for food difficult. Feeding becomes practically impossible when hoarfrost covers the snow and all vegetation. Each blade of grass becomes a stalagmite, and animals spend an immense amount of time nibbling at plants to free them of their icy sheaths. As a result, an animal cannot get enough food in the course of a day to make up for the energy it expends.

Luckily, the hoarfrost usually lasts for only one or two days, but if it persists, the *djout* occurs. *Djout* is a Russian word from the Mongol *dzoud,* meaning death of a great many wild or tame ungulates because of unfavorable weather conditions. Within a month or two, such a condition, usually extending over very large areas, can cause the loss of hundreds of thousands and even millions of ungulates in the sheltered places where they seek refuge from gales.

The only species spared by this catastrophe is the elk, which flees to wooded zones where it survives because of the length of its legs and its winter diet of bark and branches. The *djouts* affect the population of all other hoofed animals of the steppes and semideserts. If it recurs only at intervals of from eight to twenty years, as is the rule, the populations can build back up again. But if the *djout* occurs in two consecutive winters, it may cause the local extinction of some species, especially in isolated habitats on plateaus or mountains.

In this way, after recent severe winters, the mouflon disappeared from Transbaykalia and from the Ustyurt (east of the Caspian Sea), the goitered gazelle from the steppes of Minusinsk on the Upper Yenisey in Siberia, and the wild ass and wild horse from Kazakh. The ungulate that recovers most rapidly from the rigors of the *djout* is the saiga because of its special adaptability to life in open spaces. In the first place, this antelope lives in immense herds that may number as many as 100,000 individuals. The herds move constantly and very rapidly, never pasturing too long in barren regions and enabling the animals to escape in large measure from the effects of local storms. Thus saigas fleeing a zone struck by a cold wave often lose only 30 to 40 percent of their numbers, while the mortality of goitered gazelles, making only short movements in the same region, reaches 80 to 90 percent.

The rapid maturation and the fertility of the saiga are

The saiga antelope (Saiga tatarica) *lives in large herds on the Eurasian steppes. It is believed that the trumpet-shaped nose, particularly grotesque on adult males (above), filters the dust raised by the herd.* (W. Roschek)

astonishing: the female ordinarily reproduces at the age of ten months and usually bears twins. And although this is not a characteristic of adaptation, the mortality of males is distinctly higher than that of females, especially at the beginning of the winter during the rutting period. As a result, the saiga's natural enemies, and wolves in particular, attack dead or dying males and spare most of the females and the young of the year. After a very severe winter, the number of adult males may not exceed 3 to 5 percent of the total population. This does not, however, hinder normal population growth, for the saiga is polygamous and each male surrounds itself with a "harem" of four to twenty females. Mortality of the young is only about 20 percent before winter arrives, and 40 percent of those remaining survive until the following spring. The total increase in population varies from 60 to 80 percent yearly, eloquent evidence of the saiga's capacity for expansion of the species.

This prodigious reproductive capacity together with a few protective measures have allowed the saiga to progress in thirty years from the status of an almost extinct animal to that of the most abundant in the region. At the close of World War I, saigas, still hunted everywhere for the horns used in Chinese pharmaceuticals, numbered no more than a thousand head. Today there are estimated to be two and a half millions, with five hundred thousand of them living on the European steppes. This permits an annual round-up of about three hundred thousand, by preference usually young males, furnishing hundreds of thousands of hides, six thousand tons of excellent meat, industrial fats and various pharmaceutical products.

RIVER VALLEY INHABITANTS

Although the low regions of Central Asia are generally arid, they are crossed by a number of rivers and streams, the best-known being the Amu Dar'ya and Syr Dar'ya and their tributaries. Plant formations, quite different from those found on the steppes or surrounding deserts, cluster about these waterways. Most frequently, there are impenetrable expanses of grasses or reeds, sometimes growing taller than a man on horseback. In some places bushy plants predominate and form tunneled forests similar to those along the rivers in arid zones of Africa or tropical Asia.

The presence of water and plants enables certain animals to survive in the least hospitable regions of Central Asia. As A. N. Formozov notes, the intensity of animal life is particularly striking during summer days when the cries of pheasants, of bee-eaters, herons and small hawks, the songs of reed-warblers and sedge-warblers, the bustling of countless sparrows, the croaking of frogs, and the buzzing of myriad insects are in striking contrast to the silence of the adjacent deserts and semideserts. A comparison of the number of bird species in the river valleys and in the surrounding regions is evidence enough of the wealth of the valleys. Only 62 species nest in the Kara Kumy desert, while 128 have been counted in the Turkmenian part of the Amu Dar'ya Valley.

The population is not homogeneous all along the Amu and Syr Dar'ya rivers. The middle stretches of the rivers are too turbulent to suit wading birds, but the lower streams and the deep, calm deltas choked with reeds and aquatic plants shelter countless herons, pelicans, cormorants, grebes, terns, geese and ducks. Taking advantage of these natural corridors, some animals from temperate regions penetrate far into the southern deserts and, conversely, numerous tropical species go upstream quite far northward. Among the first is the rook (Corvus frugilegus), widely dispersed throughout cold and temperate Asia and also an inhabitant of the Aral-Caspian deserts. Tropical species are represented by the common myna (Acridotheres tristis) and the Indian lapwing (Lobivanellus indicus) which we shall see in abundance in India and which goes far northward along the Amu and Syr Dar'ya rivers. The same route is followed by ring-necked pheasants, spectacled Indian cobras and innumerable insects: crickets, mantises, walking sticks and several species of malaria-carrying mosquitos. Until quite recently these mosquitos made life for humans and domestic animals absolutely impossible during the summer months. According to a Russian who traveled through the region late in the nineteenth century, all one had to do was pass near a bush for it to burst into hungry life. Millions of mosquitos rose like clouds of smoke, buzzing deafeningly and pouring down on rider and horse, who, blinded and eaten alive, could find safety only in flight. Although there are fewer mosquitos today because of the war waged against them by anti-malaria teams, the number of other stinging insects has not diminished. The worst of them are the gadflies that attack camels more than any other domestic animals. On the first fine days that warn of the imminent massive hatching of mosquitos and gadflies, nomad shepherds lead their cattle into the deserts or up into the hills, hundreds of miles from the river valleys and marshes.

The vast stretches of reeds bordering the rivers and lakes of Central Asia are the favorite habitat of black-footed boars, one of the largest races of the Eurasian boar (Sus scrofa). Since local populations, Turkomans, Uzbeks, and Kazakhs, are Moslems, who do not eat pork, the boars have suffered less from hunting than other large animals of the region and are still numerous. The tall grasses are furrowed with paths traced by families of boars roving about in search of roots, tubercles and such animal food as insect larvae, worms, mollusks and fish. In winter when the frozen ground is too hard for rooting one can see herds of the animals out in the open desert, digging up the bulbs and seeds laid aside as provender by desert rodents. These bands of boars can travel great distances and will unhesitatingly go up and back between the valleys of the Syr Dar'ya and the Amu Dar'ya.

The Buchara or reed deer, a comparatively light-colored race of the red deer (Cervus elaphus), was also abundant until recently. Excessively hunted, it owes its survival only to protection measures. According to A. N. Formozov, it holds out best today in the Amu Dar'ya, Piands, and Vakhch valleys probably because of a balance by deer from Afghanistan. The Afghanistan route is used by the marsh tiger, another tropical animal linked to the river valleys, where it finds the deer and boars that are its usual prey. Once widespread in all Central Asian swamps, this splendid beast has been destroyed in most of this habitat. Isolated specimens, often from Iran or Afghanistan, are still spotted from time to time, the last definite record being made in 1966.

Other less important carnivores are the Kaffir cat (Felis libyca), the reed or jungle cat (F. chaus) and the jackal (Canis aureus), whose yelps are the sound effects of the Central Asian nights. In dry places, jackals dig burrows and give birth in them to litters of from four to ten young. When the soil is too damp, they simply bear their young in lairs in the shelter of the reeds.

Among the prey of the small carnivores are all kinds of birds and rodents and another tropical animal, the short-tailed Indian bandicoot (Nesokia indica). This is a very large, yellowish-furred rat, ten to fourteen inches long, including a tail of from three to five inches. With the spread of irrigation, this rodent moves further and further north, for it has a preference for cultivated fields where it finds both plenty of food and light soil for its burrow. The burrow may be seen from a distance for its opening is surrounded by a pile of fresh earth similar to a molehill. Inside, a passage as long as sixty feet leads to a circular rest chamber about two feet below the surface. Other chambers and store-rooms are fitted out along the tunnel and in them the bandicoot stores up large quantities of grain, rice or wheat according to localities. It really earns its reputation as one of the rodents most harmful to crops.

The Caspian tortoise (Clemmis caspica), *shown in the Hula swamp in Israel, has stocked the entire semidesert zone of Central Asia by moving upstream along rivers. (Werner Braun)*

The Empty Quarter

The Deserts of Arabia

5 The widest desert belt in the world, broken only by a few isolated mountains, stretches from the Sahara to the Gobi, across Arabia, Iran, Afghanistan and the Aral-Caspian depression. This immense Asiatic desert covers more than 2,500,000 square miles, an area twelve times the size of France or two thirds as large as the entire United States.

Nevertheless, the imposing Arabian plateau is, in terms of its plants and animals, merely an isolated fragment of Africa. The sunken ditch of the Red Sea, dating probably from the end of the Tertiary Era, is not a significant geographic dividing line or barrier. Certain plants and animals characteristic of what is called the Saharo-sindian desert may be found from the Atlantic coast eastward as far as northern India. As one moves eastward, the number of typically African species diminishes, while that of Asiatic forms increases. It is difficult, however, to mark the precise limits of Ethiopian and Oriental populations.

This difficulty does not occur in Arabia, for few species of the eastern Sahel are not found east of the Red Sea. From the botanical standpoint, the only area with a few endemic plants is that which biogeographers call Abyssomalia, a region made up of the junction of Somaliland, Abyssinia and Arabia. As to the animals of the Arabian peninsula itself, with rare exceptions they may be considered subspecies of typically African forms.

In spite of its apparently privileged location at the crossroads of two continents, the plant and animal life of the Arabian peninsula are among the poorest in the world. This immense arid zone has always hindered the interchange of plants and animals between Africa and Asia. Only species best adapted to life in these regions have been able to cross the barrier during the few comparatively humid periods in the great glacial epochs. Except for the coastal mountains, rising in places to 12,500 feet, and the southwest, which benefits from some monsoon rains, the entire peninsula is today nearly one million square miles of desert.

The Arabian desert is comprised of two vast expanses of dunes, one in the north, the other in the south. In the north these form the Dahna and the Nafud, and in the south, the lest-known and least-explored of the world's deserts. The Arabs call this southern desert Rab' al Khali, the Empty Quarter, for these 385,00 square miles are barren of human life. Narrow strips of *hamadas,* hard-topped stony plateaus, and *ergs* or dunes start east of the Dahna and join the Nafud in the north. The Nafud itself is nothing but a great sea of sand upon which rains fall only two or three days a year, or in some years, not at all.

Between these two deserts, the Dahna and the Nafud, is a vast stretch of cliffs and low plateaus occupying the east central part of the peninsula. This is the Najd, the heart of Saudi Arabia. Geographers are always astonished to note here the succession of hills and cliffs cut by valleys as a result of intensive fluvial erosion. The Najd has a nightmarish appearance because it is furrowed by countless stream and river beds that are almost all without water. Once, during the Quarternary Era, this region was crisscrossed by a complex water system; today these ghost rivers are almost all choked with desert sand. When, however, the rains do come, a few wadis (a word derived from the Arabic *oued* or stream) sometimes flow hundreds of miles before vanishing into the dunes. In fact, it rains regularly enough in winter for true springs to be found on these mountains. And even in the beds of dried-up wadis, one can in most places reach water by digging just below the surface.

Because of this comparative abundance of water, the Najd province is called "Green Arabia"; it is the country of date palms, mulberries, pomegranates, peach, fig and apricot trees. Grapes, wheat, barley and alfalfa are grown there and large herds of domesticated camels are not uncommon. Up to fairly recent times, it was a paradise for wildlife.

Vast flat areas of alluvial soil stretch between the mountains and the scattered hills. Vegetation is astonishingly abundant here and quite different from what one usually expects in a desert region. During the dry season it consists principally of clumps of woody and often spiny bushes separated by expanses of scant pasture where wild hoofed animals find little to graze on. But when the rains come, there is a truly explosive growth of plant life, an unbelievable proliferation of grasses and annual or biennial plants whose seeds or bulbs have lain dormant throughout the dry period.

TOUGH PLANTS OF THE DESERT

Only the stony deserts or *hamadas* are truly lifeless, for the little water they receive evaporates immediately, so that plants cannot take root. On sandy deserts the water is sucked down, thus escaping evaporation and remaining accessible to plants whose roots plunge deeply into the lower layers. Sandy deserts are thus much more hospitable than we think and are usually colonized by bushy plants or even trees, very sparsely of course but nevertheless guaranteeing existence to animals adapted to such arid conditions.

The principal trees are parasol-shaped acacias with the most common species *Acacia radianna,* characteristic of the Saharo-

On slopes protected from the sun, networks of surface roots retain rainwater or nocturnal condensations and enable these plants in the Negev Desert to survive. (Werner Braun)

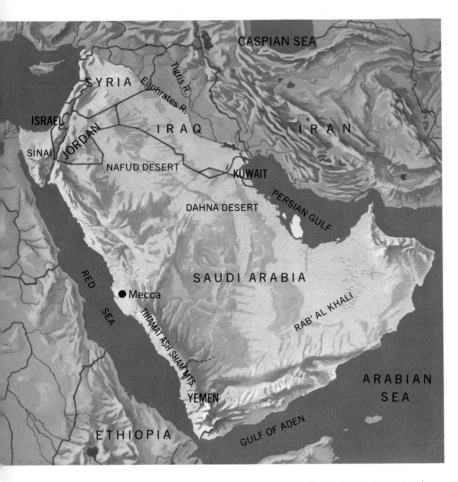

Except for a mountainous coastal region the entire Arabian peninsula is nearly a million square miles of desert. This arid zone bars the exchange of most plants and animals between Africa and Asia.

sindian deserts from Mauritania to Gujarat in northern India. Another characteristic acacia is *Acacia ethbaica,* an Abysso-Somalian native found around the Red Sea. Another leguminous tree, the carob *(Ceratonia),* common in the Mediterranean area, is very important in the desert. Its large brown pods contain a string of large seeds bathed in sugary pulp. A great many animals seek these pods and seeds, while human beings are very partial to a flour made from the pulp.

Among the shrubs, the most characteristic are the tamarisks, the *Callipogon,* which is also found in the Central Asian deserts, and the *sidr,* a small acacia growing no more than five to ten feet tall. One of the most unusual features of the landscape is the large cactus-shaped euphorbias armed with clusters of menacing spines. These euphorbias are characteristic of Southern Africa, and Arabia is the eastern limit of their distribution. The grassy covering here is made up mainly of bulbous plants and grasses of the genus *Aristida,* including several Saharo-sindian species, and *Brachyaria,* common in arid zones of Africa.

Most desert plants are xerophytes, that is, adapted to life in a dry climate, and generally have tough branches and thick leaves, sometimes covered with a grayish fuzz or even transformed into spikes. The barks are usually thickened or cork-like. All these modifications help reduce loss in transpiration and the evaporation of internal water. Other plants, such as the succulents, store water within themselves.

Summer is the season when desert plants lie dormant. In all of them the life processes slow down and they seem dead, withered by the pitiless sun. But as soon as the first drops of winter rain fall, life bursts out everywhere. Buds crack their thick shells, leaves unfurl, and flowers bloom. In some seemingly quite barren places, myriads of plants that have survived as seeds or bulbs spring from the earth with almost supernatural suddenness.

A MASSACRE OF ANIMAL LIFE

Many animals also undergo the same alternation of activity and lethargy. Dependent on the cycle of the seasons, most of them are vegetarians that eat certain plant species and those that do so only at a particular stage in a plant's development such as when it is green or in the fruit or the seed stage. Thus reptiles and rodents feeding exclusively on above-ground portions of desert plants estivate, sinking into a dormant period for more than eight months out of the twelve. Many insect-eaters are also affected by the seasonal cycle, for their favorite prey, dependent on certain plants, may become abundant only at a certain time of year.

The reproductive period of each species usually coincides with the most favorable season for feeding the young. Clearly, this period will vary according to the animal's feeding habits. It is thus logical that seed-eating birds should choose to nest at the beginning of the dry season when annual grassy plants end their growth cycle and wither away, leaving to the seeds the task of insuring the continuity of the species. Insect-eaters will choose the beginning of the wet season since the first rains usually bring a proliferation of insects that have spent the summer dormant, most often in the nymph or pupa stage.

Small animals, reptiles, rodents and birds also present a whole series of adaptations to the dryness and the extremes of desert temperatures. We shall find many examples of such adaptations in the Central Asian deserts, where the alternation of day and night temperatures combines with that of hot and cold seasons. Large animals, of course, are less dependent on these variations but more closely linked to the presence of food, for they cannot escape scarcity by becoming dormant or by accumulating reserves in burrows. The hoofed animals of the Arabian deserts seek out the short-lived pasturages that spring up in certain places following rainfall, which is itself dependent upon the topography.

Up until the last war, the first rains brought countless herds of gazelles, represented in Arabia by three forms, one of which, *Gazella g. arabica,* is endemic. Today it is rare for a traveler to see one of these animals in the course of a day. Their disappearance is linked to the discovery of oil. Spouting in geysers from the desert, the oil suddenly enriched countless Arab feudal lords, transforming nomad chieftains into princes out of *The Arabian Nights.* But the magic wand of the oil fairy was also the signal of death for the magnificent animals that lived on the land.

For all these new princes, imitating European and American oilmen, quickly adopted the most modern methods of hunting —by automobile. The flat, stony stretches, and the open areas

A wadi or seasonal stream in Israel, cutting through sandstone and granite, shows traces of ancient fluvial erosion. (Livna Yigael)

of hard sand were well suited to this technique. These "hunts," which visiting foreigners attended enthusiastically, usually brought together from forty to sixty vehicles but sometimes as many as three hundred, and these swept the desert in a murderous line, massacring every living thing in their path. According to witnesses, some riflemen managed to kill one hundred gazelles in a day. Such figures give some idea of the animal population in this area barely thirty years ago. To crown this massacre, the oil companies fed their personnel by calling in meat dealers who worked with desert vehicles armed with machine guns.

Today, Arabian gazelles have managed to survive only in places where the terrain is too rough or the sand too soft for automobiles to follow them. Since such areas, however, are also unfavorable for the gazelles, the number of these graceful animals that survive is necessarily very small.

"THE DOCTOR OF THE ARABS"

Although the disappearance of gazelles seems particularly dramatic because they were up to recently so abundant, other animals have also not been spared. The Arabian ostrich, a subspecies related to that of Africa, has also recently been exterminated. Apparently the last two specimens were killed in 1948 near the junction of the frontiers of Iraq, Jordan and Saudi Arabia. Another bird, the houbara *(Chlamydotis undulata)*, a bustard the size of a turkey, is also in grave danger because it is hunted by automobile. Although the bird can fly, it ordinarily does not rise from the ground except directly in front of a car and then it can easily be brought down.

The most beautiful Arabian animal is the white oryx *(Oryx leucoryx)*. A magnificent beast, it has ringed horns, straight as swords, that may be twenty-five inches long. From afar, it looks pure white, but closer inspection reveals brown legs and a few darker patches on head and tail. According to the American ecologist Lee M. Talbot, the oryx has always been sought by the Arabs because they believe that whoever kills and eats it acquires its bravery, strength and endurance. One of its vernacular names may be translated as "The Doctor of the Arabs." The nomads known as Bedouins call it *jawasi,* meaning "he who does not drink," for the oryx is reputed to be able to get along without water. The Bedouins consider its flesh a panacea able to cure every ailment from a stomach ache to a fractured limb.

Once upon a time, the skill of a hunter was measured by the number of oryx he had slain. These antelopes were hunted in the desert on camelback, generally in autumn or winter when the mount could travel without drinking for two weeks. This type of hunt was not at all dangerous to the survival of the oryx as a species. The coming of the automobile and

Left: Parasol-shaped acacias with tiny and often thorny leaves are the most familiar trees of the desert regions. The Acacia radiana, *here shown in Israel's Negev, is one of the most common. (Anna Riwkin: Full Hand)*

Right: The toad-headed agama of Arabia (Phrynocephalus *sp.) escapes enemies by burrowing into the sand. When it cannot flee, it opens its mouth wide to frighten its foe. (All, Standard Oil Company)*

modern arms raised the odds against it greatly. These animals preferred hard sand or stony deserts where they could run faster; but such terrain was precisely the best-suited to motorized vehicles. The oryx was eliminated from these regions within a few years. When survivors found refuge in the soft sand of the Nafud and the Dahna where automobiles could not follow them, the hunters decided to use airplanes or helicopters; it is difficult to think of any species capable of withstanding such weapons.

The most pessimistic predictions concerning the fate of the oryxes have proved justified: with the possible exception of a dozen animals in the southern part of the peninsula, the Arabian oryx has disappeared in the wild state. The World Wildlife Fund has taken a step that will perhaps save one of the most beautiful animals in the world from extinction. An expedition to Arabia recently managed to capture three of the remaining oryxes. These have been transferred to a zoo in Arizona where conditions closely approximate those of the Arabian habitat. If breeding succeeds—as well it may since two females have already borne young—there is no reason why the Arabian oryx, like Przewalski's horse and Père David's deer, should not live in captivity long after it has disappeared from the wild. And who knows whether one day the Arabs themselves, belatedly seeking to restore their native animals, will not restock their reserves with descendants of the few oryxes saved at the last moment from the great massacre.

Carnivorous animals have suffered greatly from the decrease in their prey as well as from being hunted. Even the cheetah, fastest of mammals, capable of a speed of seventy miles an hour, cannot outrun vehicles with tireless motors. Resembling the leopard in its spotted coat and round head with small ears, but doglike in its tall silhouette and in claws that are not retractable, it has forced zoologists to create a special group for it, the Acinonychines.

The panther, quite common in the mountains, is replaced in the desert by four species of cats and small-sized lynxes found in both Africa and Asia. The best-adapted to the environment is surely the desert cat *(Felis margarita)*, which is slightly smaller than the domestic cat and has a very pale fur on which one may distinguish a few blurred transverse stripes. Its head is flat and topped with small erect ears. It spends the

Left above: The desert or migratory locust (Schistocerca gregaria) *is found in two forms, one of which makes migrations in vast clouds and is the plague of all arid regions. (Werner Braun)   Left: In desert regions, sedge or carex* (Carex sp.), *whose pith soaks up water, forms thinly scattered tufts sought by herbivorous animals. (Aramco)*

Right above: The palm lizard or whip-tail (Uromastix aegypticus) *of North African, Israeli and Arabian deserts suffers in the dry season and awaits the fresh plants that appear in spring and autumn. (Walter Ferguson)   Right: The stone curlew* (Burhinus oedicnemus) *runs rapidly along the ground, hunting insects and mollusks. When in danger, it flattens out, stretches out its neck, and relies on its earth-colored plumage to camouflage it. (Livna Yigael)   Far right: The roller* (Coracias garrulus), *found throughout the Mediterranean region and in Asian deserts, hunts from cover, letting itself fall on insects. (Walter Ferguson)*

day in the coolness of a burrow dug into the sand and comes out only at night to hunt rodents, lizards and even insects.

Two other felines, larger in size, are the caracal *(Felis caracal)* and the lynx chaus or jungle-cat *(F. chaus),* both resembling the lynx in having ears topped with a tuft of black hairs. The caracal's ears, black outside and white within, are huge in comparison to the size of its head. The jungle cat is a heavier animal with a shorter tail. Both of them hunt birds, hares and a strange little animal, the dassie or hyrax.

But the most interesting of all these cats is the gloved or Libyan cat *(Felis lybica),* which most zoologists agree is the ancestor of our domestic cats. It was domesticated in the remote past by the Egyptians, who venerated it as a god and portrayed it on many bas-reliefs. Carefully mummified cats have been found in the tombs of Pharaohs inside the pyramids. Through selection of various mutations, these gloved cats became the ancestors of all the living races of domestic cats, and some zoologists believe that the wild cats *(Felis sylvestris)* of Europe and Western Asia are only color variations of the gloved cat.

LIVING TOYS AND MINIATURE ELEPHANTS

Canines are represented in this area by the common jackal *(Thos aureus),* whose habitat extends from the southern part of Africa to the eastern part of India, and by three species of foxes: the desert fox *(Vulpes leucopus);* Rüppell's fennec *(Vulpes familicus),* which has large ears; and the common fennec *(Fennecus zerda).* The latter is a dainty creature the size of a small cat; it has a pointed muzzle, big black eyes under large, constantly moving ears, a bushy tail and thick, cream-colored fur as soft as down. This living toy spends its days in a burrow in the sand and at night hunts its favorite prey, small rodents and grasshoppers.

The desert fox mentioned above truly deserves that name, for it is extremely pale and sand-colored. This leads us to the influence of the desert on animal coloration. Among the modifications that appears in desert-dwelling animals, one of the most noticeable is that of the hue of fur or feathers. On the whole, these animals are duller in hue and paler than those of the same species living in temperate regions. This variation becomes even more striking when comparison is made with forest species, normally deeper in coloration. Thus foxes, various kinds of cats, hares and small rodents are always much lighter in color than those of the same species living in

Left above: A pair of scarabs or dung beetles (Scarabeus sacer) *rolling their ball of camel dung. Having buried it, the female lays her eggs in the future foodstore for her young.   Center: The Arabian gazelle* (Gazella gazella arabica) *has almost disappeared from its native habitat, victim of local potentates and oil company employees who hunt from automobiles. (Both, Eric Hosking)   Left: The fennec* (Fennecus zerda) *lives only in the sand deserts of Northern Africa and Arabia, emerging from its burrow at nightfall to hunt rodents, lizards and locusts. (Okapia)*

Right: Parts of the Rab' al Khali desert of southern Arabia have no plants or animals and receive only a few millimeters of rainfall a year. (Aramco)

more humid regions. The same is true of birds: larks, chats, owls and small diurnal birds of prey all have plumage with hazy markings and a generally sand-colored tint.

One is immediately tempted to believe that these modifications are true adaptations and that the pale color of desert forms is mimetic. But it is difficult to be absolutely certain of this, for there is no proof that this characteristic is not due to a climatic factor such as the dryness of the air. Mimetism is, however, the simplest explanation and seems to be confirmed by recent observations, such as that of a French explorer, Hubert Gillet, who crossed stretches of black basalt in the southern Sahara. He observed birds, notably larks, and rodents whose general coloration was very dark, almost black. These can hardly be attributed to climatic factors since the climate was exactly the same as in nearby areas where the animals were typically pale in hue.

We should note here that these characteristics are found among animals in all deserts, but that they are most striking in Arabia, perhaps because of the extreme aridity of the region. In any case, the palest desert forms of mammals and birds occur in the Arabian deserts.

Another interesting small desert carnivore is the zorille, the image of the American skunk and with the same trick of lifting its tail to spurt a jet of fetid liquid at an enemy. The author and animal collector Ivan T. Sanderson swears that it smells worse than any other animal. He also tells a story of five lions intimidated by a zorille and forced to wait to devour their prey until "the father of all stinkers," as the Sudanese call it, had eaten its share.

We may not end our little inspection tour without speaking of the hyrax (Procavia). The best way to describe it is to compare it to a rabbit with its ears cut off. But on closer inspection, we see that its toes do not end in claws but in little hoofs that resemble those of an elephant reduced several hundred times. It was no error of zoologists that induced them to create a special order for this strange little animal, that of the Hyracoidea, placed beside that of the Proboscideans (elephants) in the zoological system.

Despite the strange shape of their feet, hyraxes are excellent climbers and manage to scale the smoothest and steepest rocks. Some of them, the Dendrohyrax, found only in African forest regions, have become complete tree-dwellers. Experts have never been able to explain how these curious beasts manage to climb. Some say that the soles of their feet, smooth and slightly concave, act like suction cups. Others explain this ability—not without humor—as simply a nervous expression or a sheer act of will power: they can climb because they have made up their minds to do it.

Hyraxes do not go about unnoticed: the night echoes with their lamentations, so heart-rending that in my early days as

Left above: Like many other desert animals, the wheatear (Oenanthe leucopyga) *nests and shelters from the heat of the day in rodent burrows.   Left: Temminck's horned larks* (Eremophila bilopha), *typical of the dry zones of Northern Africa and Southern Asia, feed their young. (Both, Eric Hosking)*

Right: This lesser horseshoe bat (Rhinolophus hipposideros) *of Israel belongs to a genus found almost everywhere in the Old World. They are insectivorous bats and have horseshoe-shaped nose-leaves. (Walter Ferguson)*

The Indian crested porcupine (Hystrix indica), *a wary, nocturnal creature, ranges from Israel to India. (Walter Ferguson)*

a naturalist I constantly thought that some ferocious beast was murdering an antelope. Natives explain that hyraxes wail this way to fool their principal enemy, the leopard. While it climbs, the little hyrax cries, "I'm coming down," and when it comes down, it moans, "I'm going up!"

Hyraxes have another strange habit, that of always leaving their feces in the same place and sprinkling them with urine. The combination solidifies and forms small blocks called *hyraceum* in the Middle Ages, when it was considered an infallible remedy for many ailments and was sold at fabulous prices in Europe.

A GALAXY OF RODENTS

As in all desert regions, the best-represented mammals are the rodents. Some of them are peculiar to Arabia. Among these is the black-tailed dormouse *(Eliomys melanurus)*, a relative of European dormice. Like them it is basically a tree-dweller and can fall into an almost comatose state when climatic or feeding conditions become unfavorable. Among other natives of the peninsula are the spiny rat or golden acomys *(Acomys russatus)*, merion *(Meriones rex)*, and two gerbils with naked

paws, *Gerbillus poecilops* and *G. famulus*. All of these rodents are related to forms living in Africa or other parts of Asia.

Besides these natives, one may meet many species in Arabia that are also common in the Sahara or in Western or Central Asian deserts. One of the most amusing of these is the little desert jerboa *(Jaculus jaculus)*; with its long hind paws and a long tail that serves as a balancing pole when it jumps and as a base to rest on, it resembles a miniature kangaroo. The species that has the greatest problem in getting food is surely the fat psammomys *(Psammomys obesus)*, which feeds almost exclusively on the succulent parts of certain plants; it must

Right above: The palm lizard, Uromastix ornatus, *of a genus widespread in North African and Arabian deserts, is mainly vegetarian but does not scorn a few insects. (Werner Braun) Right: The rough-tailed gerbil* (Gerbillus dasyurus), *found from Arabia to southern Iran, is a nocturnal rodent that haunts the salty clay deserts where the Chenopodiaceae grow. Far right: The golden spiny mouse* (Acomys russatus) *lives in Arabia, Israel and Egypt. A black pigmentation beneath its skin is due, according to some experts, to its diurnal mode of life. (Both, Walter Ferguson)*

find these all year round, for it has no estivation period. It is thus forced to set up its colonies near the beds of the best-irrigated wadis.

Among species living both in Arabia and in other deserts in Asia, there is the jerboa of the Euphrates *(Allactaga euphratica),* which is distinctly larger than the preceding species and recognizable by its long ears. The Indian tatera *(Tatera indica)* and another spiny rat *(Acomys cahirinus)* are equally abundant. Some rodents have managed to colonize practically the entire strip of desert from North Africa to Central Asia. The most common are merions, *Meriones crassus* and *M. libycus,* and the little sand gerbil *(Gerbillus gerbillus).* The desert hare *(Lepus capensis),* which is smaller and paler than the hare that lives in Europe and the Asiatic steppes, has the same distribution.

The birds that enliven the peninsula's deserts are the same as those found in the Sahara; we will also meet them in the dry zones of Central Asia. They are mainly crows, larks, wheat-ears grouse and a few falcons and nocturnal birds of prey. One also finds the cream-colored courser *(Cursorius cursor),* whose rapid movements animate the sandy or stony reaches of Southern Europe and North Africa.

The reptiles are principally Saharan species, such as the sand skink that moves about in light soil with such ease that the Arabs call it "the fish of the sands." The uromastix or palm lizard is another Saharan reptile. Basically vegetarian, it is commonly called the palm lizard because its spiny tail resembles the stem of a palm tree. The horned viper *(Cerastes cornutus)* is also common and buries itself in the sand to await its prey, rodents or gekkos whose large eyes with dilatable pupils indicate that they are normally nocturnal.

The fact that so many of these animals are the same as or very closely related to African species confirms what we said at the beginning of this chapter: the Red Sea is a too recent natural barrier and does not draw a line between the natural inhabitants of Arabia and those of Africa.

In the bed of the torrent that formed this canyon lives a shrubby growth of Chenopodiaceae whose deep roots enable it to withstand the rare but violent floods in the Negev Desert. (Uzi Paz)

Sand, Salt and Clay

The Cold Deserts of Central Asia

6 Immediately north and east of the Arabian peninsula, a succession of plateaus and barren depressions cuts diagonally across Asia from the Euphrates to the spurs of the Great Khingan Mountains.

Forming Iran and Afghanistan, the Plateau of Iran lies on the west, fringed north and south by high mountain ranges. Two series of transverse chains link these mountains together and cup three vast desert basins: the arid plateau of Isfahan, the salt deserts or *kavirs,* and the stony wastes of Afghanistan and Baluchistan, where only the marshy province of Seistan provides a more verdant note.

Farther to the east lies the vast low plain of western Turkistan or the Aral-Caspian depression. During the Miocene Epoch this area was covered by a sea of which the Black Sea, the Caspian, the Aral Sea, Lake Balkhash, Lake Alakol', and many other salt lakes are the merest residue. As has been quite rightly pointed out, these three seas are no longer worthy of the name. They are really huge lakes with slightly saline waters: 19 percent saline in the Black Sea, from 12 to 13 percent in the Caspian, and 10 percent in the Aral Sea. Their deep waters are rich in hydrogen sulfide produced by sulfur-reducing bacteria. These bacteria preclude living organisms in the depths, but as compensation, a comparatively large number of animals, many of them endemic species, has managed to survive on the surface. The most interesting are found in the Caspian; although this sea lacks such groups as crabs, cephalopods, echinoderms, tunicates, sharks and cetaceans, more than 80 percent of its mollusks and 60 percent of its crustaceans and fish are endemic. The present level of the Caspian is about ninety feet below that of the other seas and continues to fall partly because the rivers that feed it do not make up for the vast evaporation of water. Countless salt lakes throughout the deserts of Central Asia share this fate, for most of the water carried into them by even the strongest rivers is lost through evaporation and through filtering into the sand.

The topography of Caspian Turkistan is remarkable for its flatness. Elevations higher than 650 feet are rare. The entire

The Nemegt Basin in the Gobi Desert presents a typical landscape of deep valleys rimmed by steep cliffs. (Ryszard Gradzinski)

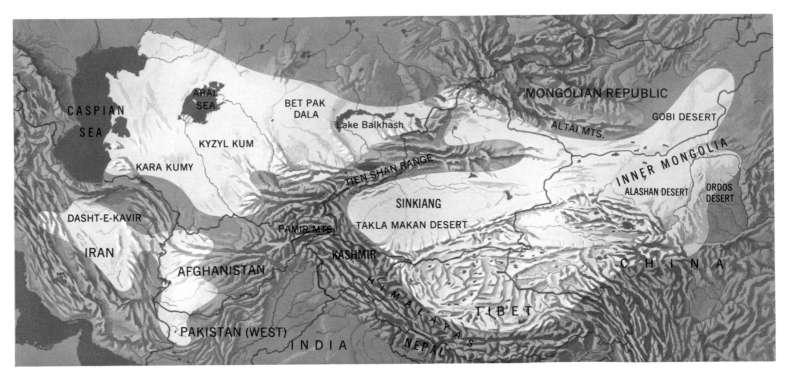

A wide band of temperate or cold deserts, broken by a few mountain chains, stretches from Iran to Mongolia. After the sandy deserts of the Aral-Caspian depression come the clay deserts of Kazakh and the stone deserts or gobis of Mongolia.

plain is strewn with shallow basins and marshes, the remains of ancient salt lakes that are gradually drying up. The Pamir and Tien Shan ranges separate Caspian Turkistan from Oriental Turkistan. The latter is a vast plateau with a mean altitude of 4,250 feet and, although crossed by many streams, is almost completely a desert. West of the great salt lake of Lop Nor, another relic of a sea now evaporated, is the Takla Makan Desert, the largest expanse of barren sand in Central Asia. Eastward, the Gobi (called *Shamo,* or "ocean of sand," by the Chinese) forms a basin with its bottom lying at a mean altitude of about three thousand feet and the rim rising to nearly five thousand. It is a succession of salt deserts, stretches of loess or yellow earth, clay, and ancient alluvial valleys full of pebbles the Mongols called *gobis,* the name applied to the entire region by the first western visitors. It is so arid that one pioneer, the Russian zoologist and explorer, N. M. Przewalsky, traveled a thousand miles without seeing a single stream. Two areas of the Gobi that are particularly desolate, the Ordos and the Alashan, consist of shifting sand dunes. "These sands," wrote Przewalsky, "beget a sort of stifling anguish of the spirit. If you climb one of these mounds and survey space, no vegetation gladdens your eyes. You will not see a blade of grass, no animal except the lizard. The silence is unbroken even by the song of the cricket; you are lost in a sea of sand, surrounded by the quiet of the tomb. . . ."

All these deserts have a continental climate, characterized by burning summers and generally severe winters. Although the Aral-Caspian desert is in the same latitude as Spain and the south of France, its mean diurnal temperature in July is higher than that at the equator. The thermometer often reaches 85° F, with some places getting above 120° F in the shade. During the night, the mercury falls abruptly, the difference between day and night temperatures often approaching 70° F. The surface of the earth exposed to the sun may reach 175° F

during the day and fall to 70° F at night, a difference of over 100 degrees in a few hours.

Autumn is generally sunny and mild in the Central Asian deserts, but winter is severe. The Aral Sea remains frozen for four or five months and floating ice may often be seen in May. On the banks of the Syr Dar'ya River, the mean January temperature is almost 0° F, colder than on the Gulf of Finland. The absence of any barriers between the icy Arctic Ocean and the mountains of Iran makes possible brutal cold waves that cause the mercury to fall as low as –20° F. Only the sheltered regions of the plateau of Iran have mild winters, with mean temperatures higher than 50° F in January.

Unlike the steppes, the deserts of Central Asia have very few winds and these are not very violent. The sky is rarely overcast and sunny days predominate. The almost constant sunshine and the meager rainfall intensify the aridity of the climate. The mean annual rainfall, usually occurring in spring and fall months, ranges between three and eight inches. The summer months, July, August and September, are practically without rain. There are a variety of soils and landscapes in these deserts, the only factor they have in common being their dryness. The salt deserts or *kavirs* of Iran are succeeded by Turkistan's sand or clay expanses and Mongolia's loess or stone deserts. As we noted in Arabia, it is sand that best conserves humidity. In the stone deserts, rain water streams into the valleys to form temporary rivers, while on bare clay stretches, frequent in Kazakh, where they are called *takyrs,* water forms huge, very shallow lakes that dry out, leaving the ground covered with cracks as in a mosaic.

Dasht-e-Kavir is a huge saline desert depression in the center of Iran. The area is often shaken by violent earthquakes. (Paul Almasy)

100

DESERT PLANTS

The stone and clay deserts are almost barren of vegetation, but the sand deserts turn green with the first rains. These plants help to keep the soil in place, and where they have been destroyed by excessive grazing, the sand becomes unstable and forms *barchans,* successions of crescent-shaped dunes that shift with the wind. It is in the deserts of Kara Kumy and Kyzyl Kumy (Turkoman names meaning black sands and white sands) that the barchans cover the largest surface.

Only at the onset of spring does the vegetation of the sand deserts appear as a more or less thick carpet of grasses, sedges, and dicotyledonous annuals. Long before summer comes, most of these ephemeral plants disappear, burned off by the sun, and only a few xerophytic species survive at wide intervals. Often thorny, they show interesting adaptations to the dryness. Among the most curious are shrubs of the genus *Calligonum,* which are distributed from the Sahara to Mongolia, but are most typical of Central Asian deserts and occur there in more than forty species. When their tiny threadlike leaves fall in midspring, respiratory exchanges take place through their small branches, which themselves fall off at the end of June. Evaporation is thus reduced to a minimum and the plant survives until the following spring. The saxaouls *(Arthrophytum)* are also characteristic and are represented by two species, the white saxaoul *(A. persicum),* which grows on neutral sand, and the black saxaoul *(A. aphyllum),* which prefers saline soil. The first has very small leaves and the second none at all. Both breathe through their branches, which fall at the beginning of the summer, leaving what seems to be the skeleton of a dead plant. As the years pass, dry branches pile up around the trunks and sometimes completely bury the plants. As a result, forests of saxaouls covering immense areas of the desert between the Caspian and Lake Balkhash provide a strange spectacle. No matter how dense these forests are, there is always light as well as stifling heat within them, for the bare branches do not shut out the rays of the sun and the closely spaced trunks form a shelter against the wind. Since animals do not awaken before the close of day, the silence is complete, and the sensation of desolation and death emanating from the skeleton-like trees surrounded by heaps of dry branches is most oppressive. Many of the trees have been dead for a long time, but continue to stretch their whitening limbs toward the sky. Saxaoul wood almost never rots and is so hard that it soon blunts the edge of an axe. The absence of leaves may be noted also on the *Eremosparton,* a leguminous bush. In other species, the leaves become thorns, a classic development in the struggle against evaporation.

Most of these plants survive in the soft sands by developing a complex root system. *Aristida karelini,* always the first grass to settle on the sands of the Kara Kumy, sprouts long threadlike roots in all directions, from which rise new tufts of grass. Some of the *Calligonum,* the "sand acacias" *(Ammodendron)* and the *Eremospartum* have roots that extend more than a hundred feet from the parent plant. The sand acacia *(Ammodendron conollyi),* a shrub growing thirty-five feet tall, has aerial roots as high as ten feet up the main trunk. These roots anchor the plant firmly in the shifting ground.

In some places, milk vetch *(Astragalus),* wormwood *(Artemisia),* ephedra *(Ephedra),* and, on saline soil, saltwort *(Salicornia)* form almost pure growths. On the Bet Pak Dala or "steppe of hunger," actually a vast desert between the Aral Sea and Lake Balkhash, one may also find a remarkable umbelliferous plant, the asafetida *(Ferula foetida),* which gets its name from its repulsive odor and is used in pharmacy as an antispasmodic.

Ephemeral plants are particularly important in the loess deserts that occupy immense tracts from the Caspian Sea to Mongolia. Appearing in March when the rains begin, the plants release their seeds at the end of April. They develop so rapidly because most of them are perennials whose growth cycle begins in the autumn and is broken off during the winter months. This two-stage cycle represents a remarkable adaptation to the brevity of the spring rains. It is truly astonishing to see these deserts, during most of the year strewn only with widely scattered plants, suddenly covered with a green carpet of sedges and meadowgrass sprinkled with blue veronicas, red poppies, yellow ranunculus and purple iris. The most important of the ephemerals is bulbous meadowgrass *(Poa bulbosa),* a perennial grass twelve to fifteen inches high and self-reproducing. At the base of its stalk it forms a kind of bulb that is highly resistant to drought. The Russian botanist L. S. Berg cites instances of the bulbs growing after a period of ten years in a herbarium. Bulbous meadowgrass reproduces in an even more astonishing fashion. Within the spike, another sort of very tiny bulb appears instead of seeds. These bulbils form very rapidly. The same botanist mentions a case where the spike made its first appearance on April 5th and the bulbils on the 16th of the same month. As soon as they fall, each of these bulbils, fifty to a spike, grows into a tuft of meadowgrass.

The sedges *(Carex pachystylis* in the loess deserts and *C. physodes* in the sand deserts) take second place among the ephemerals. In some places, the sedges crowd out the meadowgrass and form the spring covering alone. Like many desert

The strange Cistancha salsa *of Turkmen is among the countless ephemeral plants that cover the desert when the spring rains come. (Novosti)*

A venomous snake, the saw-scaled viper Echis carinatus, *found in the sand deserts from Africa through Central Asia to India, is reputedly quick to strike. (Novosti)*

plants, they reproduce by fragmentation of their bulbous roots. This permits them to colonize regions that do not have rain each year or have too brief a rainy season to allow for the flowering and ripening of seeds. By the end of April, the plant carpet begins to turn yellow and by the middle of May, meadowgrass and sedges are quite burned by the sun. In their place comes a creeping spurge *(Euphorbia chamasyce)* that forms little patches separated by soil that is either bare or covered with lichens.

ANIMAL LIFE IN THE DESERT

The brevity of the growing period of most desert plants influences the life cycle of desert animals. The land tortoise *(Testudo horsfieldi)* and the yellow suslik *(Citellus fulvus)* eat only the green parts of ephemeral plants and thus have food only from the beginning of March until the end of May. To stay alive for the rest of the year, they have found no better solution than to sink into a lethargy and sleep more than eight months out of the twelve. Large animals such as gazelles, saiga antelopes, hemiones, wild horses and camels escape starvation only by constantly moving about in search of greener pastures.

Some animals solve their main problem in the desert, lack

of water, by quenching their thirst with the liquid in plants. The camel, represented in Asia by the two-humped species *(Camelus bactrianus),* ran wild in the most remote Mongolian deserts until quite recently. It seems to have disappeared completely about ten years ago, and the few herds now sighted from time to time are usually composed of domesticated beasts that have run wild. Wild or tame, the camel is famous for its capacity to endure thirst. When the ephemeral plants cover the desert in spring, the camel can do without water entirely, provided it does not overexert itself. In summer, when the ephemerals are burned by the sun and the thorny bushes *(Alhagi camelorum)* that only the camel can eat are quite dry, it can still go long periods without drinking. It is not true, however, that the camel stores water inside its body. Its main source of liquid lies in its body tissues and it can lose as much as 25 percent of its total weight without apparent harm. Truly remarkable, the camel is adapted to life in dry regions in still another way. Its body temperature can rise as high as seven degrees, a state of fever, apparently without causing it to suffer. It thus saves the large quantities of water that other animals lose by sweating or expiration to reduce body temperature. Of course, after such privation, the camel becomes almost totally dehydrated, and makes up for its losses as soon as possible by drinking as much as twenty-five gallons of

Another view of Echis carinatus, *a viper that feeds mainly on rodents and lizards. (Novosti)*

water at one time. Food and rest are also required for the rebuilding of the fatty reserves.

Other large desert animals such as wild asses and horses, gazelles and saiga antelopes lack this capacity to endure thirst and must drink at least every two or three days. Since water-holes are rare in the desert, these animals travel great distances to satisfy their needs. Similarly, many birds, such as turtle-doves, sand-grouse, and rosy pastor starlings, often in huge flocks, fly a score of miles, early in the morning or late in the evening, to reach water. Even though protected by law, large animals have died off in many places simply because shepherds and their flocks have preempted the only watering place in a region. This is what happened to the gazelles and wild asses of Central Asia and it seems likely to have been the fate of the last herd of Przewalsky's horse in Mongolia.

Many desert rodents can also do without water. Some make use of green plants, while others get all the water they need from seeds, although these usually contain not more than 10 percent water. These species live in constant balance with their environment and they cannot survive any abnormal loss of water. They remain in their burrows all day, where the humidity ranges between 30 and 50 percent, and emerge only at night when the air is cool. Upon returning, they close off the entrances to their dens to prevent any evaporation. In

addition, they scarcely urinate and thus they loose little of their internal liquid. An underground shelter thus protects the rodent not only from the heat of the outside air but also from the dryness. Measurements have shown that when the temperature on the surface is nearly 140° F it may go no higher than from 60° to 70° F twenty inches down. It is not surprising that the vast majority of desert animals spend their days in burrows and go out only at night. Not only do burrowing animals behave this way, but so do other species usually content with surface shelters. In these deserts even a hare, which generally lives in a simple hollow in areas where plants or rock formations provide shelter from the sun, digs burrows in the sand and hides completely. During the hottest daylight hours even birds, such as larks and chats, take shelter in the burrows of rodents or small carnivores.

Proof that the nocturnal life of most Central Asian animals is a method of escaping the deadly heat of the day comes in winter when most animals reverse the cycle and emerge during the day. This is true of many insects, some lizards, snakes, and a few rodents. Except for the species that become lethargic for lack of food, hibernation is less common in the temperate and cold deserts than on the steppes.

In the Aral-Caspian region and in Mongolia, it is not unusual to see animals and reptiles emerge from their shelters at midday as early as January. They serve as food for many insect-eating or predatory birds, enabling the latter to remain in these regions throughout the winter or to migrate only a short distance. The jerboa (Dipus sagitta), for example, almost never hibernates in the Kara Kumy desert, although in colder regions like Kazakh it becomes lethargic from October to March. The animal's paws have hairy soles, permitting it to move about easily on the overheated ground. Many other animals possess physical characteristics that enable them to withstand the burning sand. The most curious is that observed in one particular species of sand-grouse (Pterocles orientalis) by the Russian naturalist A. N. Formozov. This very short-legged bird can remain active during the heat of the day because it has distinctly thicker skin on its belly than on its back and this underbelly skin is not directly attached to the flesh but forms an air chamber that isolates all parts of the body in contact with the ground. This strange air-pocket effect is well developed even in the newly hatched chicks.

Other animals show color adaptations, the great majority wear cryptic colors that harmonize with the environment. The fox, various wild cats, the hare, and many rodents, birds and reptiles are much paler than their fellows on the steppes or the taiga. From the tundra to the steppes, the ermine, for instance, is a tawny beige in summer and all white in winter except for the black tip of its tail; but in Central Asian deserts, where it rarely snows, the animal wears its summer coat, lighter in tint here than elsewhere, all year round.

Oddly enough, these desert tints can be seen on nocturnal species, such as owls and rodents, as well as on diurnal ones. It is always the visible part of the body that is subject to protective coloration. Butterflies are light on the undersides of their wings, moths on the upper surfaces—in both cases the surfaces exposed when the insect is at rest. This harmonizing with environment sometimes reaches perfection. The toad-headed agamid (Phrynocephalus mystaceus) and the reticulated lizard (Eremias grammica) have ocher-colored backs sprinkled with tiny black specks that correspond in effect to the particles of black quartz found in the sand they live on. A study of these two common Central Asian desert reptiles has shown that in the reticulated lizard this adaptation is stable and hereditary within a given population in a particular locality. The toad-headed agamid, on the other hand, displays an adaptive coloration like that of the chameleon. Cells of the dermis or true skin, rich in black pigments, dilate and contract according to impressions received by the eye of the animal. As it passes from one type of desert to another it can harmonize instantly with sands more or less rich in black particles.

Some adaptations are linked to locomotion on sand and generally involve an increase in the bearing surface of the body, thus diminishing the pressure exerted on the ground. Many running insects, lizards, larks, chats, and such rodents as the slender-toed ground-squirrel accomplish this by means of lengthened tarsi, phalanges, claws, or, as in sand-grouse, enlarged toes. A few animals form "snowshoes" made up of hairs, as in the jerboa Dipus sagitta, or thin, horny "combs," as in the gecko Crossobamon eversmanni or the jerboa Paradipus ctenodactylus. This jerboa also uses the combs to smooth its fur, for unlike most rodents it does not seem to clean itself by powdering with sand.

Some animals without special physical adaptations for walking on sand compensate by unusual behavior. The saw-scaled viper (Echis carinatus) crawls diagonally, like the Saharan horned viper or certain American desert rattlers. Instead of trying to glide along on the sand, which offers no hold, it whips its body sidewise and progresses obliquely, leaving a series of parallel tracks behind. Others, like small boas of the genus Eryx and skinks or sand lizards, thrust about just under the surface of the loose sand.

A PREVALENCE OF LIZARDS

Remarkable adaptations such as we have just noted permit a far richer animal life in the arid zones of Asia than one would expect.

The presence of countless lizards fleeing before an intruder's footsteps has always astonished travelers in the most desolate areas. In fact, the Central Asian deserts are rich in unique forms. The most common forms are lizards of the genus Eremias, agamids (Phrynocephalus), geckos, skinks, and one varan or monitor lizard that reaches a length of five feet. The strangest desert lizard is probably the toad-headed agamid, distributed from Iran to Lake Balkhash. In times of danger, this little lizard burrows into the sand with astonishing speed. But when cornered, it turns upon its adversary and adopts a threatening attitude. Solidly planted on its back legs, it lifts the forepart of its body and opens a huge, bright pink mouth made larger by folds of skin on both sides. In summer all the agamas take refuge in shallow burrows or merely bury themselves in the sand.

Geckos, very numerous in the tropics, are represented here by about ten usually nocturnal species with large eyes that have a narrow vertical pupil. The comb-toed gecko (Crossobamon eversmanni), adapted, as we have indicated, to movement on loose sand, may be seen as far north as the semideserts of Kazakh. The gray gecko (Gymnodactylus russowi) seeks regions with a firm substratum: clay or stony deserts and also saxaoul forests. Two other geckos with unadorned toes, the Caspian (G. caspius) and the Turkistan (G. fedtschenkoi), often live inside houses, where they hunt insects attracted by the lights.

The lizards are very important in the life of Central Asian deserts for they are an essential link in the feeding chain that binds various groups of animals together. Very numerous and active day and night, they are the principal consumers of desert insects, ants, spiders, locusts and bugs, and are in turn eaten by some snakes and many carnivores and by birds of prey from the desert shrike to the long-legged buzzard. Among the reptiles, the arrow or dart snake (Taphrometopon lineolatum) is the major enemy of the lizards. It hunts in cat fashion, taking advantage of every obstacle on the terrain before leaping on its prey. Although it has a fearful reputation among local residents and its venom kills a lizard in five or six seconds, it is completely harmless to man. This is not true of the saw-scaled viper, which is always ready, according to students of its habits, to inject its very active venom. The most widely distributed and most abundant snake in these regions, in summer it hunts rodents at night, whereas in spring and fall it leads a diurnal existence. Between November and January or February it hibernates, either in a natural shelter or in a rodent's burrow. Also common on the desert are the Orsini's viper (Vipera ursini) in the north and the lebetine viper (Vipera lebetina) in the south, the latter reaching a length

of six feet and the thickness of a man's arm. Two especially poisonous species are found in the southern deserts: an Asian mocassin *(Ancistrodon halys)* and also the cobra *(Naja naja),* which extends as far north as the Samarkand region, clinging to river valleys, for it seems to require more humid conditions than other snakes of the area. Among the strictly desert species living in loose sand are the little burrowing boas of the genus *Eryx,* the most common being *E. miliaris* and *E. tataricus.*

DESERT TERMITES AND MIGRATORY LOCUSTS

As astonishing as the liveliness of reptiles and lizards is the number of insects both by day and night. The first to attract attention are generally the large hunting ants of the genus *Cataglyphis* running rapidly across the sand on long legs. Although these desert species live in colonies like all ants, they hunt alone. One, *C. pallida,* is so protectively colored that Professor A. N. Formozov asserts that when it runs one sees only its moving shadow on the sand. The harvester ants of the genus *Messor* are vegetarians and live in ant-hills that are often immense. Entrance to the nest is surrounded by a wall of earth and other rubbish, and the paths leading from it are spotlessly clean and may be 250 feet long. In summer, when the ground cools at the close of day, dense black columns of ants pour out along these tracks and branch off in all directions, looking for seeds of grasses to store in the nest.

Although practically invisible, desert termites of the genus *Acanthotermes* are even more numerous than ants. Of the six species in the region, only one, the Caspian termite *(A. ahngerianus)* builds a mound, raising a clayey structure about twenty inches above a subterranean nest. All other termites here live such a life in their infinitely branching subterranean tunnels that they generally go unnoticed. But one may see telegraph poles covered from base to summit with a solid clayey crust, evidence of the activity of these insects, which attack practically anything not made of metal. Some idea of the damage they do can be gained from a count by Russian scholars that showed as many as fifteen large termite colonies per acre, with each nest covering from eighty-five to one hundred thirty square feet and descending as much as sixty feet below the surface.

Among the other plagues that beset desert plants and cultivation, first place was held until recently by the migratory locust *(Schistocerca gregaria),* which arrived in clouds from its usual breeding places in Africa, Arabia, and northern India. Spraying with insecticides on their gathering places has now

Left: The tawny eagle (Aquila rapax) *lives on arid, brushy plains. Not very energetic, it spends much time on the ground hunting small reptiles, frogs and carrion. (Eric Hosking)*

Right above: An outcropping of porphyrian and basalt rocks contrasts sharply with the surrounding flat plains in western Mongolia. (Gunther Peters) Right: The eared-agama (Phrynocephalus mystaceus) *takes its name from large folds of skin on either side of its mouth. It tries to intimidate a foe by showing its pink throat and spreading its skin folds. Far right: The gray monitor lizard* (Varanus griseus), *about five feet long, is the most northern representative of a genus widespread in all the hot regions of the Old World. (Both, Novosti)*

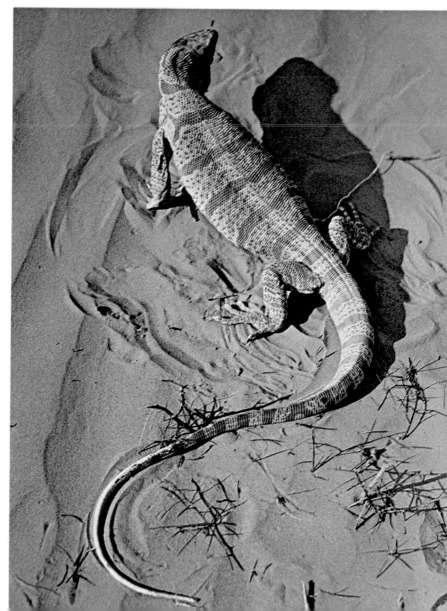

reduced to insignificance the damage they may cause. Native Central Asian locusts are not gregarious and their density is never greater than one per square yard.

Strictly insectivorous mammals are represented only by one small species, the white-backed shrew *(Diplomesodom pulchellum)*, which is peculiar to the region. Hedgehogs, which are classed among the Insectivores but have a more varied diet, are common. One species *(Paraechinus hypomelas)*, called the bald hedgehog, has a higher forehead than the common European hedgehog but has no quills on it. The other, *Hemiechinus auritus*, has large ears, a trait often noted in animals living on deserts where sound carries far and sharp ears are useful not only for detecting predators but for rallying other members of the same species scattered across vast spaces. It has been discovered that the tympanic bullae, bony sounding boxes located at the base of the skull, are more highly developed in more purely desert species, that is, those living in an environment where lack of food permits only very thin populations. According to the French zoologist, F. Petter, who has made an intensive study of mammals of the Sahara and of Iran, this adaptation must help maintain the rate of reproduction of the species by enabling the two sexes to communicate over long distances.

Among other insect-eaters, we note that moles are absent from the arid zones of Central Asia simply because of the absence of their principal food, earthworms. The role of earthworms in the formation of humus is taken in the desert by wood lice of the genus *Hemilepistus*. Recent research in the Soviet Republic of Turkmen has shown that there are as many as 500,000 of these terrestrial crustaceans per acre and that they bring to the surface over five hundred pounds of subsoil and about half a ton of excrement rich in cellulose. Their tiny tunnels go down as deep as two and a half feet and facilitate the penetration of rainwater into the soil. Over hundreds and thousands of years their activities have been extremely favorable to the formation of a fertile surface layer and the growth of vegetation.

GROUND-CHOUGHS AND SHRIKES

The most characteristic bird of the immense deserts of Central Asia is incontestably the ground-chough *(Podoces panderi)*. Several varieties of this bird have been noted between the Caspian Sea and the Gobi Desert. Although it looks like and has plumage approximating that of the Eurasian jay, it leads a purely ground existence. As the English naturalist Douglas Carruthers has noted, it seems to fly with great difficulty. It is found only in the most arid regions. In places where sand desert and stony desert touch, two races live together without mixing, each remaining in its own habitat. Silent and solitary, they run rapidly over the ground on stout legs with a well-developed hind toe and long claws like those of larks. Only at breeding time do they rise above ground and build a nest of twigs in a saxaoul or tamarisk bush, or occasionally in rock hollows or abandoned burrows.

Equally typical of the desert is a close relative of the domestic sparrow, the saxaoul sparrow *(Passer ammodendri)*, strictly linked to the saxaoul shrub. Among the other small birds that inhabit these shrubs are the booted warbler *(Hippolais caligata)*, the desert warbler *(Sylvia nana)*, other warblers, and great gray shrikes *(Lanius excubitor)*. Many species of wheatears *(Oenanthe)* have established colonies in stony or clayey

zones in the sand. These little birds nest in burrows, using the abandoned tunnels of rodents. Ground-loving creatures, chats sometimes flutter in one spot above the ground, like kestrels, to spot the insects they are hunting.

Larks, equally ground-loving, are more fond of grain. As numerous as the chats, they inhabit true deserts as well as semideserts and steppes. Short-toed larks *(Calandrella cinerea* and *C. pispoletta)* and crested larks *(Galerida cristata)* are the most common. In the sandy areas there are desert larks *(Ammomanes deserti)*, small, dull-plumaged birds also common in North Africa. In the clay deserts, one finds the spotted lark *(Melanocorypha bimaculata)* and the calandra lark *(M. calandra)*, while two related species, the black lark and the white-winged lark, occur at the edge of the steppes. Most of these larks remain here during the winter, making only limited migrations to look for seeds.

It is not by chance that those species most specialized in the search for seeds, notably the sand-grouse or gangas, prefer clayey or stony deserts. Fallen grass seeds remain uncovered for a longer time on this type of ground than on sand, and are thus available to birds, even in winter, for snow is rare in these deserts. During the driest years, the total absence of rain prevents the formation of new seeds, but those of the preceding year do not sprout and are generally sufficient to feed the birds. Sand-grouse are not strictly Asiatic since some species also live in Africa, but they may be considered the most typical of the desert birds. The size of a pigeon, they have the same kind of small round head and fairly thick, short beak as that bird; but they differ from pigeons in their long, pointed wings and more rapid, vigorous flight. Unlike other desert birds, sand-grouse, trusting to their black-veined ocher plumage to hide them, do not take flight at danger, but nestle down so inconspicuously on open ground that it is possible to pass without seeing them. Wearing the same cryptic colors, eggs and newly hatched chicks rest on the bare ground without a trace of a nest to betray their presence. To feed the young birds the parents fly in couples or large flocks to the nearest water twice a day, and return with seeds and water, the latter carried in the crop. Two species of sand-grouse are distributed from North Africa to Central Asia: the black-bellied sand-grouse *(Pterocles orientalis)* and the pin-tailed sand-grouse *(P. alchata)*. Two other species, Pallas' sand-grouse *(Syrrhaptes paradoxus)* and the Tibetan sand-grouse *(Tchangtangia tibetanus)*, are exclusively Asiatic.

Other essentially ground birds are the stone curlew *(Burhinus oedicnemus)* and the dun-colored courser that we have already met in Arabia, for these two species are distributed from Southern Europe and North Africa to Central and Tropical Asia. The desert bustard *(Otis undulata)* also inhabits dry regions of North Africa and the Middle East and is found as

Right above: Although mostly stony, sterile valleys, the Gobi Desert has sandy patches that hold water longer and permit sufficient plantlife to feed desert herbivores. (Rondière: Rapho Guillumette) Right: The tiny-eyed spalax or mole-rat (Spalax ehrenbergi) leads a completely subterranean life. Far right: In the dry hot regions of the Old World, the most widespread member of the dog family is the jackal (Canis aureus), whose carrion-eating habits are well known. (Both, Walter Ferguson)

The Nemegt Basin in the Gobi Desert, the site of recently discovered dinosaur beds, is bordered on the north by the Nemegt Range, which is seen in the distance. (Ryszard Gradzinski)

far north as Mongolia. Like the stone curlew, it hunts large insects, mollusks and small lizards.

The abundance of small and medium-sized birds, reptiles, and rodents allows a number of birds of prey to dwell in the desert. During the day, one may see the imperial eagle, the golden eagle or bierkut, the steppe eagle and the harrier eagle *(Circaëtus ferox).* The most common of the nocturnal birds of prey is the desert little owl *(Athene noctua),* which does not hesitate to show itself well before nightfall. It nests in abandoned burrows, in crevices, or under rocks, and hunts rodents as well as lizards, scorpions and large insects.

SUSLIKS AND JERBOAS

Although the mammals in Central Asian deserts are plentiful and diverse, they generally remain hidden from the traveler's eye, for the great majority are nocturnal and burrowers. The easiest to observe are some of the rodents, particularly the large gerbil, *Rhombomys opimus,* which is active during the day. At first glance, this gerbil resembles a common rat, except for a tail covered with soft reddish fur and tipped with a tuft of black hairs. Large gerbils are not timid and it is often possible to draw as near as a dozen paces and watch them as

they gnaw a branch or stalk. When alarmed, they scurry toward an entrance of their burrow, sit on their hind legs and tail and watch the object of their uneasiness while emitting a two-syllable cry of alarm that has earned them the Turkoman name of "bib-bib." As many as fifteen gerbils live in one burrow that has ten or fifteen openings. In sectors of desert rich in grassy plants, families of gerbils live so close together that there are sometimes more than 2,500 burrow openings to an acre, creating a terrain dangerous to pedestrians and horses. The slopes of sandy ravines are pitted with tunnels and chambers in which the rodents store reserves of hay. It is hardly necessary to add that these legions of rodents cause inestimable damage to desert vegetation. On the other hand, their digging loosens and enriches the soil, allowing saxaouls and other plants to take root and hold together the sand in places abandoned by the rodent colonies.

In earlier chapters we have met some representatives of another group of rodents, the susliks, which live in colonies, are active during the day, and are related to the ground squirrels. While the yellow suslik *(Citellus fulvus)* spends part of the year in a lethargic state and wakes up only during the months when ephemeral plants grow, the slender-toed suslik *(Spermophilopsis leptodactylus),* recognizable by a tail scarcely longer than its hind paws, is active all year round and in winter grows a thick silky mantle with a well-developed undercoat. It eats green plants, bark, insects and larvae, as well as seeds, bulbs and rhizomes that it digs up when food is lacking on the surface. It ventures several hundred yards from its burrow in search of food and, when surprised, flees in powerful leaps, back paws spread wide and tail lifted to show a large black spot on its underside. Professor Formozov believes this spot is an optical signal for other susliks and he points out that it is found on some desert lizards, the agamas, which also lift their tails when alarmed.

The most common among nocturnal rodents is the large family of jerboas *(Dipodidae)*, represented in Central Asia by sixteen species, some discovered quite recently. They are all timid and spend their days in burrows which they close from within. Only in the glare of a flashlight or a headlight can one see their tiny kangaroo silhouettes with large hind paws, very short forepaws, and a long tail that is used as a balance as it leaps along and as a support when it stands still. The species range in size from that of a mouse to that of a young rabbit. All are perfectly adapted to nocturnal desert life. The astonishing running speed, the keen hearing indicated by long ears in several species, the large eyes for seeing in the dark, are the results of a long selection under the most difficult living conditions. Their little forepaws are used only for digging or carrying food to the mouth. Their short, shallow burrows, closed during the day to conserve humidity, serve as a place of hibernation during the cold season.

The most important group of jerboas is one whose back paws have five toes and that is adapted to life in deserts with firm clayey or stony ground. There one finds the large jerboa *(Allactaga jaculus)*, called a "hare" by local populations because its size and its long ears resemble those of the American "cottontail." It inhabits the northern part of the region between the Caspian and the Aral Seas, and is replaced in the south by the Severtzov's jerboa, a slightly smaller animal.

The three-toed jerboas form a separate group, including species we have met in discussing adaptation to locomotion on soft sand. Of these, the hairy-pawed jerboa *(Dipus sagitta)* has the widest distribution in Asia since it is found in all sandy deserts from Iran to northern China. It eats mainly shoots, flowers, and seeds of desert plants, as well as many insects and larvae. It travels long distances during the night and takes shelter in its burrow at morning, closing the entrance with a long sand plug. The comb-toed jerboa *(Paradipus ctenodactylus)*, whose curious strip-like structures on the soles of the paws we have already mentioned, is even better adapted to life on the sands of the Kara Kumy and Kyzyl Kum. Despite the softness of these sands, this little animal can progress in a series of ten-foot leaps that give an impression of ground-level flight rather than of running. Unlike the preceding species, this one eats branches of desert bushes that it gathers as high up as five feet.

The most interesting group of jerboas is the dwarf jerboas. To the uninitiated, they are charming toys with thick, cream-colored fur, round heads, and large, velvety black eyes. To zoologists, they are rare, little-known animals. Some species were described in the nineteenth century, but they are still represented by only one or two specimens in the world's largest museums, and their way of life is still unknown. Others were not discovered until quite recently: for example, Vinogradov's jerboa, which was first captured in 1958, and *Salpingotus michaeli* from Baluchistan, described by an English scientist in 1967.

The population densities of all these jerboas is very low and, considering their nocturnal proclivities, their concealment of the entrances to their burrows, and their avoidance of traps, a stroke of fortune is required for their capture. Douglas Carruthers tells how, despite a long stay and unremitting work in Kyzyl Kum, he failed to catch several species later discovered by Russian zoologists, but how, while passing rapidly through another region, he captured a new subspecies because he happened to pitch his tent above its burrow.

WILD ASSES AND GAZELLES

One of the most astonishing aspects of life in the desert was the presence up until recently of countless large animals—gazelles, antelopes, wild sheep, wild asses and wild horses. Huge herds of gazelles *(Gazella subgutturosa)*, saiga antelopes and wild asses or hemiones *(Equus hemionus)* still roved the Central Asian deserts at the close of the nineteenth century. It is said that after the building of the Achkhabad railroad one could see large groups of gazelles and hemiones from the train. Today, even gazelles are rare along the line and only strong protective measures taken between the two wars have enabled the animals to hold out or, in some instances, to increase.

The killers of these ungulates are the wolf, in the form of a small desert race with thick, pale fur, and the cheetah, represented by a few that may still survive between the Caspian and the Aral Sea. Rodents and hares are briskly hunted by various small and medium-sized carnivores, chiefly by the desert foxes *(Vulpes corsac, V. cana)* with pale fur. Even the common red fox *(V. vulpes)*, ubiquitous north of the Himalayas, exchanges its bright colors here for a sand-colored garment. Several species of cats, rarely seen because they are so timid, occupy the desert dunes and bushes. Four of them, *Felis margarita, F. libyca, F. caracal* and *F. chaus*, also live in Northern or Eastern Africa. The last two of these, the caracal and the jungle cat, are related to the lynx and have similarly tufted ears. The only true desert cat of temperate and cold Asia is Pallas' cat *(F. manul)*, whose long pale fur has led some students to believe that this species is the ancestor of our Persian cats. This is erroneous, the race called Persian being only an "angora" mutation of the common domestic cat, which probably descends from *F. libyca*. Also among the carnivores whose habitat extends from Southern Africa to northern India are two carrion-eaters common in the Central Asian deserts, the striped hyena and the jackal *(Canis aureus)*.

The marbled polecat *(Vormela peregusna)* is the only desert carnivore with bright fur, a perfect adaptation to life in open, arid zones. Unlike other carnivores, it hunts by entering the burrows of rodents in the manner of the ferret. A concealing colored fur would appear useless but since it is also provided with glands under its tail that emit an odor repulsive to other animals, its bright colors serve to warn its enemies from afar.

The Roof of the World

The Mountains of Central Asia and Szechwan

7   The most formidable mountain barrier in the world crosses the entire continent of Asia from the Mediterranean to the Bering Sea. In the central portion alone, between the plains of Siberia and the valley of the Ganges and between the Pamirs and the Greater Khingan Range, this enormous rampart covers an area almost as large as the United States. Dominating the continent from an average height of ten thousand feet, the gigantic succession of mountain chains and plateaus slopes progressively upward toward the south, rising to 29,000 feet in the highest peaks in the world. The rampart drops down toward the north, but is rarely lower than sixty-five hundred to ten thousand feet.

Right: Lake Band-i-Amir in the Hindu Kush, a mountain range whose high summits join the Iranian Plateau to the Pamir Mountains. (Harrison Forman)   Below: The Nubian ibex (Capra ibex nubianus) *is an agile mountain goat of Israel, Egypt and Arabia. Shown here is the female. (Jacob Dafni)*

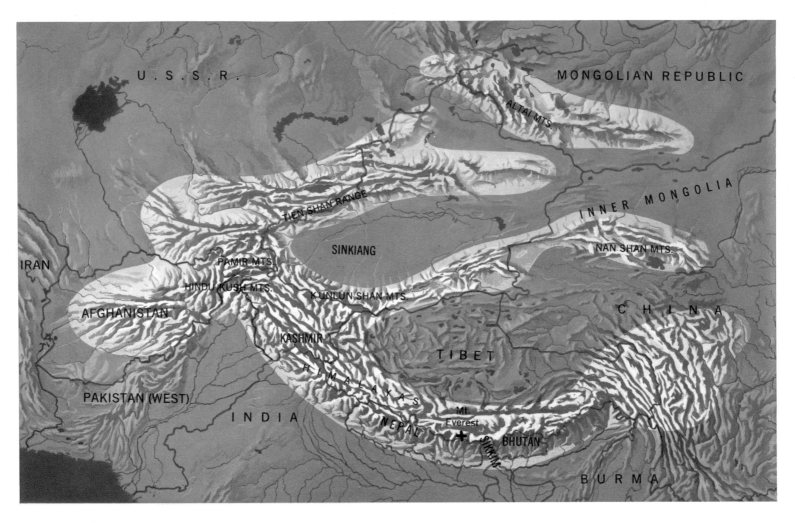

The heartland of Asia is covered by mountains that thrust out spurs in every direction. The mean altitude of the area is about ten thousand feet and the peaks on its southern border are the tallest in the world.

For a long time it was believed that the central core was completely locked in by the peripheral ranges and even at the beginning of the twentieth century reputable geographers linked the Himalayas directly to the Greater Khingan Range. A glance at a modern map shows that all these mountain chains run in more or less parallel lines toward the east and then turn abruptly either north or south as if to avoid the Chinese Mountains. Only the Chin Ling Shan Range holds to its original course and digs in like a wedge between the valleys of the Yangtze and Huang (Yellow) Rivers. The general east-west direction of the rocky undulations of Upper Asia is explained by the region's geological history. Originally covered by a sea, the Tethys, it sprang up in stages under the pressure exerted from both north and south by the very ancient Indian and Siberian continents.

It is easy to see the importance of this colossal barrier that isolates the cold or temperate sections of the country from its tropical border, so much richer botanically and zoologically. Impoverished by successive glaciations, the palearctic region north of the Himalayas was prevented from receiving any additions from the south except for a few plants or animals that managed to round the barrier by way of the Great Plain of China, the only avenue between the two large natural divisions of Eurasia. It is not surprising that the plants and animals of the center of Upper Asia are generally poorer than those of the marginal (peripheral) mountains, which are in

direct contact with the richest regions of the continent.

The point on earth most distant from any sea is in Dzungaria in the mountains of Upper Asia—1,600 miles from the Indian Ocean. Marine influences are scarcely felt in this interior region and the climate is typically continental, dry and marked by extremes of heat and cold. Przewalsky asserts that winters are so cold there that he saw mercury freeze. Temperatures close to $-75°$ F are frequent in Irkutsk, where in summer the thermometer rises to $104°$ F. All year long, violent gales from the west raise great clouds of yellow dust that darken the air and penetrate everywhere. One November and December on the mountain spurs over which the Great Wall of China runs, I had the taste of sand in my mouth constantly. The air is so dry that everything is charged with static electricity and I had merely to comb my hair or brush a woollen or fur garment to set off a shower of sparks. Summers are scarcely more humid since the encircling chains of mountains intercept all rain-bearing clouds.

By contrast, precipitation is abundant on the periphery; and some hill stations, especially in the Himalayas where 80 to 120 inches of rain fall each year, are among the best-watered

The absence of plant cover and the alternation of hard and soft strata have encouraged the erosion of this mountainous region of Iran. (Aerofilms Limited)

114

places in the world. Rivers abound on the circumference of the central plateau, whose high mountains make it a reservoir whence almost all the great rivers of the continent flow. It sends the Irtysh, Ob', Yenisey and the Lena toward the Arctic coast. Toward the Pacific and Indian Oceans flow the Amur, Huang, Yangtze, Mekong, Salween, Irrawaddy, Brahmaputra, Ganges and the Indus. Other rivers—the Syr Dar'ya, Amu Dar'ya and the Ili—flow into inland seas or great salt lakes. Still others simply lose themselves in the sands of Central Asia. The Chu literally vanishes into the Kazakh desert, and the Tarim, at first about 650 to 1,000 feet wide and from ten to twenty feet deep, sinks gradually into the reeds and salt marshes of Lop Nor.

The main contrast between the center and the periphery of Upper Asia is found, of course, in the vegetation. The Tibetan plateau is basically a succession of steppes, semideserts and high deserts. Even on the steppes, the heaviest vegetation is far from forming a complete ground cover. Plants found are principally tufts of feather grass *(Stipa glareosa),* milk vetch *(Astragalus dilutus, A. brevifolius),* halophytes *(Anabasis)* and bush plants of the genera *Caragana* and *Ephedra.* Laurel-leafed poplars *(Populus laurifolia)* grow in some valleys and there are stands of larch on the less arid slopes. Some more favored plateaus, covered with a layer of brown earth, support couch grass *(Agropyrum cristatum),* wormwood *(Artemisia),* and cinquefoil *(Potentilla)* mixed with such alpine plants as edelweiss *(Leontopodium alpinum)* and alpine poppy *(Papaver alpinum).*

YAKS, ANTELOPES AND WILD ASSES

Despite the rarity and the extreme dispersion of water holes, the high plateaus of the sub-deserts and steppes of Tibet are an ideal habitat for ungulates. The wide open spaces permit them to see great distances and to take flight before their natural enemies—most of all the wolf—can draw near. Before the spread of firearms even in regions isolated from the rest of the world, one could see large herds of gazelles, antelopes, yaks, wild sheep with magnificent horns, and wild asses. Such great herds are exceptional today and are seen only in areas most distant from caravan routes and from pastures used by nomads who keep sheep. Nevertheless, the high Tibetan plateaus are still the region of Central Asia where large animals have held their own with most success.

These large animals are rarely seen in the same area at the same time, for each species shows a preference for a given type of pasturage at a certain altitude. The German naturalist Ernst Schäfer, who traversed these regions between the two world wars, was probably the first to note these differences and to distinguish three principal habitats, each characterized

Left: The males of the Nubian ibex (Capra ibex) *of the mountains of Palestine and the Sinai Peninsula hold endless domination tournaments, violent in appearance but rarely ending in injury. (All, Uzi Paz)*

Right: The Turkish plateau, the most westerly in Asia, is bounded by steep escarpments as shown in the landscape here. Its southern slopes enjoy a Mediterranean climate. (Walter Fendrich)

by one large herbivorous animal. Comparatively rich pastures in the high valleys between 9,800 and 12,000 feet up support many Tibetan gazelles *(Procapra picticaudata)* and countless rodents and small carnivores. At about 13,000 feet lie the colder and drier steppes where the wild asses called kiangs *(Equus hemionus)* live. Yaks *(Bos grunniens)* and the orongo or chiru antelopes *(Pantholops hodgsoni)* live on the barest and coldest steppes, lying between 18,000 feet and nearly 20,000 feet. Other large mammals, like the wild sheep *(Ovis ammon)* and the brown bear *(Ursus arctos),* have a greater range of distribution and seem indifferent to the altitude.

All these animals are known only through observations by a few hunters or naturalists. The most familiar animal is the yak, domesticated milleniums ago by the natives of the high plateaus who use them as pack animals and a source of leather, wool, meat and milk. Even dung is used as a fuel and, mixed with a little tobacco, as smoking material. Without the yak, life for most of the mountain tribes would be quite impossible. Wild, the yak is a splendid animal, growing to five and a half feet at the shoulder and weighing between eleven hundred and thirteen hundred pounds. Its heavy, thickset build is accentuated by a coat of long brown-black hairs that covers its head and body and gives it a grotesque and ferocious air. The hairy coat, lined with a thick, woolly undercoat permits the yak to live at the highest altitudes, where conditions are at once arctic and desert-like. In summer, yaks ascend as high as 20,000 feet to browse on tough grasses and creeping bushes. Like all bovines, they love to roll in mud or water and often bathe in the icy streams that flow from the glaciers. The females give birth in April when fresh grass assures abundant food. During the nineteenth century, herds of as many as two thousand yaks were common, but such gatherings are apparently rare today. The domesticated yak, often distinguishable from the wild animal by a piebald coat, is gentle and docile by nature. It is frequently crossed with domestic cows to obtain animals more resistant to the comparatively high summer temperatures of the lower regions. The hybrids, called *dzo* or *zo* in the Himalayas, northern China, and Mongolia, look like short-legged cows. They are used mainly as pack and milk animals and may commonly be seen in the streets of Peking pulling heavy carts at a snail's pace.

The other peculiar animal of the high plateaus is the Tibetan antelope or chiru. It is notable for its enormous muzzle, swollen like that of the saiga antelope. Since each nostril has a sort of lateral sac, some believe that this strange nasal appendage helps the animal breathe the ice cold air in high places. The chiru lives only on the highest steppes and deserts of Tibet and northern Ladakh. Its thick coat protects it from the cold, and the animal takes shelter from the wind by sleeping in narrow trenches that it digs in the sand with its back hoofs. The males grow to about thirty inches tall at the shoulder and have long, slender, ringed horns that are apparently very fragile since one-horned individuals are quite common.

The Tibetan gazelle, sometimes called Przewalsky's gazelle, differs from species in Central Asian deserts in its lack of facial markings and the large white patch surrounding the short tail. The summer coat is slate-gray for the race living on the Tibetan plateau and in Ladakh and dark brown for the one in China and Mongolia. Horns, present in both sexes, are finely ringed and rise vertically before curving sharply backward. Like its lowland relatives, this gazelle lives in herds that may be quite large and undertake long migrations in search of richer pastures.

WILD SHEEP AND SNOW LEOPARDS

The high plateaus between the Himalayas, as well as the Altyn Tagh and the Greater Khingan Ranges also shelter the Tibetan wild sheep or argali, a large Eurasian mouflon *(Ovis ammon)* characterized by a winter fleece of long white hairs on neck, chest and shoulders. Male adults stand nearly four feet high at the withers and carry magnificent spiral horns, four feet long and twenty inches in base circumference. The female's horns are much shorter and are curved like a saber. Indifferent to height, the Tibetan argali lives in valleys and on pastures at an altitude of thirteen thousand feet. It is, however, more particular about the terrain than other mouflons, avoiding the rocky places enjoyed by wild goats and searching out open undulating plateaus where it can see great distances and flee from its principal enemies, mankind and the wolf. The mouflon's visual acuity is well known to hunters and may be compared to that of a man with eight-power field-glasses. Their sense of smell is equally acute: with a favorable wind they can smell a man a quarter of a mile away.

Sociable by nature, mouflons form winter herds of as many as one hundred head under the leadership of a very cautious old female with astonishingly keen senses. In spring and summer, the large groups break up into smaller ones, females and young males together, adult males apart. During the autumnal coupling period, the males fight seemingly terrible battles. Two adversaries retreat thirty or forty paces apart and then dash at each other and clash head on with such force

Left: The black-capped marmot (Marmota camtschatica) *lives on high mountain prairies from northeast of Lake Baykal to Kamchatka. (Novosti)*

Right: The piebald coats suggest that these Mongolian yaks are domesticated. Wild yaks, once numerous all over the mountainous center of Asia, now live only in the least accessible areas. (Ralph Herrmanns)

that the shock may be heard several miles away. These combats, lasting several hours, are merely tournaments to determine the supremacy of one male over his rivals. No serious wounds result, for the animals always strike each other on their extraordinarily thick forehead bones.

The herbivorous animals, hares and rodents such as marmots and pikas, attract carnivores of all sizes. In addition to the wolf and the fox found throughout all of cold and temperate Asia, one may here find the snow leopard, the wild dog, and a Tibetan race of the brown bear. The snow leopard or ounce *(Panthera uncia)* is surely the most beautiful of the felines. Its thick velvety fur, pale gray on top and white underneath, is decorated with spots and rosettes distinctly less marked than on the slightly larger leopard of the low regions. Very few people have observed this splendid animal even though it inhabits the entire Himalayan chain and the high plateaus of Tibet as far as the Altai. Like all wild animals, it follows the movements of its habitual prey, going up over 16,000 feet in summer and descending below 6,500 feet in winter. Its primary foods are wild goats, mouflons, marmots and probably various birds, especially pheasants, tragopans or horned pheasants and brilliant metallic-green monals *(Lophophorus impejanus)*.

The wild dog *(Cuon alpinus)*, much better known through the Indian race as the dhole, is also found throughout open areas of Upper Asia and into Far Eastern Siberia. Although not a member of the genus *Canis*, being different from dogs and wolves in certain aspects of anatomy, the cuon looks astonishingly like a domesticated dog with a thick yellow coat and a bushy tail. Living in small family groups of five to fifteen, it hunts on the run and bays animals as large as the mouflon or the wild ass with a chorus of sharp barks audible for a great distance.

The Tibetan brown bear *(Ursus arctos)* is distinguished from the Eurasia forest race by its long-haired coat and light-colored shoulders. It lives on the high steppes and pastures extending above the wooded zone to the level of eternal snow. It grazes in spring on new grass and turns over every stone to find insects, larvae and rodents. It rarely attacks wild grass-eating animals or the herds of nomads. In summer and autumn, it gorges on fruits, all kinds of berries and nuts, and digs up bulbous plants; it spends the winter in a cave or under a rock in a state of lethargy interrupted by waking periods. In December or January, the females bear two or three young; these will be strong enough to follow their mothers when they come out of their dens in May.

THE WESTERN MOUNTAIN RANGES

While the Tibetan plateau is remarkably uniform throughout, the peripheral ranges present a great variety of topography and vegetation. Their geologically recent appearance explains their often tormented aspect, while the diversity of their plants is mainly determined by their distance from the sea and their orientation to the monsoon winds. The ranges of northern China and those stretching from the Caspian to the western Pamirs in the most arid regions of the continent are generally dry. Those that border the Siberian taiga and the Manchurian forest and those that form the southern barrier of Upper Asia are watered by the rains coming from the Indian Ocean.

The variety of climatic conditions is particularly evident in the mountains that border the plateau of Iran or divide its center into more or less isolated basins. While the ranges of Kurdistan and the Zagros Mountains benefit on their western slopes from the humidity of the western winds, and winds from the Caspian Sea benefit the Elburz Mountains, the Makran Ranges to the south, the Khorassan Ranges to the north, and all the central mountain ranges suffer from complete aridity during most of the year. Consequently, these mountains develop along two different lines: dry and humid.

In the humid regions, countless torrents and rivers, sometimes descending from a height of 13,000 feet in barely thirty miles, cause deep erosions despite a thick forest cover. The Zagros and Elburz ranges have many gorges and ravines cut by such streams. In the arid regions, the rocks, unprotected by any plant cover, alternately expand and contract from the extremes of temperature, resulting in a landscape of naked peaks emerging from heaps of debris that often extend quite far around the base of the mountains.

The naturalist must therefore distinguish between mountain faces exposed to sea winds and abundant rainfall and those that are turned toward the interior and get scarcely more rain than on the central deserts. These two climatic variations account for the two types of animal and plant life: a temperate type related to that of the Palearctic Zone, and a desert type closer to that found in North Africa, Arabia and beyond the Hindu Kush Mountains in the deserts of Turkistan and Kazakh.

The orientation of the slopes is also important and, as in the Alps, one may distinguish a shaded slope from a sunny one. In Kurdistan and the Zagros Mountains, the shaded slopes are covered with fine forests of oaks, often very tall, with maples, walnuts and wild almonds in some places. The slopes exposed to sunlight bear a Mediterranean type of vegetation dominated by evergreen oaks and bush (or scrub) oaks. High up, the shady slopes are covered with pastures, while the sunny slopes especially those with chalky soil, are invaded by a jungle of scrub oaks not more than six or seven feet tall. The dry pastures turn green only during the spring rains, toward the end of April. Then the slopes are covered as far as the eye can see with all sorts of flowers such as milk vetch and both red and yellow wild tulips. This plant carpet begins to dry out at the beginning of June and soon only a few thorny plants like "camel grass" *(Alhagi camelorum)* and similar species remain.

The animals of Kurdistan and Zagros, like the plants, are similar to those living around the Mediterranean. One of the most characteristic large animals of the region is the Oriental mouflon or urial, a race intermediate in size and coat between the Tibetan argalis and the mouflons dwelling in Asia Minor and on the Mediterranean islands of Cyprus, Corsica and Sardinia. The males wear handsome horns forming a complete spiral, and in winter they grow a regal white beard from the base of the neck to the chest. Urials behave like other wild sheep and, besides man, have no greater enemy than the wolf.

Wolves are abundant in Iran and are found in almost all open spaces, very rarely venturing into a forest. One may see them during broad daylight even near cities. For several months, a Belgian zoologist, Dr. Xavier Misonne, observed three wolves in a lair not far from the village of Akinlu in

Mountains of the Himalayas with blunted summits are covered with glaciers that leave the vast moraines shown here in the foreground. (J. Allen Cash)

Kurdistan. Bones of young mouflons and boars, remains of hares, sheep, goats and even cows and donkeys were piled up in the dens. The wolves never went out before about four in the afternoon. In one night they killed twenty-eight sheep from a herd that a shepherd had neglected to enclose in a special corral of earthen walls trimmed with thorny branches.

Wolves attack only isolated prey. It is not unusual to see a shepherd with a herd of goats on a mountain and one or two wolves patiently waiting, a stone's throw away, for one of the animals to stray. At ploughing time, the peasants go up on the plateaus, each with an ox and a donkey carrying his belongings. Leaving the donkey in a corner of the field, each man works with his ox. When the donkey's owner is far enough away the wolves surround the animal, which begins to bray and run toward its master. The wolves follow, one of them leaping at the beast's throat, and try to bring him down before the peasant can put them to flight.

Primarily for protection against wolves, Kurdish villagers raise large, ferocious-looking dogs. Without these vigilantes, the wolves would enter villages even during the day. Misonne tells of a four-year-old child carried off during his visit. And in 1954 he saw 28 wounded Kurds come into the Pasteur Institute of Iran; while sleeping in the courtyard of a house one night they had been attacked by a rabid wolf. Two other writers, Baltazard and Godssi, tell of a band of fifty wolves that settled near Zindajan, a lively city of fifty thousand, and several times attacked the city from dusk to dawn, taking young children right from the courtyards of inhabited houses and wounding more than forty people. It took a concerted drive to rid the area of the ferocious beasts.

AUDACIOUS BOARS

Except when very young and separated from their mothers, wild boars *(Sus scrofa)* are not afraid of wolves. Even more common than mouflons, the boars grow very large and quite heavy, often reaching a weight of almost five hundred pounds, according to Misonne. He saw bands of thirty and more on the plateaus of Kurdistan, where they seek the bulbs and roots of various plants. In winter, the boars break into the burrows of gerbils of the genus *Meriones* to steal a store of seeds that may amount to as much as ten pounds. Their winter reserves thus plundered, the occupants of the burrows are almost certainly condemned to death. The boars thus render a great service to man, for the rodents are not only harmful to crops but are the main source of plague in Iran. Unfortunately, the boars exact a payment for their services, themselves causing much damage to the crops. Not content with eating ripe wheat on the stalk, they tear open sacks of garnered wheat. Misonne surprised twenty-three boars around the sacks one evening, while near-by eighteen other boars ate the unharvested grain. The boars are also very fond of grapes, especially when the fruit is spread out to dry in the sun. The farmers beat tin cans to frighten them off, but the boars are not afraid to attack young boys among the guard.

Another animal interesting primarily because it lives in a

These yaks, shown at a height of 16,000 feet in Nepal, are indispensable to the mountain people, furnishing them with meat, milk and wool. (Detlef Hecker: Bavaria Verlag)

semidomesticated state in many parks and public gardens throughout the world is the fallow-deer. Only a few live in the wild; they are found on the western slopes of the Zagros Mountains of Iran. The species, *Dama mesopotamica,* has been distinguished by zoologists from the Turkish deer, *Dama dama,* source of the animals raised in captivity and now extinct in the wild state. They are medium-sized animals with a spotted rust-red coat and a white belly. Their branching antlers are easily recognizable for the tips are flattened and palmate, somewhat like those of the elk, but smaller in size.

Until quite recently Persian lions lived on these same western slopes of the Zagros. At the end of the nineteenth century they were still numerous in the southwestern mountains but none has been reported since 1941. Today, these lions are found no nearer to Iran than Somaliland and the forest of Gir, north of Bombay. The disappearance of this carnivore from Iran, Afghanistan, southern Iraq and Arabia is principally the result of hunting by man but probably also of the encroachment of civilization.

THE NORTHERN IRANIAN MOUNTAINS

If we cross the mountains on the northern fringe of the Plateau of Iran—the Elburz, Khorasan, Hindu Kush—we again come upon arid regions in which the plants and animals are absolutely dependent upon water for the spark of life. The high Elburz Range, benefiting from several feet of rainfall each year and from water from its snow-covered peaks, is covered by a great forest that seems tropical because of majestic trees interlaced with an incredible number of vines. The trees are, however, all related to European forms such as oaks, elms, pines, alders and other temperate species. At the foot of this massive range on the shores of the Caspian, the heat and humidity again suggest an equatorial region, an impression heightened by marshes, lagoons and stretches of tangled forest.

The Khorasan region is the driest part of this northern fringe. The peaks of Kopet Dagh located on its northern front, show arid, bald crests, but the southern facade is lower and gets a little more water. Flowering pastures cover it in spring and beautiful forests nestle in the valleys. As one moves eastward, the slopes become drier and are covered with steppe plants or, at most, brambles and shrub oaks.

In Afghanistan, the Hindu Kush raises snow-peaked summits that catch the last clouds coming from western seas. This relative humidity does not reach the central range, which remains dry and is covered with bushy plants, but it does help the northern face of the mountains, whose slopes are covered with forests and meadows, and, most of all, the southern front. The latter also receives some monsoon rains from nearby India and as a result its valleys surround a magnificent temperate forest of oaks, elms, plane-trees and almonds, with wild olive trees and evergreen oaks on the slopes. Going higher, one sees beautiful pine and cedar forests, and then birches, bushy willows, junipers, wild rhubarb and, finally, meadows as high up as thirteen thousand feet.

In all the forests from the Elburz to the Hindu Kush ranges, large animals of typically Asiatic species abound. One also finds roebucks, stags, boars and several varieties of wild sheep and goats, as well as wolves, jackals, tigers and panthers, foxes, badgers, martens, polecats, and other small carnivores and rodents such as we have met in the deserts of the interior.

123

The lesser panda (Ailurus fulgens) *lives in upland forests of bamboo from Nepal to Szechwan, feeding on bamboo leaves and shoots as well as insects and small animals. (Paolo Koch: Black Star)*

In the large northern forests, the bear also is not unusual. The brown bear *(Ursus arctos)* belongs to the species found in Eastern Europe and Siberia, but the one here is smaller and wears a paler coat than do the animals farther north. It is interesting to note that the Tibetan bear, or, more accurately, the Himalayan bear *(Selenarctos thibetanus),* whose shining long-haired coat is decorated with a white crescent on the chest, also lives in the easternmost forests of the Iranian Plateau. However, this animal is not so common here as in the mountains of northern India where its aggressive disposition is feared by hunters and natives.

One of the most spectacular animals of the mountains of the east, ranging from Afghanistan to Baluchistan, is the markhor *(Capra falconeri).* It is a member of the goat family and perfectly adapted to life on mountains, even in the driest regions.

It is now fairly well agreed that the various races of domestic goats descent from ancestors of Middle Eastern origin, for remains of these animals have been found in caves inhabited by Neolithic man some six to five thousand years B.C. The ancestor of the domestic goat is very probably the bezoar goat *(Capra hircus),* which has long crenellated horns and is common in the islands of the Aegean Sea, in Crete, Turkey, the

Caucasus and in the Elburz Mountains. Furthermore, when domesticated goats are abandoned and return to the wild state, as often happens in many uninhabited or sparsely inhabited islands, they revert after a few generations to a type very close to the true wild goat.

The markhor is a thickset animal, almost heavy in appearance, and is covered with a long fleece of coarse hair. Its horns are erect, flat and twisted upon themselves, like a sword turned into a corkscrew by a practical joker. Unlike the mouflon, the markhor seeks steep, rocky slopes upon which to prove its astonishing agility. It does not go up so far as other goats for its lack of wolly undercoat makes it more sensitive to cold. Like mouflons, markhors form large herds in winter, but old males live apart from the herd during the summer and seek females only in autumn.

The western location of the Pamir and the Tien Shan ranges makes them the meeting place for animals from the deserts

The pleasant aspect of these valleys of Bhutan results from heavy rainfall dumped by summer winds from the Indian Ocean as they strike the first Himalayan slopes. (P. P. Karan)

of Central Asia and India, the Siberian forests, the Himalayas, and the high plateaus of Tibet and Mongolia. The area is therefore comparatively rich, harboring, according to Formozov, about 120 species of mammals and nearly 50 species of birds, including migrants.

All of these animals, whatever their origin, adopt habitats in the western ranges that approximate those of their native lands. The high zones above about ten thousand feet are thus populated by animals with Tibetan affinities. Among the mammals one may meet snow leopards, wild dogs or cuons, mouflons, marmots and pikas, some of these slightly different from races in Upper Asia. The mouflon of Pamir is often called Marco Polo's sheep for the Italian traveler mentioned it in the thirteenth century, whereas it was not officially discovered until 1840. Each of its horns, considered a most desirable trophy by mountain hunters, grows to a length of over five feet, nearly a foot and a half longer than the horns of the largest race of mouflons, that of the Altai.

Characteristic Tibetan birds include the Mongolian plover (Charadrius mongolus), a sort of curlew, Ibidorhyncha struthersii, and the bar-headed goose (Anser indicus). The most remarkable are the snow cocks (Tetraogallus tibetanus, T. himalayensis), particularly wary, little-known birds, much sought by hunters for they grow as heavy as five or six pounds. The golden eagle, the bearded vulture and the griffon vulture, which are also found in Tibet, are distributed over a vast area of the mountains of temperate Eurasia.

AN ASSEMBLY FROM TAIGA AND DESERT

At a lower level the coniferous forest zone is inhabited by many birds that we have met on the Siberian taiga: three-toed woodpeckers, nutcrackers, crossbills, hawk owls, and Tengmalm's owls. In the leafy forests live a host of small familiar European birds such as orioles, grosbeaks, blackbirds, goldfinches, greenfinches, bullfinches, woodpeckers and, among nocturnal predators, horned owls. Some are distinctly Indo-Himalayan, such as the Indian orioles and swallows, the blue nightingale of the Himalayas (Myophonus coeruleus), the thick-billed or jungle crow (Corvus macrorhynchus), and the talking myna.

Below the zone from 5,000 to 6,500 feet, the influence on animals of the surrounding desert becomes evident, and such mammals appear as djeiran gazelles, yellow susliks, various jerboas and gerbils, moles, and large-eared hedgehogs. Desert birds like sand-grouse (Syrrhaptes paradoxus, S. tibetanus) and wheatears (Oenanthe isabellina) also ascend as high as about 10,000 feet. Reptiles are much more abundant here, since very few go above 6,500 feet. A dozen species have, however, managed to adapt to life at high altitudes: the steppe viper (Vipera ursini), a mocassin (Ancistrodon himalayanus), the scheltopusik (Ophisaurus apodus), two skinks (Ablepharus altaicus, A. deserti), three lizards of the genus Eremias, and an agama, Phrynocephalus theobaldi, that is probably the champion mountain-climbing reptile since it can live at 17,500 feet. As in low regions, the distribution of the various reptiles is determined by the heat required for hatching eggs. Ovoviviparous species keep their eggs within the cloaca and can thus assure them the optimum temperature by choosing the best exposed places all through the day. In the Tien Shan Mountains, the percentage of ovoviviparous reptiles is 33 percent at

5,500 feet, 75 percent at 7,800 feet and 100 percent above 12,000 feet.

Among the amphibians it is the green toad (Bufo viridis), which reaches the highest altitudes, sometimes being seen as high as 15,000 feet up. It adapts to the extreme cold at such heights by going hunting only during the day, whereas it is rather a nocturnal animal in the lowlands. Examination of the stomach contents of toads captured at high altitudes reveals that 90 percent of their food consists of diurnal insects.

As one follows the peripheral ranges northward and eastward across the Altai, the Sayan Mountains, and the Yablonovyy and Stanovoy Ranges toward Kamchatka, the animal life grows poorer in Central Asiatic elements but richer in species from the taiga and in native animals like the Siberian ibex and the Asiatic bighorn. The Siberian ibex forms a special race, distinguished from the wild goats of Iran only by its massive silhouette and thick, long, barely curving horns. The Asiatic bighorn or snow sheep is actually the same animal as the bighorn (Ovis canadensis) of North America, an animal that gets its popular name from its very thick horns. It dwells on all the ranges east of the Yenisey up to and including Kamchatka, where it replaces the ibex and the western mouflon, which do not cross the Yenisey. In these mountains, it occupies the habitats of both goats and mouflons and is as comfortable here as on the high plateaus and tundras.

Beside the bighorn, the mountains of Far Eastern Siberia contain a few small native rodents such as the Altai suslik (Citellus undulatus), the black-headed marmot (Marmota camtschatica), a pika (Ochotona alpina), and a field lemming (Alticola macrotis). All the other mammals of this region may be found in other natural zones of Asia. Tundra animals are represented on high by the reindeer, the collared lemming, the snow hare and, in the Koryakskiy and the Kamchatka mountains by the Arctic fox and the polar bear. Animals that it has in common with the taiga are more numerous: the brown bear, lynx, wolverine, sable, striped ground-squirrel, red squirrel, ruddy vole, root vole and three species of the shrews. Other mammals common in the mountains of the north and in eastern Siberia such as the wolf, red fox, weasel, ermine, otter, common rat (Rattus rattus), and the so-called house mouse (which can live far from any human habitation), are found almost everywhere in the Palearctic region.

Most of the birds of the Far Eastern mountain ranges we have already encountered in the tundra and the taiga. Black-throated thrushes (Turdus ruficollis), pine grosbeaks (Pinicola enucleator), yellow-breasted buntings (Emberiza aureola), Pallas buntings (E. pallasi) and shrikes (Lanius cristatus) nest in the dwarf pines, bushy alders and junipers of the subalpine zone. The alpine zone, a tundra covering vast areas even on low hills, is inhabited by ptarmigans (Lagopus mutus), Lapland longspur (Calcarius lapponicus), and a wader peculiar to the region, the slender-billed sandpiper (Calidris tenuirostris).

Right above: Dwarf rhododendrons grow above the timberline in the Himalayas in Nepal. (Michael Desfayes) Right: Male and female of the rare Bhutan Glory (Armandia lidderdalei), which is found only in Bhutan, Nagaland and North Burma. Far right: The tropical vegetation of the southern Himalayan slopes abounds in orchids and such butterflies as the red lacewing (Cethosa biblis), whose female is seen here. (Both, E. P. Gee)

RAMPARTS IN THE SKY

Two majestic landmarks, Nanga Parbat on the west and Namcha Barwa on the east, mark the great rampart of the Himalayas running along the border of the Tibetan Plateau for more than 15,000 miles. The Karakoram and Himalayan ranges, young mountains, stretch skyward in clusters of sharp crests and crystal glaciers and have fourteen peaks above 26,000 feet. Mount Everest (29,028 feet) is incontestably the most impressive, but K2, second in size, is the most beautiful, forming an almost perfect cone of ice and limestone rising 28,250 feet above a base of gneiss and granite. Thirty-three peaks higher than 23,725 feet cluster about it in an area no greater than the Swiss Alps; four of them, each more than 26,000 feet high, stand on a front barely fifteen miles long.

The immensity of the glaciers is even more impressive than the height of the peaks. No place in the world except at the poles displays such piles of ice. For more than 185 miles, both faces of the Karakorams are covered by a band of glaciers 25 to 50 miles wide. More than 455 of such great rivers of ice have been counted in the western part of the Himalayas, covering a ground surface of nearly 7,500 square miles.

Countless rivers furrow the Himalayas and flow into the Indo-Gangetic depression through narrow, deep gorges that are the terror of all voyagers. The Kosi River, before leaving Tibet, runs in a gorge 20,000 feet below Mount Makalu's summit, dropping one hundred feet per mile. To explain the dizzying depths of these valleys, many geologists accept the theory that Himalayan streams were not carved out after the formation of the mountains around them but simply dug their valleys while the mountains were springing up. Since the erosive force of the rivers was greater than the upward thrust of the earth, the rivers did not follow the ascending movement of the entire area.

The monsoon is responsible for the abundance and vigor of the Himalayan streams. The humid winds that sweep the Indian peninsula from May to September discharge almost all their moisture as they strike the ramparts of Upper Asia. Nearly ten feet of water fall on Darjeeling in the eastern Himalayas each year and the rainfall reaches its maximum in the ranges leading to the Himalayas, in the hills of Assam and Bhutan. Here is the *terai*, dense, wet jungle alternating with huge swampy areas overgrown with tall elephant grass, while a thinner forest with a thick undergrowth covers the hills. Above these rises the true tropical forest, drowned in fog and a welter of vines, tree ferns and epiphytes, and every kind of orchid. In some places, there are almost pure stands of giant bamboos. A temperate type of forest appears between 4,800 and 6,500 feet, including oaks and birches, and, a little higher up, magnolias. Dense thickets of rhododendrons of all sizes and

Left: Zoologists consider the lesser panda a Procyon, an animal akin to the raccoon, although adaptation of its head and teeth to a diet of bamboo leaves and shoots has differentiated it from other members of the family. (W. Suschitzky)

Right: Inaccessible Tibet harbors animals and plants still scarcely known today. Magnificent coniferous forests grow in the subalpine zone betwenn a height of 10,000 and 11,000 feet. (Eastfoto)

129

colors appear at about 8,000 feet; more than five hundred species have been counted in the Himalayas, which must be considered their homeland. Thereafter come conifers, pines and firs, and finally an alpine type of vegetation continues to a height of nearly 16,000 feet. Above this point, up to about 19,000 feet, only a few stunted plants manage to survive. The successive belts of plant life described here are quite irregular and often encroach on each other. Thus the increasing rainfall from west to east along the entire Himalayan chain makes the tropical forest rise much higher in Sikkim, Bhutan and Assam than in Cadakh or Kashmir.

A CROSSROAD FOR ANIMALS

The Himalayas and their spurs form the southern barrier for many animal species living in temperate Asia and a northern limit for many tropical forms. The mountains shelter a mixture of typically palearctic animals and others characteristic of the Indo-Malayan region. To these are added endemic species native to these mountains.

In the Himalayas one therefore finds not only Eurasian species like the ibex and the mouflons but also an original form of intermediate look, the bharal *(Pseudois nayaur),* also called the blue sheep because of the bluish glints in its fleece. Another completely native animal, the takin *(Budorcas taxicolor)* has long golden or brown hair and horns remarkably like those of the African gnu. Also among the ungulates of these mountains are three species of goat-antelopes with dense coats and small, barely curved horns: the goral *(Nemorhaedus goral),* which occurs as far as Manchuria along the Himalayas, the thar *(Hemitragus jemlahicus),* two species of which live

Right: Mount Masherbrum, 26,470 feet high, is one of the summits beside Baltoro Glacier in a part of the Karakoram Range where thirty-three peaks rise above 22,000 feet. (George I. Bell)   Below: Like all alpine meadows in the spring, those of the Altai in Mongolia are covered with such brightly colored flowers as the gentian (Gentianus acaulis). *(Gunther Peters)*

in South India and the coastal mountains of Arabia, and the serow *(Capricornis sumatraensis),* which lives as far south as Indochina and Sumatra.

The Himalayan black bear *(Selenarctos tibetanus)* has also spread out along the principal mountain ranges reaching Manchuria and Japan on the east, the northern reaches of Burma on the south, and Baluchistan on the west. This bear, which may attain a length of almost six feet and weigh more than 250 pounds, has a bad reputation among natives of the Himalayas. The most carnivorous of its family, it may supplement its usual diet of fruit, berries and honey by boldly stealing a sheep or goat from a village. These bears are rarely man-eating, but they are all ill-tempered and will not tolerate another animal or a human being on their accustomed paths. Natives confronted by a bear give way without running, for the sight of a man in flight incites the animal to attack. Accidents on narrow mountain trails are frequent and no Himalayan village is without its history of one or more inhabitants killed or mauled by bears.

Another carnivore peculiar to the Himalayas and the ranges to the east, the lesser panda *(Ailurus fulgens),* looks like a teddy bear with a fox's tail. Its round head, large erect ears, short muzzle, ringed, bushy tail, white face and fiery-red back make it impossible to confuse with any other animals. It lives in thick bamboo forests whose leaves and shoots form its basic diet. It probably also takes berries, insects and birds' eggs. Two little pandas that I purchased from Nepalese hunters loved sweets, milk, eggs and, although they are vegetarians, raw meat.

We know very little about the lives of these small pandas. Zoologists associate them with raccoons, but they are distinguished by wide molars supported by the strong muscles needed to chew tough bamboo leaves and shoots. Basically nocturnal, they spend the day sleeping, curled up on the highest branches of trees. The soles of their feet are covered with short, thick fur like those of the hare and the white bear. Their claws, long, curved and semiretractile, may also be considered an adaptation to life in trees.

THE CLOUDY COUNTRY

By following the Himalayas toward the east, we reach the highlands of the Szechwan province of China, one of the most fascinating regions in the world for a naturalist and one of the richest in native animal species in Asia. More than a fourth of the mammals and a third of the birds of China live in Szechwan, including representatives from cold regions as well as from temperate and tropical Asia.

The varieties of climate is the chief factor contributing to this wealth of animal life. Crossed from north to south by high mountain ranges, Szechwan affords snow-covered peaks and deep gorges through which flow turbulent streams. Its altitude rises gradually from just above 3,000 feet to almost 25,000 feet —the height of Mount Minya Konka—in a series of broad steps, each between 6,500 and 10,000 feet. While its mountain tops are covered with glaciers and tundras, its valleys enjoy subtropical climates. The growth of vegetation is favored also by heavy annual rainfall, reaching eighty inches in places. The north-south orientation of the mountain ranges forms a barrier against which the damp winds from the west discharge all their moisture. One of the characteristics of Szechwan is its

cloudy sky. There are rarely thirty sunny days in a year and the average is about twenty-five. The rest of the time the entire landscape is bathed in a strange, diffused light that forms halos around all objects. Szechwan is known in China as the land of clouds, and the name of Yunnan, the province to its south, means literally "land south of the clouds."

The region's geological age is the second factor favorable to the development of animal life. The mountains of Szechwan were formed before the birth of the bordering Himalayas. They thus served as a refuge for a number of primitive mammals: the giant panda, the golden monkey, the jerboa of Szechwan, and the mole-shrews.

The third favorable factor is the location of Szechwan, like the Himalayas, on a crossroad between two large biogeographic regions, the Palearctic and the Oriental, linked by mountains with valleys forming corridors that animals follow naturally. The imposition of palearctic on tropical forms is particularly striking in the felines. Here one sees the lynx and the snow leopard as well as the clouded-leopard *(Felis nebulosa)* and the common spotted or black leopard. The smaller species are represented by the golden cat *(Felis temminckii),* hardly smaller than a lynx and covered with a uniformly golden-brown coat, the marbled cat *(Felis marmorata),* and the leopard-cat *(Felis bengalensis),* spotted all over and scarcely larger than the domestic cat. All three are found in most tropical Asian forests. The region is also famous for the quality of the furs it exports not only of the animals just mentioned but also of the mountain red fox *(Vulpes ferrilatus),* the yellow-throated marten *(Martes flavigula),* the stone marten *(Martes foina),* the Himalayan marmot *(Marmotta himalayana),* and the Tibetan otter, a large race of the common otter.

Palearctic and tropical types are found also among the ungulates. In addition to those we will meet in Southern Asia —the sambar deer, the muntjac and the water deer—we find such Tibetan, Himalayan and forest species as the musk-deer *(Moschus moschiferus).* Distributed from Manchuria to the Himalayas, the latter is a little animal with thickset body and heavy legs ending in broad hoofs. It wears no antlers, but the male has a pair of long, pointed tusks curving down and back. Underneath the skin of its belly it has a huge gland that secretes musk, an aromatic substance prized as a fixative in the making of perfume. Musk brings high prices and the musk-deer, hunted to excess, is in danger of extinction despite its ability to flee across the most difficult terrain. A recent effort at domestication in the Maerhk'ang region of western Szechwan has been successful and it is hoped that the species will in this way be preserved. The production of musk would then be increased since the gland's secretion increases as the animal ages and one animal can continue to produce for many years and need not be killed for the sake of a single extraction. Other deer are also very much sought by hunters, especially when the horns are in velvet and can be sold at high prices to Chinese pharmacists as a tonic and as a remedy against anemia.

GIANT PANDAS AND GOLDEN MONKEYS

Szechwan is not only a meeting-place for palearctic and oriental animals, but also the richest Asiatic region for native races or species not found anywhere else. The first naturalist to visit the region was Père Armand David, whose tribulations in the imperial hunting preserve of China are well known. In

The rarest and most expensive animal in the world, the giant panda (Ailuropoda melanoleuca), *probably merely an aberrant bear, is native only to the bamboo forests of the slopes of Szechwan. (W. Suschitzky)*

1869, he went to the part of western Szechwan that then formed the kingdom of Muping. There he gathered a collection of animals, some of which are entirely unknown even today. The most famous was the giant panda or Père David's bear. He himself had been skeptical when the inhabitants of Muping told him that the neighboring mountains sheltered a white bear, for the mountains are less than ten degrees from the Tropic of Cancer. Nevertheless, he investigated and soon acquired a skin and then the living animal itself. It had the general appearance of a bear: a massive body, plantigrade paws with powerful claws, thick fur and a round head. Its head and body were white, but its limbs and ears were coal black. Each eye had a black ring around it, whence the name *hua-hsiung,* spectacled bear, bestowed on it by local hunters along with that of *pei-hsiung* or white bear.

Père David believed he had discovered a new species of bear and named it *Ursus melanoleucos,* black and white bear but since its cranial and dental characteristics are very different from those of true bears and allied to those of the lesser panda, a special genus, *Ailuropoda,* was then created for it. But more recent studies by Dwight Davis at the Field Museum of Natural History in Chicago indicate that the giant panda is definitely related to the bear family but has become differentiated because of its special way of life and its very restricted diet. While all other bears are basically carnivorous, the giant panda is a strict vegetarian. Very finicky, it eats only leaves and shoots of a bamboo of the genus *Sinarundinaria* that grows from five to sixteen feet high on the slopes of impenetrable mountains and at various heights from 8,000 to 12,000 feet. This very tough food necessitates huge chewing muscles and these have radically modified the panda's skull and dental structure, including the development of large, tuberculated

133

molars. The panda's forepaws are also different from those of true bears and the bones and muscles around the paws permits the animal to grasp and manipulate objects as small as a straw.

We know very little about the life of the giant panda in the wild state. We can be certain that a diet of bamboo shoots and leaves obliges an adult animal weighing over 250 pounds to eat great quantities for ten or twelve hours a day. It is also probable that this panda, unlike the brown bears of the same habitat, does not hibernate and keeps alive during the cold season by eating bamboo twigs left bare by the snow. In any case, it dislikes hot weather and in summer prefers shady places and moss-covered ground.

Since this aberrant bear is one of the rarest animals in the world, it has been chosen as the emblem of the World Wildlife Fund, the international organization whose purpose is to save disappearing species. Since the giant panda's discovery by Père David, not more than twenty have been taken alive, and of all the specimens that zoo directors dream about, it is, along with the Sumatran rhinoceros, the most difficult to acquire and the most expensive: about $35,000 at this time.

When I visited the Peking zoo late in 1964, five giant pandas were thriving on a thrice-daily diet of bamboo shoots and leaves, supplemented by a gruel of oats, eggs and biscuits. They moved about constantly, playing and performing acrobatic stunts to the great delight of the public. The Peking animals had adapted so well to captivity that in 1963 the female Li-li, "Beauty," had given birth to a cub, named Ming-ming, "Shining One." At birth, Ming-ming was no larger than a rat and weighed five ounces. At three months, the baby weighed twelve and a half pounds and walked alone; two months later it had gained another ten pounds. The vast difference in size between infant at birth and adult is additional evidence of the giant panda's relationship to bears: baby bears are much smaller at birth, compared to their parents, than are babies of other carnivorous groups.

The region of Lake Hsinlu and the Yunwa Mountains is the only area where one is likely to meet this very rare animal. One of the richest portions of western Szechwan, the lake is inhabited by a great many sheldrakes *(Tadorna ferruginea)*, and the surrounding forest shelters a profusion of birds that would excite any ornithologist: Himalayan blue magpies, Reeves pheasants, blood pheasants, ring-necked pheasants, golden pheasants, Lady Amherst pheasants, Temminck's horned pheasants, and metallic-green monals. Among the mammals, one finds a mixture of Himalayan, Tibetan and tropical forms:

Himalayan black bears, brown bears, leopards, snow leopards, lynxes, lesser pandas, wolves, boars, blue sheep, takins, serows, gorals, sambars, muntjacs and musk-deer, and macaque monkeys. Native to Szechwan are the giant panda, the golden snub-nosed or Roxellane's monkey *(Rhinopithecus roxellanae)*, the white-muzzled deer *(Cervus albirostris)*, the small hornless barking deer *(Elaphodus cephalophus)*, and four strange species of shrews belonging to three genera *(Uropsilus, Rhynchonax,* and *Nasillus)* of the subfamily of the *Uropsilinae.*

The golden monkey is the northernmost representative of the leaf-eating monkeys (family Colobidae) widespread throughout Africa and tropical Asia. It is truly astonishing to see a troop of these animals leaping about on snow-covered pine branches, long golden fur shining under the pale winter sun. Although undeniably tropical in origin, the golden monkey has adapted remarkably to the harsh climate of Szechwan. As the Russian zoologist A. G. Bannikov notes, this is one of the few monkeys to bear young only during the summer, for primates generally have no fixed reproductive season. The golden monkey is another of Père David's many discoveries. It was named Roxellane's rhinopithecus after the wife of Suleiman the Magnificent, famous for her small, turned-up nose. Beside having a charming nose, the monkey has very beautiful eyes: large, round, velvety dark-brown or black, and circled with bright blue as if with an eye-shadow cosmetic. The skin of the face is pale blue, contrasting with the silky golden fur surrounding it.

These monkeys have always been highly prized for their fur, which in ancient China was considered the best preventive against rheumatism and only Manchu dignitaries were allowed to wear it. Constant hunting of this splendid animal has made it quite rare and the present regime has placed it on the list of animals completely protected by law. Despite this, I recently saw golden monkey skins in several shops in Peking.

Among other native species we should note first the rather rare Tibetan muntjac or hornless barking deer, a small deer with horns reduced to simple bumps hidden under tufts of long hairs. Another very rare ungulate is the white-muzzled or white deer, for, besides lips and muzzle, it may have a white chest and antlers of a very pale color. The mole-shrews are curious insect-eaters with intermediate characteristics: they are like moles in size and general anatomical structure, but have longer legs and long tails and live on the ground like shrews.

Clustering around the major Himalayan peaks are countless lesser summits such as these near Mt. Everest. (George I. Bell)

Yellow Earth and Wandering Rivers

The China Plain, Hainan and Taiwan

With the expanses of Siberia and the masses of the Himalayas behind us, we might think that we had covered most of Asia and had only to make a rapid survey of its southern and eastern borders. However, this fringe of peninsulas and islands is, from a naturalist's point of view, the true heart of the continent, for the rich ancient lands of India, Indochina, Malaya and China offer us more treasures in animal and plant life than all the rest of the continent.

This region, known to geographers as "Monsoon Asia," is influenced climatically by alternating land and sea winds known as monsoons, from the Arabic *mausim* or season. The monsoons, whose action is based on the fact that a large body of water maintains a more stable temperature than does a continental landmass, cause a more than tropical luxuriance of vegetation in Southern Asia. During the winter, the Asiatic continent, cooling off more than its surrounding waters, becomes a high pressure or anticyclone center: the heavier cold air coming down from the upper layers spreads out as winds blowing from the land toward the sea. During the summer, the land is warmer than the surrounding water and becomes a low pressure or cyclone area: the air rises to form a vacuum attracting the sea winds.

The effect upon climate of these alternating monsoons is easy to perceive: in winter, dry, cold winds come from Central Asia whereas in summer, winds that are hot and laden with humidity come from the ocean and condense above the continent on impact with a mountainous barrier, on rising into the interior of the cyclone center, or on striking a mass of cold air. Areas north of the equator have dry, cold winters and rainy, hot summers; south of the equator, the order is reversed: the rainy season extends from October to February, and the dry season occurs in the other months.

The mechanism of the monsoons seems quite simple, but we must not conclude that any region will have rain simply because it is swept by an ocean breeze. Condensation requires a cooling process resulting either from mountains or from a passage over a barometric depression that causes the damp air to rise and meet the masses of colder air. In flat areas, without a barometric depression, the air can reach a humidity of 95 percent with no rain falling from the darkly clouded sky.

Some regions, lying in the shelter of a mountain range, receive only a small part of the monsoon rains since all the damp winds have been diverted along the way, while neighboring regions on the other side of the mountains are copiously watered.

These differences in rainfall clearly account for different types of vegetation within the same region and in the same type of soil. In other areas, differences in climate are added to the differences in rainfall, so that this entire part of Asia, although subject to the monsoons, is a mosaic of different natural regions. As a further complication, some monsoon areas lying below the equator have almost constant rainfall all year round.

VAGRANT RIVERS AND OAK FORESTS

Stretching southward from Peking to the hills of the lower Yangtze is the great plain of China, a sunken basin once covered by the sea and now enriched by the alluvial deposits of the Yellow River. These deposits are unusual because they consist principally of fine loess, carried by water and then picked up and swept away by winter winds. The coarser sand remains, often forming barren beaches and dunes near the rivers. The blown loess piles up as soon as the wind strikes any obstacle, creating terraces, steep slopes and canyons of yellow earth. In the very damp, low alluvial plains formed by this fertile soil, rivers meander among swamps, often changing course and ending in mud-choked mouths and deltas.

The French geographer Jules Sion has declared that no river in the world has altered its course more often and more disastrously than the Huang or Yellow River. Chinese history over thousands of years records it as flowing sometimes to the north, sometimes to the south of the mountains of Shantung, but never in the same bed. Twenty-three centuries before Christianity, the river turned north-northeast to empty into the sea east of Peking. The earliest chapters of Chinese history tell only of devastation and the efforts made to stop it. As soon as China was unified, an eminent mandarin was appointed to direct the control of the river. Nevertheless, it shifted more and more toward the south, leaving its ancient mouth in 602 B. C. and flowing into the sea at several points to the north of its present delta. Then in 1194 it swerved sharply toward the east, leaving the Shantung peninsula in the north, probably after a period of war when the effort to control it had slackened. Yellow River floods correspond so closely to troubled periods in Chinese history that the Chinese claim that such floods herald the fall of the reigning dynasty. Because of the predominance of loess in its basin, the river easily undermines the cliffs if it is dammed. Of all the great rivers of the world, it is said to carry the greatest proportion of alluvium: 655 million cubic yards per year, as against a mere 277 million yards for the Mississippi. Villages have been buried in as much as ten feet of mud by floods. Before the damming of the river, these inundations enriched the great plain with fertile alluvium, as do the Nile in Africa and the Mekong, the Ganges, and the Brahmaputra in Asia.

Shanhaikuan, the pass west of Peking where the mountains meet the sea, forms a natural gateway between China and Manchuria. (William P. Fenn)

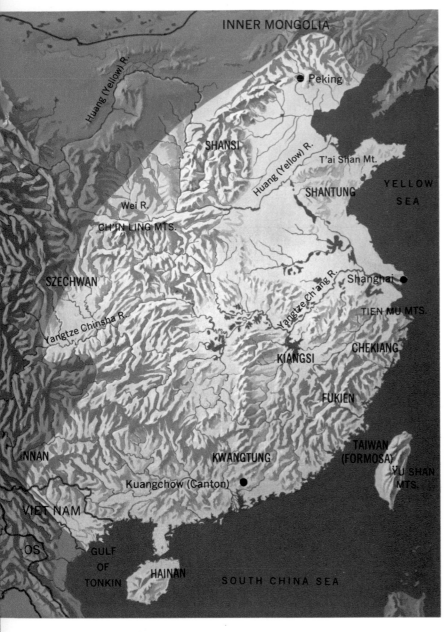

The vast expanse of the Great Plain of China, once covered with temperate leafy and coniferous forests, is now entirely bare. South of the Yangtze River, the country billows with small rounded, thickly wooded mountains cut by deep valleys and pebbly torrents.

After seven centuries of southern meanderings, the Yellow River breached its dikes and in 1853 resumed its course to the north of Shantung. The three-hundred-mile detour swept away one of the richest and most densely populated regions of China, drowning hundreds of thousands or perhaps millions of people and leaving the southern fields, dependent upon the river for irrigation, to drought and ruin.

The only break in the Chinese plain occurs on the eastern border of Shansi province where the Shantung Mountains rise like an island above the great plain and the Yellow Sea. These mountains are not very high, but they are very irregular in contour, and consist of many segments separated by wide depressions. The tallest peak, the T'ai Shan, 5,000 feet high, is the holiest of the sacred mountains of China. Confucius tells us that the Emperor Shun visited it in 2200 B.C., and to this

day pilgrims go to the many pagodas scattered through its forests.

The entire region, both in the mountains and on the plains, has a temperate climate with four distinct, comparatively dry seasons, the rainfall rarely exceeding forty inches a year. The primeval vegetation is forest with deciduous foliage, typical of subhumid temperate regions between the mixed taigas of the north and the mixed forests of the south. The dominant tree here, the oak, is represented by several species each of which will tend to form pure stands. Most of the oaks have smaller and less lobate leaves than European or North American types. The most important species (Quercus mongolica, Q. dentata, Q. liaotungensis, Q. aliena, Q. acutissima, Q. variabilis and Q. serrata) are all deciduous in winter, but in the south, on the edge of the mesophytic forest, three species are evergreen: Q. baronii, Q. glauca and Q. spinosa.

On the plain in certain places up to 4,600 feet high, these oaks are associated with ash trees (Fraxinus chinensis), walnuts (Juglans mandshurica), aspens (Populus tremula), elms (Ulmus glaucescens) with smooth little leaves, and U. parvifolia with even smaller leaves, lindens (Tilia dictyoneura), and Père David maples (Acer davidi) to form the forest's upper stratum, while hornbeams (Carpinus turczaninowii) and birches (Betula fruticosa) occupy the level immediately below. Cornels (Cornus bretschneideri), rowan trees (Sorbus acuparia) and jujube trees (Zizyphus sativa) are more rare. The jujube's round fruits, basted with melted sugar, are sold, ten to a skewer, on all the streets of Peking.

In these woods the thick, creeping bushes of Cotoneaster multiflora, its red berries familiar to European gardeners, dogroses (Rosa bella), Continus coccyria, with heart-shaped leaves and flower clusters reminiscent of florists' Asparagus, the sweet-smelling blossoms of honeysuckle (Lonicera pekinensis), spiny dwarf jujubes (Zizyphus vulgaris), and small-leaved rhododendrons (Rhododendron micranthum and R. mucronulatum) form the undergrowth. The ground itself is covered by countless herbaceous and grassy plants and xerophytes with woody, perennial roots, including Pulsatilla chinensis, Platycodon grandiflorum, Adenophora scabridula, Atractylis eroscodentata and Echinops dahurica. In areas subject to flooding, the only trees are willows (Salix mataudans), which are numerous in the countryside south and east of Peking. They give the landscape its characteristic look.

Of course, in densely populated China, relatively little remains of the old plant cover and the wildlife in it, since the Chinese, like the populations around the Mediterranean, destroy nature and are not interested in a rational utilization of plants and animals. Unlike the Japanese, who have a tradition of replanting one tree for each one cut down, the Chinese peasant has for ages been content to cut down trees and clear the land without considering the future.

As early as 1872, Père David declared: "I have often wondered what leads the Chinese to destroy the woods of their vast empire so completely.... They do not even have the pretext of pasturage, since they raise very few cattle, use no milk and little wool, to explain their passion for ceaselessly burning down the mountains.... I think one of their main

In its upper reaches, the Yangtze flows through narrow gorges hemmed by towering cliffs and dotted with rounded peaks on the banks or in the middle of the river. (Emil Schulthess)

138

reasons is a desire for security, obtained by destroying wild animal lairs. . . .

"To comprehend the sacrifices made to procure tranquillity and security, one must have lived as I did in these houses near thickets haunted by some of these terrible beasts. Experience has taught the Chinese that all cats abandon country denuded of forest and brush."

The long struggle between the Communists and the Kuomintang also led to the destruction of millions of trees, since government forces cut down all forests used as refuges by the partisans. Consequently, travelers in most rural parts of China today see nothing but cultivated fields and a few trees along roads or near villages; only around temples or Buddhist monasteries scattered on the plain or in remote mountain villages does one see vestiges of vegetation, mere hints of past luxuriance. The other hills or mountains of Lower China are covered only with grass and brush and occasionally a deformed tree. A traveler must penetrate deep into the interior, to the mountain sources of the great rivers, to find genuine forests and primitive jungle.

Happily, the present Chinese government, realizing the importance of forests as a natural resource and in the prevention of soil erosion, has begun a vast campaign of reforestation. Already, as I saw in a recent visit, young forests of pine, poplar, oak or willow cover every suitable space. From Kuang-chou (Canton) to the Mongolian border and beyond the Great Wall, hundreds of millions of trees struggle to take root in the impoverished, eroded soil of hills and mountains, stretch in double and quadruple lines along the roads, and even fill gaps between city buildings.

THE EMPEROR'S STAGS

This entire region, the heart of old China, has been for thousands of years one of the most densely populated areas on the globe and the one where man has most modified nature. The present fauna is thus only a pale reflection of that found when the Great Plain and the adjoining mountains were the meeting-place of animal species from the northern taigas, the eastern Mongolian steppes, and the southern tropical forests. Until the second half of the nineteenth century, this amazing fauna was practically unknown, so well did the Middle Kingdom keep its ancient secrets. If many really extraordinary animal species have become known to western science, credit must be given to that venturesome naturalist, Père Armand David. Arriving in China in 1861, at the age of thirty-five, he remained until 1874, journeying in every direction across that vast empire, and visiting Tibet, Mongolia, Kiangsi and Szechwan.

One day, near Peking, he came upon a wall running into the hills and learned that he had stumbled upon the Emperor's own vast hunting preserve, teeming with every sort of animal: bears, wolves, lynxes, stags roe deer and smaller game. At considerable personal risk, the intrepid missionary managed to gain entrance to the sanctuary, and one night in 1866 he smuggled over the wall the skin and two skeletons of a mysterious animal, the milou, a stag bearing no resemblance to any

other members of its family. Père David's discovery created a stir in scientific circles, and the Zoological Society of London succeeded in having a number of stags, fed chiefly on fresh alder leaves, shipped to Paris, London and Berlin. At the close of the nineteenth century, the Duke of Bedford released eighteen on his estate at Woburn Abbey; by 1948 they had increased to 255. This herd and the twenty or thirty in European and American zoos are all that remain of Père David's stags (Elaphurus davidianus), for the species is, paradoxically, extinct in its native land. Fossil remains dating from the Pliocene Era to 2000 B. C. have been found in the area between Peking and Shanghai and in Japan, but the animal, preserved only in the imperial sanctuary, remained unknown in the West for four thousand years. Since the Chinese government recently asked that a pair of stags be sent back in the hope of building up a herd on native soil, the story may have a happy ending.

SPARROWS, FLIES AND GRASSHOPPERS

After the destruction of the imperial game preserves, no large animals remained in this area. I was therefore surprised to see Chinese armed with hunting rifles in the countryside around Peking until I realized that small game abounds here: partridges (Perdix daurica), Mongolian pheasants, hares, foxes and many crows and magpies. In the few wooded mountains that remain there are roe deer (Capreolus capreolus) and birds native to Manchurian taiga—black grouse and hazel hens. The small animals are a mixture from all points of the compass: hedgehogs, voles, woodmice and little striped ground-squirrels, while the common red squirrel keeps to the wooded areas. Most of the birds are Palearctic: buntings, larks, tits, robins, thrushes, flycatchers and other inhabitants of the plains, while blue Himalayan magpies, nuthatches, and parrot-finches live on the heights.

Already seriously endangered by land clearing, all these birds narrowly escaped falling victim to the pseudo-logic of a cabinet economist. Multiplying the amount of grain consumed by a single bird by the estimated number of birds in China, he calculated that they were taking the bread from the mouths of two or three million people and concluded that the birds must be totally destroyed at once.

Since a tiny passerine can remain aloft for only about three hours without resting, the population was ordered to climb to the tops of trees, monuments and houses and make enough noise with sticks, pots and firecrackers to prevent the birds from landing or resting. By evening of this winged Waterloo, hardly a passerine remained in the most populated areas of China, and millions of others died of exhaustion or were finished off with sticks as they fell. But this experiment demonstrated that man can destroy nature far more easily than he can regulate it: a few years later in China an unprecedent invasion and multiplication of parasitic insects ruined the crops. The Chinese authorities thereupon reversed themselves, ordering the strict protection of birds. It is probable that such protective measures together with intensive reforestation will eventually restore China's rich birdlife.

Overleaf: The powerful Si Kiang River, the longest tributary of the Canton River, here crosses the chalky plateau of Kwangsi. Along the river are beehive-shaped hills. (Emil Schulthess: Black Star)

This forest of stone, an immense eroded plateau, is one of Yunnan's curiosities. (Louise Weiss)

Père David's deer (Elaphurus davidianus), *extinct in the wild state for millenia, held out until the end of the nineteenth century on the hunting reserve of the Chinese emperor. The only herd surviving today is that of the Duke of Bedford at Woburn Abbey in England. (W. Suschitzky)*

China's plans for the extermination of flies and rats were not nearly so successful, for although flies have become notably rarer than they were, this is not true of that very adaptable and prolific creature, the rat. It is indeed possible that the brown rat *(Rattus norvegicus),* the Asiatic invader who has, over the centuries, conquered the entire planet, will still be here when man and all other animals have disappeared.

The latest Chinese campaign is against cicadas. Despite their song, these insect transmitters of plant diseases are being hunted through the summer months by children and adults armed with bamboo rods tipped with bird-lime.

In spite of these communal hunts, insects still abound throughout the region, including such strange species as a very primitive grasshopper of the genus *Paratlanticus* on the prairie, and a giant scarab, *Callipogon relictus,* in wooded zones. Among the other beetles commonly found from Manchuria to the shores of Korea are several species of carabid beetles *(Carabus hummeli, C. asraël, C. smaragdinus, Calosoma cyanescens, Rosalia coelestris)* and such other species as *Phellopsis amurensis, Chloridolum silversi, Purpurianus petasifer,* and *Moechotypa diphysis.* The most common butterflies are *Papilio maacki* and *Eolimenitis eximia* and the moth *Antheraea pernyi* is equally familiar, but the best-known insect is incontestably the mulberry moth or silkworm *(Bombyx mori).*

of silk dates back, it is believed, to 2700 B. C. when the wife of the Emperor Hong watched the silkworms building their cocoons and had the idea of unrolling them to use their remarkably fine, strong thread. The thread of other species of moths is used to make fairly coarse fabrics, but the most famous silks have always been those furnished by the mulberry bombyx, especially in the region of Shantung where the white mulberry *(Morus alba)* grows abundantly.

The Chinese kept the process of raising silkworms and making silk a closely guarded secret for centuries while their caravans transported the fabric to all the markets of Central Asia, India, and the Near East. In the markets the silk brought fabulous prices from Arab merchants who, in turn, sold it in Mediterranean countries. But at the beginning of the Christian era silkworm cocoons and white mulberry plants were smuggled out to India, then to Persia and Arabia and finally in 555 A. D. to Constantinople. In the twelfth century, the tree and its precious parasite reached Sicily and then went on to Italy and at last to France. The mulberry became quite at home in the Rhone Valley and the wealth of the city of Lyon was based mainly on silk-weaving. At the end of the nineteenth century, however, the European silk industry underwent economic setbacks and a serious crisis when a silkworm disease wiped out many of the worms. Pasteur soon showed that the disease

SILKWORMS AND GOLDFISH

The use of the cocoon of the mulberry moth for the weaving

This natural "gate" or arch on Moon Mountain near Kweilin is due to chemical erosion of unequally resistant layers of limestone rock. (Eastfoto)

could be eliminated if the worms were bred under strictly hygienic conditions, but in many regions breeding never recovered from the epidemic. Today China and Japan have a monopoly of what remains of the industry.

Two modest inhabitants of China's streams, lakes and ponds also conquered the world. One, the Chinese or mitten crab *(Eriocheir sinensis)*, is easily recognized by its hairy claws. As large as the palm of a hand, this crab lives in rivers and estuaries, apparently indifferent to the degree of salinity. After millions of years in China, it suddenly appeared in Holland at the end of the nineteenth century. Undoubtedly first transported by boat, it has since continued an inexorable invasion, occupying all Holland and sapping its earthen dikes, moving upstream in the Rhine to enter Germany, and using other rivers to reach France and Belgium. After World War II, the crab was sighted at the mouth of the Seine. Nothing seems to stop this crustacean, scourge of fresh waters, where it attacks young fry, is a serious rival to native aquatic fauna, and perhaps the carrier of a particularly dangerous parasitic worm *(Paragonimus ringeri)*.

Luckily, the goldfish, China's other great migrant, is far from undesirable and owes its presence on all five continents to man's interest in it as a pet. Called *chi-yu* in China, this little fish has been raised as an ornament to house and garden for nearly two thousand years. Called goldfish all over the world, except in France, where it is known as *poisson-rouge* (or redfish), and more scientifically as the golden cyprin, it is, like the carp which have been raised for centuries as an ordinary food fish, a member of the family of cyprinids. In its wild state, the *chi-yu* resembles a very small carp, but since it is, like the fruit fly among insects, genetically unstable, mutants suddenly appear without the usual greenish-brown carp coloration but in bright orange, the source of their common name and their Latin label: *Carassius auratus*.

The first man to breed goldfish appears to have been a certain Ting Yen Tsan, governor of Chekiang province between 975 and 968 B.C. A fervent Buddhist with a deep respect for animal life, Ting built a pond to which people brought many golden cyprins, venerated for their color. Selective breeding did not begin until the Sung dynasty (960–1280 A.D.) when Emperor Chao-Ku built several goldfish pools in his Hangchow gardens and other officials followed his example, some civil servants being charged with procuring water fleas or daphnias to feed the fish. After 113 years, two new varieties were isolated: the white and the spotted black. In the sixteenth century under the Ming dynasty, breeding was transferred from ponds or pools to large terra-cotta jars. Now almost anyone could breed the fish and encourage the mating and multiplication of desirable mutants. As a result, six new varieties appeared during the century, the "classics" of today's

Known to the West through Chinese literature, the lotus adorns ponds throughout Asia east and south of the Himalayas. layas. Its seeds, eaten fresh, are considered a great delicacy. (Louise Weiss)

fanciers: goldfish with transparent or multicolored bodies, globular shapes, fantails, sailtails, elongated fins and "telescope" or bulging eyes.

When the laws of heredity became known after the middle of the nineteenth century, raising goldfish became a matter of logical breeding, and ten new varieties appeared in seventy-seven years—all with such evocative Chinese names as Eyes of the Black Dragon, Lion's Head, and Pearly Scales. In Peking's public parks one may even see huge yellow ceramic jars in which goldfish as blue as the South China Sea mingle with others of white or pink to form a remarkable spectacle in animated color.

BEYOND THE YANGTSE CH'ANG

Seen from an airplane flying from north to south over eastern China, the Yangtse Ch'ang is a sharp boundary between two large natural zones. To its north lie the gloomy loess plains sown with isolated clumps of trees; to its south are little round mountains covered with dense vegetation and separated from each other by deep valleys in which clear streams tumble over the rocks.

Left above: Early morning mists in the heart of Taiwan shroud Sun Moon Lake and the surrounding hills. (William P. Fenn) Far left: The little blue flycatcher of Hainan (Cyornes pallipes), one of many flycatchers of the temperate and hot regions of Asia, darts out on passing insects from atop a bush or small tree. (John Markham)   Left: This heron, Ardeola bacchus, common in southern China, is found during the summer in large numbers in the Lower Yangtze Basin, but in winter lives in solitude along muddy creeks and ponds. (Government Information Office, Republic of China)

Covering these crowded hills is the type of forest that is, made up of plants adapted to medium moisture, called mesophytic, and distinguished in two ways. First, it is composed of a mixture of species, generally broad-leafed and deciduous, of many unrelated families. Second, with no dominant species, the canopy is formed of a great many different trees, a complexity unusual in deciduous forests but reminiscent of tropical virgin forests with their evergreen broad-leaved formation. Most of the typical trees belong to orders found in the north, here represented by species adapted to the damp, temperate climate.

Save at high altitudes, no month has a mean temperature of less than 32° F, even though some minimum temperatures as low as 7° F have been noted. Generally, from 230 to 280 days a year are frost-free and the warm season is longer than in the deciduous forest we have just described north of the Yangtze. Only three months of the year have a mean temperature lower than 32° F, three have a mean temperature higher than 72° F, and six have one higher than 50° F. Also favorable to vegetation is an annual rainfall of between forty and sixty inches, twice that in the north, and the spread of this rainfall is over 125 to 165 days each year, with no absolutely rainless month.

The canopy of the mesophytic forest, striking in its diversity, offers more than fifty genera of leafy trees and twelve of conifers. This includes all genera found in northern Chinese forests, and, according to the American botanist E. L. Braun, all the important genera of the North American forest, except for *Oxydendrum, Platanum,* and *Robinia.*

There are three distinct layers in the forests: that of tall and middle-sized trees, that of shrubs, and the grassy floor. The upper layer is a mixture of deciduous, evergreen, and coniferous trees: fifty species of maple *(Acer),* thirty-two of sorb *(Sorbus),* eleven of hornbeam *(Carpinus),* ten of ash *(Fraxinus),* nine of birch *(Betula),* nine of linden *(Tilia),* eight of elm *(Ulmus)* and five of corktree *(Phellodendron).* There are also alders, walnuts, oaks *(Quercus glauca* with barely lobed leaves, and *Q. aliena* and *Q. fabrii* with long or oval leaves but distinctly lobed), wild apple, plum and pear trees. One also sees the kind of ornamental trees found all over the world, such as *Magnolia* and *Paulownia,* especially in public gardens. The evergreens include evergreen oaks *(Quercus glandulifera, Q. baronii* with very long, narrow leaves), subtropical oaks *(Lithocarpus thalassina)* with laurel-like leaves, camphor trees *(Cinnamomum camphora),* and such chestnuts as *Castanea mollissima,* which bears very small nuts, *Castanopsis sclerophylla* with thick long leaves, *C. eyrei* with equally thick but rounded leaves, and the Tibetan chestnut *(C. tibetana)* whose ten-inch-long oval leaves look enormous compared to those around them.

Most of the conifers are pines *(Pinus taiwanensis, P. massorniana),* yews *(Taxus chinensis, Cephalotaxus sinensis, Pseudotaxus chienii),* junipers *(Juniperus formosum),* blue firs *(Pseudotsuga* sp., *Tsuga yunnanensis)* on the heights, and cypress *(Cupressus funebris)* in the lower regions.

Relics of the flora of the Mesozoic Era are found in the forests of conifers. The most familiar is the *Ginkgo,* which also occurs in Japan and is used ornamentally all over the world. It grows spontaneously in the western Tienmu Shan, the mountainous region of the lower Yangtze valley, with larches *(Pseudolarix),* maples, magnolia, yews *(Torreya),* and evergreen oaks. Two other living fossils of the vegetable world

are *Taiwania* sp. and *Metasequoia glyptostroboides,* a relative of the North American giant sequoias. Chinese botanists recently claimed to have discovered in this region a living example of the famous *Metasequoia fossilis,* widespread 100 million years ago and believed extinct for at least twenty million years.

Bamboos appear only occasionally beneath the upper level in the primeval forest, for they can grow freely only in natural clearings along a stream or as formed by the fall of a tree. Where the forest has been cut down, however, bamboo thickets may cover vast expanses, especially on the lower slopes. Some species are planted for the shoots, which are eaten, and others serve various domestic purposes. The most common are *Phyllostachys edulis, P. pubercula, P. bambusoides, Sinocalamus beecheyana, S. latifrons. Chimonobambusa quadrangularis, Plioblastus amarus,* and, finally, several species of *Arundinaria* that form impenetrable thickets as tall as a man —a grave obstacle to a farmer trying to clear the land.

Besides bamboos, the bushy layer consists of plant species well known to gardeners: *Hibiscus, Jasminum, Ficus, Cercis, Clerodendron, Daphniphyllum, Ilex* and many others common in warm and temperate climates all over the world. Epiphytes and tropical creepers abound and it is astonishing to find such familiar climbing vines as the white-vine *(Clematis)* and the ampelopsis.

The ground is covered with plants and ferns adapted to withstanding rain, generally perennial and rarely found outside the forest. The most common fern is *Cyanopteris vestitata,* resembling our eagle-fern. In places flowers are abundant, particularly various species of wild lilies *(Lilium* sp.), and the humidity is favorable to a thick carpet of moss, with *Paraleucobryum enerve* and *Pogonatum submicrostomum* predominant.

THE GREEN HILLS OF THE SOUTH

Moving south, we gradually penetrate into another climate and another type of forest. Here the coldest mean monthly temperature is usually above 41° F and the minimum rarely below 20° F. Thus there is a growing period of about three hundred frost-free days. Moreover, the rainfall, from sixty to eighty inches annually, is spread over 145 to 165 days, and even the driest months have from one to one and one-half inches of rain. This favorable climate, together with an excellent red soil, has covered the hills of the southeastern provinces with a thick carpet of greenery, still untouched in many places, and a large-leafed evergreen forest. Of course, the word "evergreen" is not to be taken literally, for the leaves fall off like those of trees in temperate regions, but different trees lose their leaves at different times so that the forest remains green overall. This broad-leafed forest may be further divided into three distinct types: the sclerophyllous (or coarse-leafed forest), the hygrophytic or moisture-loving rain forest, and the coastal forest. The term "rain forest" generally designates tall, complex and varied tropical vegetation, sometimes with a dominant group giving its name to the whole. At other times, the terrain lends its name to a forest, as in swamp forest, mountain forest or plains forest. Rain forest is found in the low

These remarkable rock formations tower above the sea on the northern end of Taiwan. (Government Information Office, Republic of China)

Countless aquatic birds such as these gulls (Larus saundersi) *nest on an island in the salt lake of Koko Nor in northwestern China. (Eastfoto)*

southern regions and in the valleys of Yunnan Province in China, and on the islands of Taiwan (Formosa) and Hainan. It also blends into the Indo-Malaysian forests, with which it shares the same kind of flora and fauna.

The coastal forests on the shores of warm seas is a very different community, including, besides the forest proper, such vegetation as mangroves and those plants that colonize tropical islands and coral islets, mainly species typical of all tropical regions.

The permanent, broad-leafed sclerophyllous forest spreads over immense areas here, covering the entire southwestern plateau of China, all the hills of the southeastern provinces, and the mountains of Taiwan and Hainan. Unlike the northern forests, these have generally been spared millenia of destruction by man and are still in an excellent state of preservation for such a densely populated land. These forests are dominated by the perennially green trees of the oak family, which includes the commonest trees of the west: oak, chestnut, birch, hazel, beech and alder. Trees from such other families as the Theaceae, Lauraceae, Magnoliaceae, occur, and sometimes they are more abundant than the former, but it is generally the oaks with their long, shiny, tough leaves that give this forest its characteristic appearance. Moreover, when

trees from such different families as those mentioned above look so much alike and have similar tough oval or lance-shaped leaves with generally smooth or barely notched edges, it is a striking example of evolutionary convergence, most trees apparently adapting to the environment in the same way.

Where the primeval forest has been destroyed, pines, either alone or in association with oaks, cover great stretches. From a plane, thickets of giant bamboos (Dendrocalamus, Bambusa) or dwarf bamboos (Arundinaria) may be seen. Despite their height and appearance, bamboos belong to the family of grasses, although the bamboo's arborescent stalk can live a very long time, while other Gramineae are perennial and lose their above-ground parts each year.

PEKING ROBINS AND GOLDEN PHEASANTS

Both deciduous and green forests zones are inhabited by a characteristically subtropical animal life. There are very few palearctic species. Thus, among the mammals, we find only the northern roe deer and that only in the north of the region. The more mobile birds are represented, especially in high places, by such palearctic species as the black woodpecker *(Dryocopus martius)* and the three-toed woodpecker *(Picoides tricactylus).* Some insect species, following their host plants, also descend quite far into the south: for example, *Spondylus buprestoides* and *Ips sexdentatus,* one attacking the wood and the other the bark of pines, and *Melasoma tremulae,*

which devours the leaves of aspen trees *(Populus tremula).*

Southern species of fauna are of course countless, especially in the eastern provinces of Kwangtung and Fukien where no natural barrier has impeded their invasion. But in the west, mountains have hindered such expansion and favored the evolution of an original fauna, one which resembles that found in the Himalayas.

In southeastern China we meet for the first time certain animals that will become familiar in our tropical wanderings. Almost immediately we note such tropical birds as drongos *(Dicrurus* sp.), their tails long and forked, silhouetted on the tops of bushes or on telegraph poles and wires along the road. Like flycatchers, they dart out from their perches to capture insects in flight. Often they can be seen riding on the backs or necks of domestic animals, feeding on the parasites of the big beasts or on the flies buzzing around them. Another companion of cattle, also tropical in origin, the almost pure white cattle egret *(Bubulcus ibis),* stalks the rice paddies. One of the most delightful birds to watch is the paradise flycatcher *(Terpsiphone paradisi),* with various subspecies widespread in the hot forest regions of Africa and Asia. The adult male is white, with a little crest and glints of blue on its black head and two long tail-feathers that float like ribbons behind it during its undulating flight. These birds pass through two coloration phases in Africa, but in Asia both sexes are always white.

Along the streams and on the edges of the forests of southeast China, little black-backed herons *(Ardeola bacchus)* and

several species of tropical kingfishers *(Halcyon, Ceryle)* are common. On its rivers and lakes are various palearctic ducks and teals, usually passing through in autumn and winter, followed by wild geese, storks and cranes, and such tropical species as whistling teals *(Dendrocygna* sp.), great crested ducks *(Sarkidiornis),* and pretty mandarin ducks *(Aix),* familiar ornaments of most parks and zoos. An astonishing bird is the red, white and black jacana or water pheasant *(Hydrophasianus)* whose long legs and enormous claws tipped with outsize talons enable it to move freely about on tops of waterlily pads without sinking into them. It is a vivid red, white and black and has a long tail which accounts for its being called a pheasant.

These wooded zones are the northern distribution limits of many Indo-Malaysian birds. We find, surprisingly, ten species of sunbirds *(Nectariniidae),* the Old World counterparts of American hummingbirds. There are also five species of flowerpeckers *(Diceidae),* who are closely related to the sunbirds but add the pulp of various exotic fruits to the sunbird diet of flower nectar. Both birds are brightly colored and flit through the forest, like moving flowers, the sunbirds often glinting metallically. Very similar in appearance are the three species of white-eye *(Zosterops),* their black eyes encircled by clearly visible white feathers. They seek their diet of insects and berries in thickets and low trees, often in the company of the tailor bird *(Orthotomus).* The latter, a small, long-beaked gray or brown bird with a rather short, often uplifted tail, eats insects but is most notable for the nests it builds between

two large leaves with edges carefully sewn together to form a cone. Thus suspended, the nest is supposedly safe from the bird's enemies, especially egg-eating snakes.

The babblers *(Timalidae),* so called in English because they are so noisy, are represented by about ninety-five species. Poor fliers with short, rounded wings, they live on insects but have stronger beaks and legs than other insect-eaters. Many species live on or near ground level; others prefer thickets or tangles of vine. One of the most prized of cage-birds misnamed the Peking robin *(Leiothrix)*—it is not a robin at all—belongs to this group. It is the size of a sparrow, olive-green above, with an orange or red head and breast, dark gray wings prettily marked with yellow and red, yellow beak and legs. Its varied and melodious song, heard the year round, has caused it to be compared to the European nightingale.

Kin to the babblers are the bulbuls *(Pycnonotidae).* Their song, heard from afar, announces a clearing or a stream, for they are typical inhabitants of secondary growth, of cleared lands and gardens, where they remain in the tall trees. Extremely lively and constantly chirping, they eat fruits and berries and occasionally a few insects. Common in Africa and Tropical Asia, they are at the limit of their range in Japan.

Still other birds make us aware of the proximity of the tropics: a caterpillar-eating species of cuckoo-shrike *(Campephagidae),* numerous turtle-doves *(Streptopelia),* long-tailed pigeons called cuckoo doves *(Macropygia)* and various fruit-eating pigeons *(Treron, Ptilinopus).* China is particularly rich in gallinaceous birds, possessing, for example, forty-seven of the world's 165 species of pheasants. Probably the most beautiful are those found in the south central province of Szechwan, but the southeastern provinces also shelter fine species such as silver pheasants *(Lophura nycthemera)* or golden pheasants *(Chrysolophus pictus),* widespread as aviary birds. The peacock pheasant *(Polyplectron bicalcaratum),* its gray-brown plumage starred with peacock-like "eyes," lives on the island of Hainan.

The golden pheasant is a striking example of a familiar bird about which nothing is known. For although represented in Chinese art and literature for centuries, raised in Europe for more than two hundred years (Lafayette gave a few to Washington for his Mount Vernon estate), quite common in bird stores and reproducing easily in captivity, practically nothing is known of its natural life, its area of distribution or its nest. Its mass of gold, red, blue, green, and yellow feathers makes it one of the most gorgeous of birds and the male's nuptial parade is an enchanting ballet in public parks. Crest raised, feather collar spread wide to conceal the neck and the head below the eye, tail fanning out like a peacock's, the bird hops about in front of his companion to show off the beautiful colors of flanks and back, meanwhile emitting a series of hisses and resonant "click-clicks."

Left: Massive ancient mountains at Nan K'ou Pass forty miles from Peking dwarf the Great Wall. (J. Allan Cash)

Right above: The Chinese river deer (Hydropotes inermis) *is a small animal without antlers but with long canine teeth like tusks. It lives in marshy places and swims perfectly.   Right: The muntjac deer* (Muntiacus muntjac) *of southern China is the smallest of the muntjacs which live in all forests south of the Himalayas. Very cautious, it barks when alarmed, whence its common name, barking-deer. (Both, W. Suschitzky)*

HOG DEER AND PANGOLINS

Southeast China is also heavily colonized by tropical mammals, but since we shall meet them all again in the Indo-Malaysian region, we mention here only the most important. Squirrels abound in the forest, the most common being the red tree-squirrel (Callosciurus), the red-cheeked ground-squirrel (Dremomys rufigenis), and several species of large flying-squirrels (Petaurista sp.). Among the carnivorous animals are the small masked civet (Paguma larvata), a crab-eating mongoose (Herpestes urva) and the large clouded leopard (Felis nebulosa), a tree-dwelling cat that has gray-brown fur with great grayish spots often outlined in black.

Although stags have been hunted to excess for their velvety antlers, which are used in Chinese medicines, they are still common in less accessible places. The largest is the sambar (Cervus unicolor), whose habitat extends from India to the Moluccas toward the east and to the Sunda Islands toward the south. It is as large as a European stag or a Canadian wapiti and its antlers usually have only two tines. The spotted deer or sika (Cervus nippon), the size of a white-tailed deer and close relative of the Indian chital, has a brownish-red hide that is spotted with white and clearer in winter than in summer. Even smaller is the barking deer or muntjac (Muntiacus muntjac), which resembles Eurasian roe deer in size and forest habits. It is a characteristic tropical Asian ungulate and abounds from south of the Himalayas to Java. Its crooked little horns spring from bony bases several inches long, and the male has long upper canines that protrude even from its closed mouth.

But the most unusual of the deer here is the Chinese water deer or Hydropotes, a strange little hornless animal with canines so well developed as to form tusks. At its Latin name indicates it is at home in swamps and swims perfectly. It has coarse fur; and with this thick hair forming a mane on its back, with its short legs, squat silhouette higher in the hind-quarters than in the forequarters, it looks just like a pig. This resemblance is reinforced by the fact that it bears as many as seven young to a litter, boar fashion, instead of one and sometimes two like all other deer.

Abundant in this region is the rhesus macaque (Macaca mulatta), the monkey most often used in medical research. Various species of macaques are found throughout tropical Asia and we will meet them constantly throughout our journey southward.

Southeast China or, more accurately, the Yangtze River, also marks the northern limit of distribution of a typically tropical animal, the bizarre pangolin or scaly anteater. Next to the Australian platypus, it is probably the most unusual of mammals. It looks like a huge, brown, shiny-scaled pine cone with a long scaly tail. The scales, which may be compared with those of snakes and lizards, form an armor that leaves bare only the face, the belly and the inner surface of the paws. Inserted into the skin by only one edge, they can bristle like a bird's feathers. Another astonishing characteristic—but one also found in South American anteaters, Australian echidnas, and all woodpeckers—is the tongue, which can be thrust far out and is coated with sticky saliva that easily collects insect prey. The mouth is merely a toothless tube just large enough to permit the passage of the tongue. Like the other animals mentioned above, the pangolin is an insect-eater, swallowing its prey whole and "chewing" them in its stomach. The eyes are tiny—barely the size of a pea even in a three-foot pangolin—and are scarcely used, the animal depending on its acute sense of smell, as evidenced by its constantly exploring nose and quivering nostrils. Its hearing is also very sharp and the crushing of a dead leaf suffices to make the pangolin roll into a ball, with the end of its prehensile tail locked so tightly into the dorsal scales that an enemy cannot unroll it.

Nocturnal forest-dwellers, they spend as much time in trees, which they climb with agility, as on the ground, where they move clumsily about, their backs arched and their paws turned inward. They usually remain in one area living either in a hole in a tree or a burrow. Except for the reproductive period they are solitary but can coexist with other animals; I have seen a pangolin and two porcupines living cozily together in a vast burrow among the roots of a huge tree.

The pangolin feeds exclusively on ants and termites, using its strong paws to break the solid walls of anthills and termite nests. When the entrance to a gallery has been disclosed, the pangolin inserts its wormlike tongue into the opening and pulls it out garnished with dozens of insects, a process it repeats with the rhythm of a cat lapping milk. It is, in fact, the distribution of two species of termites, Coptotermes formosanus and Termes formosanus, its habitual prey, that marks off the pangolin's habitat in southeastern China and up to the Yangtze. The pangolin's method of feeding puzzles biologists, since its sticky tongue, inserted into a termite nest, should collect grains of sand or bits of vegetation as well as insects. How the tongue instantly separates the digestible from the indigestible has not yet been explained.

Above far left: Called the Peking robin in Europe, this bird, known for its melodious song, is really the red-beaked leiothrix (Leiothrix lutea) of the high forests south of the Himalayas, and of Indochina and southern China. (John H. Tashjian) Above left: The fairy bluebird (Irena puella) lives in Asia's hot regions. It betrays itself only by its mewing cry and the blue flash of its wings in the dim forest. (John Markham) Left: The mandarin duck (Aix galericulata), a native of China and Japan, has long ornamented European and American parks. (Robert Frederick)

Monsoons and
Sacred Rivers

From the Indian Desert to Assam

9 After having traveled across cold, temperate, and warm monsoon Asia from north to south and from east to west, we now penetrate India, where high temperature adds its influence to that of summer and winter monsoons.

On the Indian peninsula, the most westerly part of tropical Asia, we shall become familiar with true tropical nature, some of whose flora and fauna we have already met in south China. Bounded on the north by the Himalayas, and on the west and east by the mountains of Afghanistan, Iran and Burma, the almost perfect triangle of India and Pakistan has a 2,200-mile base, a height of 1,760 miles from Cape Comorin to the southern border of Tibet, and an area almost one-third that of the United States. Inside this triangle is another, an immense plateau, the Deccan, separated from the Himalayas by the vast plain of the Indus and Ganges rivers.

The altitude of the Deccan highland is 1,300 to 3,300 feet and it slopes from west to east, as indicated by the general direction taken by its rivers. It is bordered by three mountain chains: the Western Ghats, whose highest peak is the Anai Mudi (8,841 feet), the Eastern Ghats, seldom higher than 3,300 feet; and on the north by the Satpura, Vindhya and Maikala ranges, with altitudes from 2,300 to 4,400 feet. The alluvial coastal fringe is very narrow, barely forty miles on the western or Malabar Coast, slightly more than sixty miles on the eastern or Coromandel Coast. The Indo-Gangetic plain is remarkably flat—only nine hundred feet at the highest point.

The island of Ceylon, geologically a part of India, separated from the mainland by Palk Strait, is formed on the north by a low-lying plain and on the south by a mountain chain dominated by Adam's Peak and the Pidurutlagala (8,327 feet). There are very few other islands along India's remarkably unbroken alluvial coasts.

The Indian climate may be defined as hot and humid in the summer and cool and dry in the winter. India is, in fact, one of the hottest areas on the globe in the summer months and a region where the alternation of monsoons is most evident. A journey across Bengal during the dry season offers nothing but an expanse of parched land from which a burning wind raises clouds of dust and where emaciated cattle struggle for a few blades of sun-scorched grass. During the month of

May, the thermometer hits 115° F in Calcutta; people collapse in the streets from sunstroke, and under the trees on the avenues one may see crows, parakeets, and giant fruit bats killed by the heat. All eyes turn to the lowering sky, where black clouds begin to pile up, promising the salvation of rain. The monsoon usually begins in the Bay of Bengal about May 20th and reaches the foot of the Himalayas three weeks later. But sometimes it is not exactly on time, and the uneasiness swells to panic and Indian newspapers, ignoring important international news, present such anguished headlines as "Monsoon: Serious Delay," or such reassurances as "Slight Delay, Experts Say."

When the rains come, usually so violently that Indians speak of "the explosion of the monsoon," people become delirious with joy. The atmosphere clears and man and beast breathe freely again although it is actually hotter than at the height of summer in temperate lands. Naked children frolic in the rain, animals roll happily in the puddles, and the thirsty earth sops up water.

The rainfall is actually distributed very unevenly. Precipitation varies between sixty and eighty inches a year on the Malabar Coast, and even exceeds 120 inches in the Bombay region. Areas north and east of the mouth of the Ganges have a mean rainfall of 80 to 120 inches, and such a place as Assam, one of the wettest zones in the world, has recorded two hundred inches. On the other hand, in the west, along the valley of the Indus, lies one of the world's driest regions, Rajasthan, where in some spots precipitation barely reaches four inches a year.

Taking into account rainfall and topography, we may therefore divide the Indian peninsula into three large natural regions: the arid plains of the Indus in the northwest, the green hills of Assam in the northeast, and the more temperate Deccan Plateau in the south.

THE INDIAN DESERT

In terms of its animal and plant life, the classification of the Indian desert is in dispute, sometimes being linked to the palearctic zone and the arid regions of Iran and Afghanistan, and sometimes to the eastern zone. It is true that many representatives of palearctic desert fauna are found east of the Indus: 56.4 percent of the mammals of Rajasthan, as the Indian zoologist I. Prakash recently showed, as against 41 percent Indo-Malaysian and 2.6 percent endemic. However, we prefer to consider the area east of the Indus as being in the eastern region, first for the sake of geographical unity, since it is part of the Indian peninsula, and second because this arid zone is of relatively recent origin and caused the invasion of palearctic fauna and the retreat of Indo-Malaysian animals.

In fact, before the Christian era, the Sind-Rajasthan region had a much damper climate and was covered by vast tropical forests; from the trees in these forests, history tells us, Alexander the Great built the boats with which his armies crossed the Indus River. Fossil evidence also proves that in the middle

The Asiatic water buffalo (Bubalus bulaus), *found in the wild only in Assam (right) and parts of Indochina, is distinctly larger than the domesticated animal, weighing as much as a ton. (Philippa Scott)*

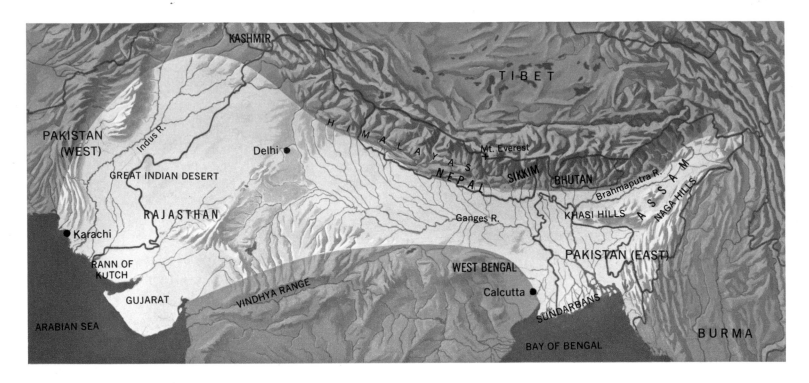

The western Indo-Gangetic plain is an arid zone, often desert-like or covered with dry forests with acacias predominant. At the foot of the Himalayas, where rainfall increases, lies the terai, *a land of green hills and dense forests. Assam, to the east, holds the world's record for rainfall and is still largely covered by forests and tropical swamps.*

of the Pleistocene Era this region was inhabited by many rhinoceroses, water-buffalos and elephants. The climate remained favorable for these large animals during the time of the famous lost cities of Mohenjodero and Harappa. The drying-out of this region began between 4000 and 1000 B.C., probably after a modification of the local climate, the consequent disappearance of two rivers, the Saraswati and the Ghaggar, and the sinking of the water table from 260 to nearly 400 feet down.

The history of the Saraswati is most curious. Hailed in Sanskrit poetry as "Queen of Rivers," it flowed, until the fourteenth century, into the sea and was lined with flourishing cities; but, choked by sands and perhaps swallowed up by such other rivers as the Djamna or the Bias, it could not hold its course across the desert. Today it is an insignificant stream.

Our use of the term desert must not lead to the impression that there are vast, completely sterile lands in India. Only stony deserts of the *hamada* type are truly dead; sandy deserts are never entirely without life, for the little water they receive suffices for the blossoming of temporary vegetation, which is immediately turned to account by animals. The arid regions of northwest India are almost clear of stones, even near the mountains, where plants grow in the gravel. All the rest of the country is covered with fine, alluvial sediment, called *khadar,* in the river deltas and more or less sedimentary sand in the intervening plains. Thus the vegetable cover is very variable and chiefly conditioned by the irregular rainfall and the melting of Himalayan snows. The latter swell the rivers in March and together with the monsoon rains raise river levels to their peaks in July and August. During September and October the water level falls rapidly and in winter the sand of the dry beds is whirled about by the wind. Water levels in streams vary greatly: the lower Indus, for example,

has a mean minimum of six inches and a mean maximum of 165 inches. The floods rush down the steep Himalayan slopes so suddenly as to take riverside communities by surprise; no wonder the people who dwelled on the banks saw the floods that swallowed up their crops as the work of formidable water deities.

Most of the region along the Indus, from the coast to the northwest of Delhi, is flat or studded with hills and covered with clumps of grass amidst large patches of bare, dark, sedimentary soil. In other places, the plain is covered with spiny thickets from which spring thorny jujube trees *(Zizyphus jujuba),* spurge and several species of acacias.

The true deciduous monsoon forest with various species of trees occurs only in the south mainly in the forest of Gir on the Gujarat peninsula. Nearly half that area is covered by teak *(Tectona grandis),* mixed in places with numerous evergreen banyans *(Ficus* sp.). Ebony *(Diospyros melanoxylon)* is equally common, as are *Terminalia* and *Butea frondosa,* the "forest flame" with its dazzling flowers. Thus, local flora, including plants found in Africa and the Middle East (such as jujube trees and acacias) and others limited to tropical Asia such as teak, banyans and forest flames show the same duality as birds and mammals.

In the Sind-Rajasthan desert proper, more than half the mammals are palearctic in origin, but have apparently invaded this region only during the last few thousand years. Oriental species, still well represented, will undoubtedly retreat as the region becomes more and more arid. Curiously, many pale-

Indians venerate the langur or sacred monkey (Presbytis entellus), *considering it the reincarnation of Hanuman, the Monkey God. (Ylla: Rapho Guillumette)*

arctic and oriental mammals are represented here by sub-species having the characteristic coats of desert animals, an indication of fairly rapid adaptation by these species but in superficial traits only.

Among the region's ungulates, the blue-bull (so called because of bluish glints in its gray-brown coat) or nilghai *(Boselaphus tragocamelus)* is typically Indian. In spite of its scientific name *(bos* = bull, *elaphus* = stag), it is not a link between a bull and a stag; its silhouette is like that of a stag, but the animal is bovidian and akin to the antelope. Since, however, the Indians consider it a bull and sacred, they generally abstain from hunting it, so that it is still abundant in the Hindu areas—northwest and central India. A handsome animal with a massive body the size of a large stag, it has, unfortunately, a very short neck and a pointed head, topped in the male by two ridiculously small horns. Another typically Indian herbivorous animal, the black-buck *(Antilope cervicapra),* is represented in the desert by a subspecies with a paler coat. This very pretty animal, as large as a gazelle, with a slender body and very long, twisted horns, is intensively hunted and is becoming rare. The Indian gazelle or chinkara *(Gazella gazella)* still common in this area is also typical of the Sahara-Sind region, the Indian desert being the eastern limit of its habitat.

Wild boars are also common in the Sind-Rajasthan. They belong to the form *Sus cristatus* widespread throughout India, but some zoologists consider it a subspecies of *Sus scrofa,* the boar of the temperate regions of Europe and Asia.

This region has two species of monkeys, the rhesus macaque *(Macaca mulatta),* already mentioned, and the sacred langur *(Presbytis entellus);* both are tropical, but the first is found from the Indus to southern China, the second only in India, and we shall meet it again in the forests of Deccan.

Among smaller animals almost as many palearctic as

oriental forms are found here: hedgehogs, shrews and bats. One rodent, the Indian gerbil with hairy paws *(Gerbillus gleadowi),* whose nearest relative is the North African gerbil *(Gerbillus gerbillus),* was discovered only as recently as 1965.

Since the balance of nature functions in the Indian desert as elsewhere, all these animals have natural enemies. The best-known was the Indian cheetah *(Acinonyx jubatus);* we say *was,* for this splendid animal, the same species as the African cheetah, may now be considered extinct in India. Once, all the Indian princes kept them for use in hunting blackbuck, then abundant. The cheetah was trained to crouch on horseback just behind a rider until the game was sighted. The hunt was very brief, for the animal overtook its prey after a dizzying sprint of a hundred yards. This sport was so popular in India that it spread to the West, where, lacking antelopes, the nobles hunted hares.

This passion for hunting with cheetahs certainly hastened their disappearance, for, to keep up the packs (some of which, like those of the Mongol emperor Akbar, numbered several hundred), it was necessary to keep capturing fresh wild animal. In fact, the cheetah, like the falcon, which works with man but is not truly a domestic animal, generally refuses to breed in captivity. Another probable cause of this magnificient carnivore's extinction is the disappearance of its natural prey, notably the much hunted blackbuck. Hunters killed off the few surviving cheetahs, the last three being killed in 1948 in a single night by a hunter using a flashlight and a gun.

With the cheetah gone, the largest carnivore in the Sind-Rajasthan is a leopard, a somewhat paler version of the forest animal. There are also subspecies of two other desert cats, *Felis chaus* and *Felis libyca.* Among small carnivores are the Indian civet *(Viverricula indica),* which is also found in southern China, and the mongooses, *Herpestes edwardsi,* of the Sahara-Oriental region, and *H. auropunctatus,* found from North Africa to Malaysia. The canids are represented by two closely linked species, which often settle a hundred yards from each other, the palearctic red fox *Vulpes vulpes* and the oriental Bengal fox, *Vulpes bengalensis.* Belonging to the species *Canis aureus* is the jackal, abundant everywhere, even in the hearts of large cities, where it quarrels with stray dogs over scraps. Wolves, disappearing all over India, are less common here than formerly. The Indian wolf belongs to the same species as that of all temperate and cold regions, but the desert wolf, sometimes considered the ancestor of the domesticated dog, is thinner, paler in coat and with shorter, sparser fur.

Surprisingly, the greatest collection of aquatic birds in India may be observed only about a hundred miles south of Delhi, on the Ghana reserve, once the private hunting grounds of the

Left: The anhinga or Indian darter (Anhinga melanogaster), *common on lake and river shores of tropical Asia, harpoons small fish with its pointed beak, tosses them into the air, and swallows them as they fall. (Loke Wan Tho)*

Right above: Siberian cranes (Megalornis leucogeranus) *are among many migratory birds that come to pass the northern winter in the more clement climate of Southeast Asia.   Right: The very long claws and nails of the pheasant-tailed jacana* (Hydrophasianus chirurgus) *permit it to run rapidly along on surface plants without sinking. (Both, Peter Jackson: Photo Researchers)*

Maharajah of Bharatpur. Until the last war, the Maharajah customarily invited the most important members of the British colony to his winter hunts. E. P. Gee, outstanding conservationist and photographer of India's animals, declares that it was not uncommon for fifty hunters to kill more than four thousand birds at one shoot.

The bird population reaches its maximum during the winter, when Ghana's waters are the rendezvous for at least twenty species of aquatic birds from Siberia, including fifteen species of ducks and teals, two of geese, one each of pelicans and cranes *(Grus grus)*. The two commonest migrating geese are the greylag and the bar-headed goose *(Anser indicus)*, which nests in Central Asia, western China and Tibet, but turns up in India and Burma beginning in October.

Non-migratory species are equally well represented. Among the reeds, aquatic grasses or stretches of water lilies slip large moorhens *(Gallinula chloropus)*, gallinules *(Porphyrio poliocephalus)*, little grebes *(Podiceps ruficollis)* and longtailed jacanas *(Hydrophasianus chirurgus)*. Wading along the banks or nesting in the trees are painted storks *(Ibis leucocephalus)*, spoonbills *(Platalea leucorodia)*, little egrets *(Egretta garzetta)*, darters *(Anhinga anhinga)*, open-bills *(Anastomus oscitans)*, little cormorants *(Phacrocorax niger)*, sarus cranes *(Grus antigone)*, gray herons *(Ardea cinerea)*, purple herons *(A. purpurea)*, night-herons *(Nycticorax nycticorax)* and, especially among the water-hyacinths, the spotted-billed duck *(Anas poecilorhyncha)*.

The little grebe or dabchick is the best-adapted to aquatic life. It spends all of its time in the water, swimming with its body scarcely visible above the surface, disappearing instantly at the slightest sign of danger, and emerging far from where one would expect. Most of its food, small fish, aquatic insects, plants and mollusks, is captured and consumed underwater. Curiously, its craw is filled not only with the gravel it needs for mastication, but with its own feathers, perhaps also swallowed to help digestion.

The most marvellous spectacle at Ghana is the nuptial dance of the sarus cranes. These great gray birds, with their yellow beaks and red heads, spread their wings and hop about each other, interrupting their dance from time to time with courtly bows. Once mated, they usually remain faithful for life, and if one is killed, the other will hover about for weeks, uttering despairing cries, and according to Indian belief as reported by E. P. Gee, will eventually die of grief. Since sarus cranes are the symbol of happy marriage, they are frequently protected by the natives and often become quite tame and approachable. Their nest is simply a heap of reeds and grass in shallow water.

WILD ASSES AND ASIATIC LIONS

Southeast of the mouth of the Indus lies the peninsula of Gujarat, most interesting to naturalists because of two large mammals, once widely diffused but now reduced to a small number: the wild ass or hemione *(Equus hemionus)* of India and the Asiatic lion.

The wild ass, also seen in Iran and in the Central Asian deserts, was once abundant on both sides of the Indus, but is now found only in an area of northern Gujarat known as the Little Rann of Kutch.

The Great and Little Ranns of Kutch are huge, sometimes muddy salt flats, where travel, often in several inches of salt water, is possible only by horse or camel. Its residents gather the salt in the dry season, and raise herds of lean buffalos and zebus during the rest of the year. When the preceding season's monsoons have been favorable, the more swampy of the two expanses, the Great Rann, is a nesting-place of tens of thousands of flamingos and pink pelicans. As the noted Indian ornithologist, Salim Ali, has observed, the flamingos practice a kind of "baby-sitting," a few adults caring for all the young birds, while the other parents search for food. The pink pelicans have jet-black chicks, in contrast to the white or gray of other species.

The Little Rann is strewn with islets that in the dry season become low hills in an absolutely flat landscape covered only with thorny bushes and a few acacias with twisted trunks. On these island-hills live the wild asses, splendid beasts about four feet tall and much larger than the domesticated kind. In color they are a classic example of natural camouflage: a golden-sand shade, with mane and dorsal stripe of deep chestnut, and white bellies, all blending into the landscape. Before the war, thousands of these animals lived here, but the last Forestry Service census put their present number at 860, a great many having died in 1960 during an epidemic of "surra," a disease of cattle and horses. The natives of the region, Hindus who will not eat meat, do not kill the animals and merely try to frighten them away from crops. They are wily and fleet; a photographer in a car going almost thirty-five miles an hour could barely keep up with them.

As for lions, even those interested in animals will be surprised to learn of their existence in India, for we consider the king of beasts a typically African animal. However, in ancient times, the huge cat lived from Southern Europe through the Middle East and into India. The last European lions probably lived in Greece and they are described by both Aristotle and Herodotus as stealing horses and asses from Xerxes' army in 480 B.C. They apparently disappeared at the beginning of the Christian era. In Palestine they were common enough at this period to be mentioned frequently in the Bible, but were doubtless destroyed during the Crusades. Until the beginning of the twentieth century, a few did survive in the wildest regions of the Tigris and the Euphrates, as well as in western and southern Iran.

In India, lions survived in certain parts of the south and center, but by the beginning of this century they had become isolated in the Forest of Gir and its environs, three hundred lions living in an area of about five hundred square miles. Some naturalists ascribe the decrease in the number of lions as due to its rivalry with the tiger, but tigers prefer damp, cool wooded zones and the lion's favorite habitat is the savanna or dry, brush-covered areas. Again it is man who must be accused. After having destroyed the lions of Southern Europe

Right above: The painted stork or pelican ibis (Ibis leucocephala) *is found on all tropical Asian shores. Except for snapping its mandibles and a raucous groaning, it is surprisingly silent. (E. Hanumantha Rao)   Right: The Indian skimmer* (Rhynchops albicollis) *uses its long lower mandible to capture small fish as the bird flies close to the surface of the water. (Peter Jackson: Bruce Coleman Limited)   Far right: The sarus crane* (Megalornis antigone), *a majestic but friendly bird, is common in India where people consider it a symbol of conjugal fidelity. (E. Hanumantha Rao)*

and the Middle East, he rapidly eliminated those in India, leaving only the few in what had been the private hunting reserve of the Nabobs of Junagadh, the Forest of Gir. The lion is also easier to hunt than the tiger. Often noisy, and preferring open places, he makes himself far more conspicuous than his solitary, nocturnal, silent, forest rival. Where the lion insists on investigating strange noises, the tiger disappears instantaneously. The last survivors in the Forest of Gir are, however, in no danger; in this protected area they are able to breed and increase their numbers.

The lions do not lack prey: nilgais, sambar deer, chitals or spotted deer, wild pigs, gazelles and four-horned antelopes. These strange antelopes *(Tetracerus quadricornis)* are related to the blue-bulls, but, uniquely among the bovidae, have four horns, two in the usual place and two smaller ones above the eyes. They are about the size of a gazelle, very timid, and live in pairs or small herds. They are found only in India and are now rare. Some overzealous animal lovers have suggested that the lions be captured and transported elsewhere, since they menace these four-horned antelopes. Luckily this proposal was not taken seriously; even if we ignore the difficulty of executing such a plan, the antelopes would be no better off since they are in much more danger from the many forest leopards. And lions also need protection. Other nature lovers then suggested saving the lions but killing the leopards, hardly a better idea since leopards kill off foxes, wild dogs, and monkeys, who would otherwise multiply overwhelmingly. As always, it is wise to refrain from interfering with nature's balance without some careful preliminary study.

RED RIVER AND BLUE HILLS

Leaving the arid stretches of the Indus, we follow the Ganges Valley to the pleasant landscape of northern Bengal, or Terai, and of Assam. This area was called the "land of golden gardens" by the Ahom, invaders from Burma, as early as 1228, a name that will seem most apt to anyone who has seen those undulating green hills covered with bamboo thickets, dense forests, and peaks crowned with majestic pines. Garden balsam, rhododendrons, azaleas and wild roses weave a carpet of green dotted with red, orange and mauve on the plateaus. Epiphytes cling to the branches of trees, and lianas with whitish bark hang from every limb. Orchids abound in the forests both on the plains and on the mountains. Perhaps the most highly esteemed is the "kapauphul" *(Aerides odoratum),* one of the rare perfumed orchids. It gives off a subtle odor of honey and is sought by young girls of the mountain tribes who wear it in their long black hair. Another popular flower, a balsam, the "bhatauphal" or parrot-flower, has recurved, red petals that look like a parrot's beak.

Assam and neighboring regions are among the richest in the world in orchids. In little Sikkim alone, E. P. Gee points out, there are more than one thousand species. And it was in northeast India that the famous "lady-slipper" orchid *(Cypripedium fairieanum)* was discovered; exhibited in London in 1857, an effort was made to cultivate the rare flower in a hothouse but it died after twenty years. Searches to discover other specimens began immediately, but no one knew exactly where the first flower had come from. Even though two thousand pounds sterling was offered for the "lost orchid," the entire region was investigated in vain. Then, in 1905, it was found in the eastern hills, at the foot of the Himalayas, at an altitude of about 3,600 feet. This orchid which has so excited horticulturists has petals gracefully lifted around the edges like a ballerina's tutu.

Assam owes its luxuriant vegetation to its climate. The entire region is damp and even swampy in the plains. The rainfall is heavy, ranging between eighty and two hundred inches per year. One of the wettest places in the world is in Assam, at Cherrapunji in the Khasi and Jaintia Hills; it has a mean rainfall of 472 inches a year, and a record of 522 inches.

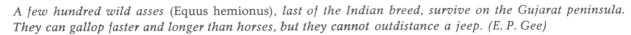

A few hundred wild asses (Equus hemionus), *last of the Indian breed, survive on the Gujarat peninsula. They can gallop faster and longer than horses, but they cannot outdistance a jeep. (E. P. Gee)*

The Asiatic lion, once found as far as Greece, belongs to the same species as the African lion. About three hundred of them survive in the Forest of Gir in Gujart. (E. Hanumantha Rao)

Nevertheless, the climate of Assam is not unpleasant. The summers are short and less oppressive than in other parts of India and start usually in March and end early in June when the monsoon rains begin. The rest of the year is cool or, at least, rarely hot.

The violence of the rains is overwhelming: rivers overflow rapidly, sweep away bridges, carry tons of red earth from the hills, and flood the low plains. This alluvium without doubt gives Assam's greatest river, the Brahmaputra, its Sanscrit name of Lohitya or Red River. (Mythology offers another explanation: after the saint Parasurama had killed his own mother, he washed his blood-stained body in this river to regain his purity, leaving the waters forever red.) Born in western Tibet, where it is called the Tsangpo, it collects several rivers from the Himalayas and the mountain chains of Assam, and then rushes in torrents through the hills and swampy

plains. For Assam is a country of hills and low mountains— the Naga Hills, Mikir Hills, Garo, Jaintia and Khasi Hills— inhabited by primitive Tibeto-Burmese tribes. From afar, these hills, always covered with bluish haze, melt into the blue sky, so that the site of the famous temple of Kamakhya is called *nilachala,* the blue hill.

Unfortunately, the floods often take on the violence of miniature tidal waves, sweeping away forests, crops, and villages, including animals and human beings in a rush of muddy water. Yet, as with the Nile, the fertile mud enriches the soil.

Earthquakes are relatively frequent in the region, and geologists place Assam in the seismic zone that cuts through Asia and joins the one that crosses the Pacific. Two of the five greatest earthquakes in history occurred in Assam, one in 1897 and the other in 1950. The first caused terrible damage

165

The Indian or Bengal tiger, most beautiful of the large cats, has been much reduced in numbers by hunting and the reduction of its commonest preys. (E. P. Gee: The World Wildlife Fund)

and took at least 1,540 lives. The second had the destructive force of several atomic bombs, but its epicenter was luckily in the least populated hills.

At one time, all of Assam, from the foot of the Himalayas to the plains of Bengal, was covered with unbroken forests. These splendid expanses have unfortunately suffered greatly from the burning and other land-clearing activities of the mountain tribes. It is painful to pass a score and sometimes a hundred miles of hillsides bristling with burned stumps among which are some thinly scattered rice fields. Despite this, Assam is still one of the most heavily forested regions of India, since primary vegetation still covers nearly a quarter of the country; it is thereby also the richest and most interesting in its wildlife.

It is in Assam that Indian elephants are still most numerous, and it was here that the technique of capturing and training

wild elephants originated, and was thence diffused to all of Eastern and Southern Asia. One of the first illustrated treatises on the subject, the *Hastividyarnava* or "Art of Elephantology," was written in Assamese in 1734. This art is still much practiced there, and some families of maharajahs specialize in the domestication of elephants. The animals are first forced into enclosures. Then, aided by domesticated elephants trained to squeeze one of the captives between them, astonishingly adroit men slip among the bellowing animals and shackle the captive. Then begins the most difficult part of the training: taming. Each wild elephant is chained between two poles in a standing position for a few days and left without water or food. The poor animal trumpets in a heartbreaking manner. Then, gradually, the trainers give it water and food, hose it down and drive away the tormenting flies. Most elephants so handled grow accustomed to man and after some weeks permit the trainers to touch them. Then the real training begins: obedience to the words and gestures of their "mahout," always the same for each animal, and an apprenticeship in the most varied kinds of work, such as carrying human beings or loads.

Domesticated elephants are astonishingly intelligent and literature abounds in examples of their mental capacities. Several times, while hunting specimens from the back of an elephant, my guide has wounded some game that managed to escape. Our mount immediately took over the trail like a bloodhound, the end of its trunk close to the ground, stopping sometimes to sniff noisily. When it found a leaf or a twig stained with blood, it seized it and passed it up to us over its shoulder, as if to say, "You see, I'm on the right track!"

On another occasion, as I was about to light a cigarette, a rhinoceros charged us. Our mount, a young elephant, became terrified and reared up, trumpeting. I was barely able to hang on to the cord that goes from the neck to the base of the animal's tail, and I dropped my lighter in the tall grasses of the swamp we were crossing. When the "mahout" had calmed his mount, I told him what had happened. He leaned over and said a few words in Assamese to the elephant. She turned and began to snuffle about in the reeds; she rummaged about in this way until I was beginning to be a bit skeptical when, suddenly, she triumphantly brandished my lighter.

Rhinoceroses seem to detest elephants and enjoy charging them. Contrary to what one might think, rhinos do not charge head down and horn forward, but head high and jaws open as if ready to bite the elephant. It always proved to be nothing more than an attempt at intimidation, often by females followed by their young or by males trying to defend their mates. Each time, the rhinoceros stopped short two or three yards from the elephant, and then, after a few snaps of the jaw, turned its back and went off. However, elephants seem terrified by these charges and even mounts long used to such threats betray their nervousness by violent trembling.

THE ARMORED UNICORN

The Indian rhinoceros of Assam belongs to the species *Rhinoceros unicornis,* one of three Asiatic species now tragically becoming extinct, but the one best represented, since about six hundred survive in India and Nepal. This rhinoceros, the largest of Asia, grows to a height of nearly five feet at the shoulder and nearly fourteen feet in length and a weight of two tons. Its one horn, thick and solid at the base, is about eight inches long, but has been known to reach nearly twenty-five inches. Its very thick hide forms great folds on the neck, shoulders, and hindquarters, giving it an armored look like that seen in old illustrations of unicorns, an effect accentuated by rivet-like tubercles or knobs scattered over its body.

Once found on hills and plains from India to Burma, the Indian rhinoceros now lives only in the Rapti Valley, in Nepal, and on a few preserves in Assam and Bengal. There it frequents wooded hills and low river valleys overgrown with tall grasses. The Kaziranga preserve in Assam, typical of the latter type of habitat, shelters most of the rhinos as well as other animals of the region. Bounded on the north by the Brahmaputra River and on the south by the Mikir Hills, the preserve, twenty-five miles long by ten miles wide, is a vast, swampy plain, periodically flooded by the river. It is covered by tall elephant grass *(Erianthus elephantinus),* rushes *(Phrag-*

A few Indian gazelles or chinkaras (Gazella gazella), a graceful, long-legged animal, kin to the Arabian gazelle, live in the arid regions of northwestern India. (Eric Hosking)

mites karka), wild sugar cane *(Saccharum* sp.) and a few scattered trees, notably *Bombax malabaricum, Lagerstroemia flosreginae,* and a relative of the acacia, *Albizzia procera.*

A river winds across the preserve and several ponds hold a great many fish, attractive to fishing birds. Unfortunately, some of the ponds, like river backwaters, are overrun by a South American plant pest, the water-hyacinth *(Eichhornia crassipes).* With its small leaves and pretty blue flowers, this plant, introduced into tropical Asia fifty years ago, has become such a nuisance that an international congress in Ceylon was devoted to controlling it. In some places, the water-hyacinths grow so thickly that irrigation canals, small rivers, and ponds are completely choked and eventually dry up. It proliferates with frightening speed; one plant will spread out over an area nearly six hundred yards square in a few months. Along

A one-horned rhinoceros (Rhinoceros unicornis) *wallows in a swamp choked with water hyacinths in the Kaziranga Reserve on the shores of the Brahmaputra. (Pierre Pfeffer)*

the great rivers, *Eichhornia* forms dense clusters, and fragments, torn off by currents and deposited in the ponds at flood time, displace all other aquatic plants and in many places make navigation impossible. Most animals, moreover, do not much like this plant. Rhinoceroses enjoy rolling in it, but rarely eat it. Only wild and domesticated pigs seem to enjoy it and, in such places as Singapore, the Chinese cultivate it especially for swine.

Kaziranga is the kingdom of the rhinoceros; it is believed to be inhabited by about three hundred of these animals, and they are so accustomed to man that they may be easily observed. The enormous beasts have furrowed the tall grasses with paths from their feeding areas to the mudholes where they bathe during the hot hours of the day and to the places where they habitually leave their excrement. For a long time, the latter places were believed to mark the territorial limits of each animal, such as other beasts have. However, since a rhinoceros has no clearly marked territory, this habit seems simply to be triggered in a rhino by the sight of its own excrement or that of one of its fellows.

The Indian rhino is easily tamed and was used like a tank in the battles between various Indian kingdoms. An iron trident was affixed to the end of the horn to increase its offensive power against soldiers and elephants of war. It is a courageous animal and both elephants and tigers, the two largest beasts of the jungle, give way before it. It is, moreover, much more agile than is ordinarily believed, and can charge at a gallop, jump, stop short, or turn as sharply as a polo pony. Its only enemy besides man is the tiger, which may carry off a newborn calf that has been left by itself. The rhinoceros, incidentally, uses its jaws, not its horn, in fighting, and many of them bear the scars of bites by their fellows. The males sometimes fight between themselves, but when one sees two rhinoceroses chasing each other, it is possibly a female in heat running after a coy male, for it is said that among them the so-called weaker sex makes the choice. Gestation lasts a little more than sixteen months and at Kaziranga births seem to occur mainly in December. The longevity record for a rhinoceros in captivity is forty-seven years, but it is probable that the span will be increased.

BUFFALOS AND BIRDS

Rhinoceroses are the star attraction at Kaziranga, but the preserve swarms with other animal life. The largest of these, after wild elephants and rhinos, are the buffalo and the gaur or Indian "bison."

The Asiatic buffalo or water buffalo *(Bubalus bubalus)* is the same species as the domesticated animal in rice paddies all over tropical Asia. In many regions it is difficult to tell whether buffalos living at large are truly wild or simply feral, but those in Kaziranga have never been enslaved. They are enormous, weighing nearly a ton, and have heavy horns with a span that may reach five feet. Except for a few solitary males, they live in herds, and, as their name indicates, are very fond of wet places. They pass most of the day in the water with only the tops of their heads showing, and dip these, too, below the surface from time to time to chase the tormenting flies. I have counted thirty-five buffalos and twelve rhinoceroses, two of them six-month-old babies, bathing peacefully a few yards apart in a pond full of water-hyacinths.

Many sportsmen would rather hunt the water buffalo than the tiger, as much for the buffalo's horns as for the excitement of its charge. But it has become so rare in India outside the preserves that hunting it is strictly regulated and subject to a tax of about fifty dollars a head.

The gaur or Indian bison *(Bos gaurus)* is even larger than the buffalo, although its weight is about the same. It stands taller and has an enormous dorsal hump, giving it the appearance of a bison and the name by which it is known in India. Rare in such swampy terrain as that bordering the Brahmaputra, it is much more abundant in the open forests of the Deccan and of Indochina. The gayal or "mithun" *(Bos frontalis),* which lives only in Assam and the north of Burma, closely resembles the gaur, the principal difference being that its horns are straight instead of curving inward. Many zoologists consider the gayal merely a local variety of gaur, simply altered by domestication or isolation. It would be interesting to discover whether these two animals live together anywhere, since this would eliminate the isolation theory. Gayals are found only in semidomesticated herds that return regularly to the villages to lick greedily the salt put out for them by the natives.

Although neither of these animals is used for transport or work in the fields or gives milk, possession of them is, among mountain tribesmen, a sign of wealth, as it is in many parts of Africa. They serve as barter money particularly for purchasing wives or they are sacrificed on certain ceremonial occasions. Cross-breeding the gayal and the domestic cow produces animals with white or piebald coats.

There is also an astonishing variety of deer in Assam, including several species already noted in nearby southwest China. The one most prized by hunters is the magnificent sambar, whose horns reach their greatest size in India, with a record of fifty and a half inches. The axis deer or chital is also common, as is the swamp deer or Duvaucel's deer *(Cervus duvauceli),* whose splendid horns branch into fourteen to sixteen antlers, with twenty the maximum recorded. Its Indian name *barasingha* means "twelve points."

Found all over is the muntjac or *kakar,* whose baying signals the approach of a tiger or a leopard. The muntjac may be lured by the nasal sound one can make by blowing on a blade of grass pressed between two thumbs; when expertly

These skinks (Mabuya carinata), *members of a genus found in all tropical Asian forests, live on the ground and feed on butterflies and other insects. (M. Krishnan)*

rendered this can sound like the call of the fawn in distress and adult muntjacs will come to the rescue. This trick is not without surprises, for instead of a deer, a tiger or leopard may appear, drawn by hope of an easy prey.

PARAKEETS AND EXTINCT DUCKS

The visitor to the Kaziranga preserve will be astonished by the richness of its birdlife. Francolins *(Francolinus francolinus)* frequently fly up from beneath the feet of riding ele-

Overleaf: Wild elephants are still numerous because India permits hunting only old rogue males that attack men, and only certain maharajahs are permitted to capture elephants. (W. Suschitzky)

phants, while quail *(Coturnix coromandelicus)* thread their way through the tall grass. Hundreds of rose-ringed parakeets *(Psittacula krameri)* perch in the scattered trees, screech deafeningly and fly abruptly away in multicolored bouquets. It is a rare branch without a purse-shaped nest, product of the industrious weaverbirds *(Ploceus philippinus)*. In the tree-tops, black drongos *(Dicrurus macrocerus)* keep watch, ready to dive upon passing insects, while various species of king-fishers mount guard on the lower branches. While the green pigeons blend into the surrounding foliage, the black and flaming red male minivets *(Pericrocotus flammeus)* stand out strikingly. Red-cheeked bulbuls *(Otocompsa jocosa)* and orange-headed Jerdon's leafbirds *(Chloropsis jerdoni)* are found everywhere; both are very popular singing birds and are widely sold in the markets.

Abounding in the marshy zones are herons of all sorts, sarus cranes and adjutant storks *(Leptoptilos dubius),* the latter with enormous beaks and bald heads and necks. The fluted notes of the warning cry of red-beaked Indian lapwings *(Lobivanellus indicus)* resound constantly while cattle egrets *(Bubulcus ibis)* flutter around the buffalos and rhinoceroses or perch on their backs.

On the rivers it is not unusual to see gray pelicans *(Pelecanus philippensis)* and various species of teals and ducks paddling about. Gone forever, unfortunately, is the pink-headed duck *(Rhodonessa caryophyllacea)*. No specimen has been sighted since the 1950's, despite a search made by the Indian ornithologist, Salim Ali.

But the Ganges and the Brahmaputra still harbor two very special animals, an aquatic mammal, the susu, and a reptile, the gavial. By a strange convergence of evolution, probably due to their similar feeding habits, both are equipped with extremely long narrow jaws, forming a sort of beak with strong teeth.

The susu or Gangetic dolphin *(Platanista gangetica)* is a cetacean related to the whales. When fully adult, it is between six and eight feet long, with the females larger than the males, and some individuals reaching nearly ten feet. It has between 117 and 128 pointed, conical teeth, longer in front than back. The susu seems to be almost blind. But sight would perhaps not be very useful to the animal in the muddy waters of the Ganges, the Indus, and the Brahmaputra, and it probably captures its basic foods, crustaceans and fish, especially catfish living in the mud, by means of its sense of smell. Fishermen hunt this unusual animal with harpoons and nets. It is eaten by certain of the lower castes and many believe that it promotes fertility in women.

This Asiatic representative of the *Platanistidae* has two close relatives in South America, one living in the Amazon, the other in the Rio de la Plata. There is also the Chinese lake dolphin *(Lipotes)* which is found in the Tung Ting Lake in Hunan Province. Such widespread but isolated groups would seem to indicate that these cetaceans were once marine animals and widely distributed. The four surviving species must owe their survival to their adaptation to life in brackish fresh water where the struggle for life is easier than in the sea.

Living in the same waters as the susu is the gavial *(Gavialus gangeticus),* a crocodile that may reach a length of more than nineteen feet. In spite of its size, it does not attack man; it is true that bracelets, necklaces and other jewels are occasionally found in its stomach, but such objects probably come from bodies incompletely burned in funeral pyres on the Ganges' shores.

The gavial's astonishingly long, narrow muzzle is, like that of the platanist, very certainly related to its almost exclusive diet of fish. The sticklike shape of the head enables the gavial to catch fish by an abrupt sidewise movement of the head and jaws. This slender structure also permits it, like the susu, to dig for fish resting in mud. This unusual characteristic of the gavial makes it a replica of the Australian theriosaurus, extinct for more than two hundred million years. Judging from fossils of the theriosaurus, the two reptiles are as alike as two peas in a pod, except that evolution has provided the gavial with nostrils at the end of its muzzle, far more helpful in detecting prey than those of the theriosaurus, which were just below the eyes.

An Indian rhinoceros in the Jaldapara Reserve in western Bengal. Long hunted for use in Chinese pharmaceuticals, only six hundred survive in Nepal, western Bengal and Assam. (H.-E. Tyndale)

Blue Hills and the Heartland Plateau

The Southern Mountains, Deccan and Sundarbans

10 Although lacking the grandeur of the Assam landscape, the Deccan plateau is an extremely picturesque region rising in terraces from the Indo-Gangetic plain to a mean altitude of between twenty-three hundred and thirty-three hundred feet. Geologically very ancient, the plateau is bordered on the north by the Satpura, Vindhya and Maikala mountain chains, characterized by flat summits, while its eastern and western margins are formed by the ranges known as the Ghats, which converge toward the southern point of the peninsula. The entire plateau slopes upward from east to west, the Eastern Ghats rising to an average of 950 feet, whereas the Western Ghats reach a height of 8,647 feet in the Nilgiris or "Blue Mountains."

Although the Deccan is a fairly homogeneous unit in terms of animal life, it may be divided into three large regions differing in climate and landscape.

The western side, including the Western Ghats, the Nilgiris, Anamalais, and Cardamom Hills and the Malabar Coast, has heavy rainfall, with a mean precipitation of over six and a half feet, and the entire region is covered with luxuriant tropical vegetation favorable to a rich wildlife. The eastern side, with the Eastern Ghats and all of the plateau south of the Godavari River, is cut off from the southwest monsoon rains by the wall of the Western Ghats. Thus precipitation varies from year to year and is generally very slight, the mean being twenty to twenty-four inches. Vegetation is stunted, with thorny plants, acacias and jujube trees predominant and with savannas covered by such grasses as *Andropogon* and *Imperata*.

The center of the plateau below the Godavari is well watered, for here the Western Ghats are low enough to permit the passage of the summer monsoon winds. Rainfall does not

The forests of teak (right) or of sal (Shorea) that cover central India form an ideal habitat for such herbivores as these gaurs or Indian bison (Bos gaurus). (M. Krishnan)

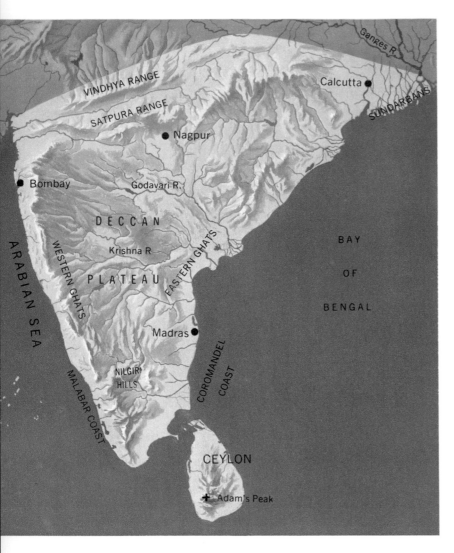

The Deccan is a mountainous triangle bordered on the north by the Indo-Gangetic plain, on the west by the Western Ghats, and on the east by the Eastern Ghats. It is tilted toward the east and all its streams run in that direction.

The region of the Nilgiris, Anamalais, and Pulni Hills, expansions of the Western Ghats, rises abruptly in a succession of plateaus and grassy hills separated by *sholas* or valleys covered by forests with persistent leaves and dense undergrowth. Elephants, gaurs and other large animals dwell in these wooded gorges, as do endemic species such as the Nilgiri langurs, lion-tailed macaques, brown mongooses, Malabar civets and spiny-rats. The high forests of the Nilgiris and Anamalais also present remarkable affinities in plant and animal life with equivalent zones in the hills of Assam and in spurs of the Himalayas. Thus we find the thar there and palearctic forms of the marten and the otter.

One of the characteristics of the entire Deccan is the appearance there of large animals indigenous to India: sloth bears, spotted deer, nilgais, blackbucks and four-horned antelopes, whom we have already met or now see for the first time, while cheetahs and Indian lions lived here before their extermination by man. In addition, most of the five hundred oriental species live in central India also, but since the majority are found as far as Indochina and Malaysia, we shall discuss only those peculiar to the Indian forest.

LORD OF THE JUNGLE

The most representative animal in central India is the tiger, symbol of all the dangers of the jungle and all the flamboyance of hunting for wild animals. The tiger is one of the most beautiful animals in the world and a glimpse of its long, supple, gold and black-striped body slipping silently through the greenery, is one that will never be forgotten.

There was a time when these magnificent beasts were found all over India, but today most of them haunt the broken terrain of low forests that still abound in game. A native of cold regions, as we have seen, the tiger seeks cool, shady places near water in which it can bathe or remain submerged—completely unexpected behavior for a member of the cat family. It begins hunting only at dusk, solitary and silent, and prefers to follow cleared pathways such as the trails of boar, deer, and bovidians, its favorite prey.

The tiger uses its remarkably developed sight and hearing when hunting, but very little of its fairly fine sense of smell; nevertheless, it can follow bait dragged along the forest floor for a considerable distance. Once the game is spotted, the tiger waits until it is within reach or makes the best use of the terrain to approach it. Its ability to blend with a landscape is absolutely uncanny. I once stared for more than five minutes at a low bush in a grassy clearing where I knew that a tiger was hiding but I could not see him until he moved away.

Each tiger has his own territory, and natives who move about a forest know each animal of the sector almost as well as we know our neighbors. Merely by looking at its footprints, they can tell which tiger has passed and describe it so accurately that the beast is recognizable if it is later killed. This territory varies with the terrain and the abundance of game, but, according to George B. Schaller who studied the tigers of

fall below twenty-four inches and generally exceeds thirty-nine in the Maikal chain. The region between Goa, Bombay, Indore, and Nagpur is covered with basaltic lava, contributing to form a black soil famous for the growing of cotton. The entire country consists of low hills covered with monsoon forests strangely like those of temperate lands, with short, low-branching trees that differ sharply from the smooth straight trunks of trees in the equatorial zone. West of a line through Nagpur are volcanic formations covered with forests of teak and composite species, while to the east are forests of *sal (Shorea robusta)* and bamboo, strewn with heaps of crystalline rocks and blocks of sandstone. Here and there, grassy stretches provide excellent pasturage for the large animals of the region.

Gazelles, four-horned antelopes, nilgais, hares, small rodents, Bengal cats, common foxes, mongooses, hyenas, wolves, jackals and leopards live on the savannas. The monsoon forests are more favorable to sambars, gaurs, spotted deer, muntjacs, sloth bears, tigers, and wild dogs. In the wettest region, which benefits from the monsoons from the Bay of Bengal as well as the Arabian Sea, we find, in addition, swamp deer, a few rare buffalos and elephants.

The Indian wild boar (Sus cristata) is more abundant in places where tigers, its worst enemy, have been killed off. (Max Hemple)

176

Unlike most other members of the cat family, the tiger loves to bathe. It always seeks cooler air, withdrawing during the heat of the day to shady thickets. (E. Hanumantha Rao)

the Kanha Reserve, may reach from twenty-five or thirty miles in its largest dimension. The home range of the man-eaters is even larger, and may reach from three hundred to fifteen hundred square miles.

Normally, tigers show the greatest indifference to man. The man-eater is thus almost always physically or psychically abnormal, or it is an animal forced by circumstances to attack prey it generally ignores. The first type are animals weakened either by age or wounds and unable to capture their normal game; frequently these are tigers crippled by gunshot wounds. Other accidents may also affect its hunting habits. For example, tigers adore the flesh of the porcupine, but are so clumsy in killing this rodent that they are often found bristling with barbed quills that cause them great suffering. Jim Corbett, the famous English tiger hunter, tells of killing a man-eating male that was lame because of thirty spines in one paw; and a tigress that had lost an eye and had fifty quills in its shoulder and between the pads of its foot.

The underlying reasons for certain tigers' preference for human flesh sometimes come from their rearing; thus the young of a man-eating tigress may well become man-eaters. Another cause may be natives who habitually chase a tiger from its prey and carry off the quarry, as do some primitive tribes in central India; the animal then may consider man a competitor and attack him without hesitation. Finally, during epidemics of plague or cholera, cadavers lie around the villages, and tigers, who like carrion as well as flesh game, may get into the habit of eating human flesh and may thereafter attack human beings.

THE KINGDOM OF THE MAN-EATERS

In one area of Asia all the tigers are reputedly man-eaters. That is the forests of the countless islets forming the Ganges and Brahmaputra deltas in the west of Bengal. This region, the Sundarbans, is an astonishing example of the adaptation of animal life to exceptional conditions. It is a vast surface of salty swamps, formed mainly by the alluvial deposits of two great rivers. Its tiny islands are in large part covered by spring tides and animals have only brackish, often quite salty, water to drink. Grass grows only on the seacoast or near it, and the ground, usually muddy, resembles a fakir's bed of nails with its dagger-like respiratory roots of mangroves sticking up everywhere.

This habitat would appear completely unsuited to all but such semi-aquatic animals as the marsh crocodile *(Crocodylus palustris)* and the monitor lizard *(Varanus monitor)*. Yet an enormous colony of water birds has been recently discovered here and placed in sanctuary. It has been estimated that during the nesting period from June to August, it will shelter more than fifteen thousand birds. Snakes are also numerous, notably deadly cobras and pythons, and marine crocodiles *(Crocodylus porosus)*, more dangerous than the sharks, abound in the network of canals between the islets.

Inhospitable as this area surely is, a number of large animals have managed to survive in it. The water buffalo and the lesser one-horned rhinoceros *(Rhinoceros sondaicus),* still found in Java, lived in the Sundarbans until their extermination by European hunters at the end of the past century. Boars and spotted deer are common, and the muntjac survives where the water is not too brackish.

Astonishingly, tigers are plentiful in this muddy jungle and it is said that they are all man-eaters. Doubtless this special habitat and the periodic scarcity of large animals, often drowned or carried off by exceptional tides, have forced the tigers to eat whatever is available—fish, crustaceans or reptiles. For a continually underfed tiger, man is evidently a choice morsel, guaranteeing several days of meat; and since the cubs learn about hunting from their mothers, the Sundarbans tigers may all be hereditary man-eaters.

Few people, however, venture into this swampy hell. Woodcutters exploit the mangroves or *sundri* (from which the name Sundarbans comes), and, between April and June, they gather the honeycombs of wild bees *(Apis dorsata)*, which yield more than 440,000 pounds of honey each year. At the same time they also collect such important pharmaceutical plants as *Swertia, Rauwolfia* and *Aconitum*. And the most regular visitors are fishermen who come not only for fish but also for mollusk shells which, ground into lime, they chew with betel.

Aware of the ferocity of the Sundarbans tigers, all these men take extraordinary precautions each time they come. Fishermen remain a safe distance offshore, tying their boats to a root or branch by means of long cords and do all their cooking, eating and sleeping in their craft. But the cunning tigers may spend days waiting for the moment when the men approach the shore to untie the ropes, and then pounce on them.

DOG ROBBERS

The tiger may be disappearing rapidly in India and Asia, but its cousin, the leopard, or panther, still thrives. The leopard has so adapted itself to man's presence that every wooded or rocky hill a few hundred yards away from a dwelling seems to shelter one. It sleeps peacefully during the day in a bamboo thicket or on a rock, waking from time to time to observe its human neighbors at their business. When night falls, the leopard lithely descends toward the village, lit by fires and oil lamps and humming with life. Unlike the tiger, who approaches houses only when driven by hunger, the leopard walks straight into the village, seeking a careless chicken asleep on a low branch, a poorly sheltered goat, or a dog rummaging in the garbage.

The leopard's preference for dogs is well known to natives, and hunters often use dogs as bait in traps or when hunting at night. A leopard will not hesitate to enter a house in pursuit of a dog. A large village dog that had taken a fancy to me usually slept on the veranda of my forest hut, but one night he crawled into my bedroom and under my camp bed, whining piteously. Taking my flashlight, I went outside and saw the phosphorescent reflection of a leopard's eyes not fifty paces from the house. Without doubt, the leopard would have followed the dog, save for the sound of my voice.

Used to prowling around villages at night, a leopard will not hesitate to drag off a sleeping human being, and since they are agile climbers, it is very difficult to be safe from them. With their cunning and their awareness of man's ways, it is also much more difficult to kill off a man-eating leopard than a tiger and some are shot only after months of patient efforts. Luckily, man-eating leopards are very rare.

AN IRRITABLE HONEY-LOVER

The sloth bear *(Melursus ursinus)*, peculiar to India, was once extremely common. Even today, after decimation by hunters, it is found frequently in the more heavily forested areas of the Deccan. A dumpy animal, it measures well over five feet in length and weighs 300 pounds or more. Its body is covered with long black fur, except for a white crescent on the breast. Its long and very mobile muzzle is well adapted to its diet of fruit, honey and the larvae of bees, beetles, white worms and termites. Its favorite fruits are those of the jujube tree *(Zizyphus jujuba)* and the ebony tree *(Diospyros melanoxylon),* the jaman *(Eugenia jambulana)*, the aromatic orange-like bel *(Aegla marmelosa)*, and various species of figs, notably *Ficus indica* and *F. glomerata;* it is also very fond of the pods of the drumstick tree *(Cassia fistula),* the fleshy flowers of the senna *(Cassia latifolia)* as well as the juice of the sugar cane.

The sloth bear's sight and hearing are not remarkable and it therefore relies on its highly developed sense of smell in finding its food. Anyone near a sloth bear as it gathers fruit at the base of a tree can hear it sniffing and huffing noisily about. It can smell a beetle's larva at the bottom of a tunnel two feet deep; it then uses its enormous claws to dig out the morsel. It also extracts termites from their combs by a sucking so violent that it may be heard hundreds of feet away. The sloth bear climbs readily and gathers honeycombs from the tallest trees. Protected from bee stings by its thick fur, it gets rid of bees on its muzzle by huffing and puffing furiously. In the south of India, they regularly raid the jars placed in palm trees to collect the sap used in making palm wine, and according to the natives it is not uncommon to find bears quite drunk and very aggressive as the result of a prolonged drinking bout.

The sloth bear's disposition is unpredictable. In the jungle it may pass a man without turning, or it may fall on him, tear him with its terrible claws or bite him severely. Females followed by their cubs are much more aggressive than males and it is probable that they attack intruders out of a defensive

instinct rather than out of true aggressiveness. They practically never eat meat in the wild, and a man-eating sloth bear is an exception.

The gestation period for the sloth bear lasts seven months and there are usually two in the litter. From the age of two months, the cubs are carried about by the mother, hanging to the long hairs of her back, so that, from afar, a she-bear with its little ones seems huge and hunch-backed. The young follow the mother until they reach adult size at about the age of three. The babies, like all bear cubs, are playful and affectionate.

CARRION-EATERS AND "WOLF-CHILDREN"

Hyenas, jackals, vultures and crows are the jungle's scavengers. Since they immediately take over any prey left uneaten by a large carnivore, a tiger will use leaves and branches to camouflage the remains of a meal and the more agile leopard often hoists leftovers into a tree.

The striped hyena *(Hyaena striata),* whose cry resembles the mocking laugh of its spotted African cousin, grows to a length of five feet and a weight of seventy-five pounds. Hyenas usually go about in pairs, and live in caves, or among piles of rocks, or in porcupine burrows that they enlarge. The hyena is usually despised for its cowardice. Although it has jaws and teeth strong enough to crush the hardest bones, it may flee animals more feeble than itself. On the other hand, it often attacks goats, sheep and any young and defenseless creature. Only the leopard bows before it, abandoning its prey without resistance although the big cat can easily kill a dog the size of a hyena. This relationship is undoubtedly part of the order of nature and seems to be completely accepted by the leopard. Surprisingly, if captured young, the striped hyena becomes as tame as a dog. The one unpleasant feature of this unusual pet is the strong odor secreted by its anal glands.

In the jungle the hyena's tracks, sometimes confused by inexperienced hunters with those of the leopard, may be recognized by the clear imprint of the claws—which is not true of feline tracks—and by the distinctly larger prints of the forepaws. The presence of hyenas is also revealed by their droppings, made up mainly of bone fragments; upon drying these form such indestructible balls that they have been found fossilized in caves once inhabited by prehistoric species.

It was the practice in India to chase the hyena with a pack of dogs and hunting spears. When the hyena realized that it had no chance to escape, it feigned death, letting the dogs bite it until they abandoned it. Dunbar Brander tells of planting a spear in an apparently dead hyena, whereupon it tried to leap up and escape.

Left: Very common in India, more supple than the tiger, and an excellent climber, the leopard is the monkey's great enemy. (Max Hemple)

Right above: The white-backed vulture (Gyps bengalensis) *is a valuable scavenger in Indian cities. It haunts the Bombay Towers of Silence to eat the corpses of followers of Zoroaster. Right: The largest species of tropical Asian mouse deer (Tra-gulus memmina) lives in India. They are timid forest animals no larger than a hare. (Both, M. Krishnan)*

Another "street-cleaner" of India, the jackal *(Canis aureus)* is a species found all over the Middle East to Northern and Eastern Africa. It is a small canine, rarely exceeding twenty pounds or a length of thirty inches. In color it ranges from dun to pale russet, with the hair on its back more or less mixed with black. The jackal is common not only in the forest and in open country, but also around villages and large cities. On occasion, I have seen them even in the streets of Karachi, capital of Pakistan. The night echoes with their howls and strident barks when a number of them crowd around the carcass of a cow or buffalo. The jackal's cry as it searches for a carcass is familiar to anybody who has ever camped in the wilderness: a long ululation repeated three or four times on a note that becomes sharper and sharper, followed by a series of three barks also repeated three or four times. Hunters say the jackal is crying, "Dead Hindu! Where? Where? Where?," an accurate if rather sinister transcription of the cry.

Another familiar canine of central India, especially in open country, is the little Bengal fox *(Vulpes bengalensis)*. During night hunts by lamplight, one sees greenish eyes moving along at ground level on all sides and after a while discerns an animal with a long, low body, a pointed muzzle topped by big ears, a fluffy tail and small, rapidly moving feet that seem to glide rather than run. This fox is thirty inches long, but the tail takes up more than a third of this, and an adult rarely weighs more than six or seven pounds. In India one sees them all along the roads and in the fields. They feed on small reptiles, frogs, insects, and rodents and also like fruits, especially the very refreshing berries of the jujube.

Wolves, once as abundant in India as foxes, are today rare. Their disappearance seems puzzling since they have never been especially hunted; it is probably due to the decrease in the game they feed on, or perhaps to such diseases as rabies, very widespread in these regions.

When wolves were still common, they were regularly accused of carrying off village children and rearing them with their own offspring. These stories seem to be supported by the discovery of abandoned children who were unable to talk and who walked on all fours. Kipling's tale of Mowgli has contributed greatly to this belief. But all these stories of "wolf-babies" are pure fantasy and simply describe abnormal or retarded children, abandoned by their parents because life is so difficult in India. Even if a she-wolf were inclined to adopt a baby and could drag a child to its lair without harming it, it would be unable to nurse it for more than six to eight weeks, the normal lactation period for a she-wolf. And it is difficult to imagine a human nursling able to eat the game furnished by a wolf mother.

The wild dogs or dholes, found all over central India, chasing in packs after prey, are neither true dogs nor wolves, since they have two, and not three, molars on either side of the lower jaw. They are thus separately classified in the genus *Cuon.* We will discuss them when we meet them shortly in Southern and Eastern Asia.

MISCHIEVOUS AND SACRED MONKEYS

Monkeys abound in India, both in the country and in the crowded cities, where human beings treat them with respect or indifference. They are represented by two large groups: the macaques and the langurs.

The various macaques are distinguishable only by such minor characteristics as the length of the tail or the arrangement of hair on the head or cheeks. The only distinctive one is the lion-tailed macaque *(Macaca silenus)* of the Western Ghats, which is all black except for an abundant whitish-gray mane encircling its head and a rather short tail ending in a whitish tuft. All other monkeys of this group are tawny-brown, or occasionally grayish, with light-colored, often flesh-pink faces. This group, and most of all the rhesus macaque, furnishes not only the majority of monkeys in laboratories but in zoos or animal shows. Although they are rather bad-tempered, particularly as they age, they are frequently kept on verandas or tied to a stake, with an empty packing-case serving as a kennel. They are intelligent and easily learn all kinds of amusing tricks. Although the Hindus do not consider them sacred, they respect them as they do all living creatures. The macaques, however, take advantage of this, displaying no regard for their protectors and doing serious damage. For example, while I was visiting a government office in Calcutta, a band of macaques burst in through the windows and scrambled over the desks, tearing up papers, and knocking over inkwells and cups of tea: nobody dared to protest.

These macaques live so intimately with man that they are rarely found in the forest except in places where there are remains of forts or temples. During the epoch when the temples were in use, the monkeys probably lived there with the human occupants and continued to do so after the buildings had been abandoned. They eat grass and fruits, and pick up beetles and grasshoppers. They take fresh-water crabs and shrimps along streams and cross water without hesitation, for they are excellent swimmers.

If macaques may be considered the Asian counterpart of the African baboons, then the langurs are the counterpart of the *Colobus* monkeys. Their digestive system, with a stomach divided into three parts, not unlike that of ruminants, is adapted to a strictly vegetarian diet of leaves, young shoots and occasionally fruit. The best-known of the Indian langurs, the sacred langur *(Semnopithecus entellus)* or hanuman (so called after the monkey-god of Hindu mythology) is a large, beautiful animal, with long silky gray, brown or golden fur framing a bare, black-skinned face and shining brown eyes. It is found in the most remote parts of the jungle, if there is water nearby, as well as in temples and villages, usually on the banyan tree at the center of every Indian town. No monkey is easier to observe, and American anthropologist Phyllis Jay has studied forty troops in various villages of central India.

Like all the higher primates, langurs are well developed socially and live in groups of from five to one hundred and twenty with about twenty-five the mean: these groups remain stable for as much as a year. A langur group often admits a few rhesus macaques as temporary or permanent members without the least sign of discord between the two species.

Right above: The blackbuck (Cervicapra cervicapra), *long hunted by maharajahs using trained cheetahs, has almost disappeared from India, its only habitat. (W. Suschitzky) Right: The chital or spotted deer* (Cervus axis) *is still fairly common in certain reserves, especially in Kanha, in southern India, where about a thousand survive. (Max Hemple)*

THE DEER OF KANHA

Buffalos are rare in the Deccan, but gaurs are more abundant than in Assam since they prefer a forest broken by clearings or by savannas of short grass. They are even more numerous in Indochina, where we shall find them living with two other large bovidians, the banteng and the kouprey.

The deer family, although the primary victims of hunting by headlights, are still comparatively numerous in this region. The largest, the sambar, measures five feet high at the shoulder and seven feet in length. Males weighing six hundred pounds are not unusual and Dunbar Brander killed one weighing seven hundred pounds, including one hundred and ten pounds of entrails. The record length for their antlers is slightly more than four feet, but any trophy over forty inches is considered good.

Most sambars lose their antlers at the end of March or the beginning of April and begin to grow them again a few weeks later, being "in velvet" from the beginning of the rainy season. Since the horns are at this time very sensitive to a blow, the animals avoid the wooded areas and keep to grassy clearings. When the antlers reach full growth in October, the deer clean them of dead skin by rubbing them against tree trunks, especially that of the incense tree *(Boswellia serrata).*

In discussing Assam, we mentioned the barasingha or swamp deer, called Duvaucel's deer by zoologists. In central India the name swamp deer is misleading since this area has no such swamps as occur in the humid zone at the foot of the Himalayas. The barasingha is in fact no more dependent on water than other Indian deer and it requires only plains or grassy clearings. It rarely penetrates the forests that cover the hills, preferring their borders.

Once widespread, the barasingha now lives only in the most remote localities. They may also be found in the Kanha National Park. This ninety-seven square-mile reserve in the heart of the undulating, forested hills of the Satpura chain has exactly those *maidans* or grassy stretches the barasingha prefers. And Kanha's central plain is certainly by far the Indian area richest in the variety of herbivorous and carnivorous animals. Besides Duvaucel's deer, there are spotted deer, blackbucks, gaurs, tigers, leopards, wild dogs, and many smaller animals here. The animals flee at the sight of a man on foot, but it is possible, as in Africa, to approach very close to them in a car. This lack of fear of vehicles together with the hypnotic effect of headlights has made the animals the easy victims of unscrupulous hunters using jeeps. Figures recently published by the American ecologist George B. Schaller, well-known author of the *Year of the Gorilla,* show that in 1964 Kanha harbored between 900 and 1,000 spotted deer, 200 to 300 sambars, 75 barasinghas, about 125 barking deer, 100 four-horned antelopes, 20 blue bulls, 18 blackbucks, about 150 wild pigs and from 165 to 210 gaurs. The park supported from 10 to 15 adult tigers all or part of the time, and very few leopards and wild dogs. The spotted deer or chital is thus the most abundant; it is also the most graceful of all the cervidae and certainly the most common of them in India.

The Indian varan or monitor lizard (Varanus monitor), *sometimes more than five feet long and an excellent climber and swimmer, feeds on carrion, small mammals and birds. (M. Krishnan)*

The sloth bear (Melursus ursinus) *feeds mainly on termites that it extracts from their mounds with its long tongue or sucks in with its lips pursed. (Max Hemple)*

Besides Ceylon, where it was probably introduced by man, it is found only in India. It is the third largest of the peninsula's cervidae, measuring three feet high and weighing 190 pounds, and its three-pronged antlers are usually about thirty inches long. Its white-speckled bright russet coat has a wide black dorsal band bordered by two lines of white dots, and a large white patch forms a kind of bib at the base of the neck, contrasting sharply with the deep color of the chest.

Unlike some deer, chitals are gregarious all year round, living peacefully together in great herds of males, females and young. Because they are very prolific, they have been more successful than other Indian deer in withstanding destructive forces. The female usually has two and sometimes three young at a time, and mates again six months after she has whelped. Yet they are easily killed because they do not fear man and

even more because they go foraging during the day, unlike most other hunted animals. They also have other enemies: the tiger, the leopard, the marsh crocodile and the wild dog, as well as the hyena and the jackal, who kill the fawns.

PRIMITIVE MONKEYS AND GIANT SHREWS

We have space enough here to discuss only those medium-sized and small animals of the central Indian jungle that are found only in India or are most typical of the country.

Perhaps the strangest of these is an archaic primate, one of two representatives in Asia of the Lorisoids. This strange little creature, the slender loris *(Loris gracilis),* found only south of the Godavari River in India and on Ceylon, is like a little

185

plush bear with an owl's head. Its thin body, covered with short gray fur, stands no more than six inches tall, but it has equally long arms and legs that end in hands with slender fingers that seem uncannily human. Its enormous head is dominated by immense round eyes that are set close together and peer nearsightedly under lids that blink constantly during the daylight hours. A nocturnal animal, the slender loris is not very well known. It is strictly a tree-dweller and feeds on young shoots, leaves, some fruits, insects, eggs or baby birds and small lizards. Natives say it loves wild bees' honey, the sweet sap of certain trees and the nectar of flowers of the coral tree.

It moves slowly, as if weighing each movement, but it can seize an insect with astonishing rapidity. It is hopelessly clumsy on the ground and sways constantly from side to side as if about to fall. Because of its large eyes and the capacity of its pupils to dilate, it moves about in the dark with ease, but during the day it sleeps in a hole in a tree or, as it clings to a branch, rolled into a ball with its head between its legs.

Among the small animals that a visitor sees from the first, we must not forget little striped squirrels or palm squirrels *(Funambulus palmarum)*, found only in India and Ceylon. They are abundant everywhere: in open spaces as well as in city gardens. In the forest there is another variety, also striped, but of a slightly darker hue. A third smaller than European red squirrels, they are usually sandy or grayish, with a brown, sometimes nearly black, back displaying three longitudinal white bands. Another species, *Funambulus pennanti*, has five stripes, lives in the same regions and has the same habits. Constantly in movement, whether on the ground, in trees or on roofs, they are so tame that they run into houses and climb on the tables looking for a choice morsel. Their cry, similar to the "chirp" of domestic sparrows, is part of the sound effects of Indian gardens and is hushed only during the mid-day heat.

The most spectacular of the many squirrels of central India is the giant or Malabar squirrel *(Ratufa indica)*. Nearly forty inches long, this beautiful animal's body is a bright brown and black, its belly is beige and its tail almost black. It is found in all the forests of the peninsula, where it lives in tall trees and comes down only to drink. It builds a large nest of leaves and branches and bears from two to five young. When captured young, they become very tame and can be handled without danger despite their impressive teeth. Two that I brought to the Paris zoo have been living there for nine years.

Among India's tree-dwelling rodents is the Malabar dormouse *(Platacanthomys lasiurus)*, found only at an altitude of almost 2,000 feet in the hills of Travancore. Analogous to the European dormouse, it is a small animal, no more than eight inches long, with a reddish-brown back, a white belly, and a long fluffy brown tail. It lives only in large trees, in which it digs holes that it fills with leaves and moss. It feeds on seeds and fruits, notably of varieties of *Artocarpus*.

Surely the most bizarre animal in Indian homes, one that would horrify a Western housewife, is a musk shrew. On the evening of my arrival in a forest bungalow in central India, I saw a rat-sized shaggy-haired cylinder with a long pointed

Although not venerated like langurs, bonnet macaques (Ma-caca radiata) are respected in India and boldly pillage harvests and steal everything within their reach. (M. Krishnan)

187

snout and a rat tail slip into my bedroom. When I called the caretaker and protested, he said, "Don't be disturbed sahib, it's only a muskrat. There's always one in the house." I realized then that the object of my disgust was a large house shrew, incorrectly called "muskrat" because it gives off a strong odor. Its name is musk shrew *(Suncus caeruleus)* and it is, like all shrews, insectivorous. It is a welcome nocturnal guest in every Indian house, for it chases the enormous, swarming tropical cockroaches and all other vermin, including scorpions and rats. It is nearly ten inches long, half of which is tail, and has highly developed side glands from which drips the characteristic musky odor.

To litter, these shrews make a nest of straw, leaves and other debris inside a burrow or similar shelter. Two or three little ones are born at one time and they soon follow their mother, hanging on tightly with their teeth to the tail of the one in front.

BIRDS AROUND MAN

The Indian peninsula, as the largest part of tropical Asia, has an extraordinarily rich bird fauna. Of the 25,000 known species and subspecies of birds in the world, it has more than twenty-four hundred, with less than five hundred of them winter migrants from the north.

Like the mammals, the bird population of the entire eastern region is extremely homogeneous and, with a few exceptions, the commonest birds in each area generally belong to the same genera but are represented by different species and races. We will here focus only on those birds peculiar to a region or among the most common in it. Even the least observant visitor is immediately struck by the teeming abundance of a few species closely associated with man and lumped together as "carrion-eaters": crows, vultures and kites.

The common crow *(Corvus splendens)* is probably the boldest and yet wariest of all Indian birds. It is at home everywhere, in cities as well as villages, constantly looking for something to eat, which means everything from carrion and garbage to small animals and nestlings. Its close kin, the jungle crow *(Corvus macrorhynchos)* may also be found in the cities and villages but prefers the forests. It is equally undiscriminating in its eating habits.

Around carrion we generally also find vultures. The most common and most repugnant-looking of these is probably *Neophron percnopterus,* called Pharaoh's chicken, a bird about the size of a large hen, usually a dirty white color and with a bald head as yellow as its beak. In places, the Bengal vulture *(Pseudogyps bengalensis)* is even more abundant. It is larger, and blackish brown, with a large white band on the back and a naked head and neck. The king vulture *(Sarcogyps calvus)* is a little less common than the other two and rarely gathers in such great numbers around the prey. It is the size of a goose, almost entirely black, with a naked crimson head and neck and crimson legs. Despite their ugly appearance and the scorn they evoke, vultures have a particularly useful function in a country such as India where sewers are practically nonexistent. By rapidly eliminating wastes and car-

A troop of sacred monkeys or langurs (Presbytis entellus) *can be found in the central square or the customary banyan tree of almost every Indian village. (M. Krishnan)*

casses, they help clean villages and limit the spread of many diseases.

Also among the scavengers are the kites, which immediately attract attention by their numbers and their daring aerial acrobatics among tangles of electric wire, fences and other city obstacles. The most common in populated areas is the pariah or migrator kite *(Milvus migrans)*, of which two races are seen in India. It feeds mainly on wastes, whereas the Brahminy kite *(Haliastur indus)*, found in harbors and along rivers, prefers dead fish.

Luckily for bird lovers, the carrion-eaters are not the only birds around man's communities. Streets and gardens are lively with other winged visitors, some noisy and turbulent, others so quiet that most people are unaware of their presence. Among the noisy, the domestic sparrow, the common myna and the pink-collared parakeet are certainly most widespread in the cities and villages. The sparrow *(Passer domesticus)*, differing from the European race only in its white cheeks, is considered almost as much of a plague as the rat. It gets into everything, pillaging and soiling provisions, boldly putting its nest in the most improbable places and waking the people at dawn with its quarrelsome cries.

Despite its common name, the yellow-throated sparrow *(Gymnorhis xanthocollis)* is not really a sparrow. Although not quite so domesticated as the other, it is found all over the country, as it is in Persia and Afghanistan, and often nests in gardens, preferably in a hole in a tree or in an abandoned woodpecker or parakeet nest. It generally collects in sizable groups in rice paddies, on grassy savannas or in villages.

The common myna *(Acridotheres tristis)* is a starling with bright yellow legs and beak, purplish-brown plumage that is almost black on the back and a large white patch showing on the wings during flight. With rapid, confident steps, it moves about in pairs or small groups, looking for anything edible: insects, worms, refuse, fruits, seeds and even very small animals. Despite its Latin name, doubtless a reference to its plumage, the myna is not at all sad. Constantly on the move, it is very noisy and always ready to fight to defend its living space. Man has carried it, like the sparrow, into several islands in the Indian and Pacific oceans, where, with no natural rivals, it has rapidly increased and become a pest, as it also has on Tahiti.

The common myna often associates with the crested myna *(Temenuchus pagodarum)*, which is distinguishable by its long, full black crest. Not quite as man-loving as the common myna, it may live far from human habitations, for it likes open spaces; but the lawns of public squares and gardens suit it perfectly.

Since the dull plumage of sparrows and mynas hardly corresponds to our idea of exotic birds, the western traveler to India is pleasantly surprised to see hundreds of green parakeets flying about rapidly and chattering shrilly. Of the three species found all over India and Ceylon, the most common is the Alexandrine parakeet *(Psittacula krameri)*, often exported as a cage bird. Nearly fifteen inches long, three-quarters of its length being tail, it is almost entirely a delicate green, with a bright red beak, a pink collar on the male, and blue on the

Macaques are even more closely linked than langurs to man's settlements. When they are found in mid-forest, it is in abandoned temples overgrown with vegetation. (W. Suschitzky)

189

The Indian pangolin or scaly anteater (Manis crassicaudata) *eats only termites, using its long, sticky tongue to reach far into their galleries. (M. Krishnan)*

underside of its tail. Parakeets, like most birds of this family, are normally tree-dwellers but adapt perfectly to any other place and may be seen in gardens and on sidewalks. They usually waddle clumsily because of their long tails and short legs with two claws pointing forward and two back. This arrangement, peculiar to climbing birds, makes them extremely adroit on trees and telegraph wires, and it permits them, like all parrots, to carry their food to their beaks as if using a hand. Their flight is astonishingly swift and one may see them in the evening gathering in noisy bands all moving toward the trees they have chosen for sleeping. The cry of these parakeets is usually piercing and fairly unpleasant, but when the male courts his mate he emits a musical warble while scratching the top of her head and "kissing" her on the beak.

The two other species of parakeets common in the parks and on city trees are the large Indian parakeet *(Psittacula eupatria),* distinguished from the smaller bird by its size, nearly twenty inches, and the blossom-headed parakeet *(P. cyanocephala),* recognizable by the purplish tint of the top of its head. These two species are also very common in India as caged birds. They become very tame and can learn to pronounce a few words, but do not reach the vocal mastery of true parrots.

GARDEN BIRDS

A great many birds, not so closely linked to man as these, enjoy parks and gardens where lawns, flower beds and fruit and ornamental trees supply them with an abundance of foods. It was thus that Malcolm MacDonald, a British High Commissioner to India and a reputable ornithologist, was able to observe 136 species of birds in his New Delhi garden, including thirty that built nests before his eyes. In the introduction to his book *Birds in My Indian Garden* he wrote: "Some of Delhi's species are as beautiful as any to be found

in the world, for they include exquisite creatures like golden orioles, Indian hoopoes, white-breasted kingfishers, blossom-headed parakeets, blue-tailed bee-eaters, green pigeons, white-eyes, yellow wagtails and golden-backed woodpeckers. Although my garden has no sheet of water except a small goldfish pond, river birds like terns, lake birds like darters and cormorants, and swamp birds like egrets, herons, storks and ibises, often fly above its lawns. My visitors run the whole gamut of sizes from gigantic sarus cranes and griffon vultures to diminutive whitethroats and Hume's leaf warblers; and they include birds who build many varied types of nest—a slim platform of sticks plaited by ring doves, a wondrously suspended globe of grasses woven by purple sunbirds, a hole in a wall sparsely furnished by spotted owlets, two leaves firmly stitched together by tailor birds, or a hammock slung across the forked branch of a tree by a pair of black drongos."

We must content ourselves with describing only the most common, most spectacular or otherwise outstanding birds of such gardens. Among the most remarkable are the bulbuls whose roulades and trills, frequently melodious, are heard from the break of day on. This large family is typical of the Orient, even though a great many are also found in Africa. They range from the size of a finch to that of a blackbird, are generally drab in color and sometimes wear a crest. Although mainly fruit-eaters, they also consume insects. The most common in gardens are the red-vented bulbul *(Molpastes cafer),* the white-cheeked bulbul *(M. leucogenys)* and the red-whiskered bulbul *(Otocompsa jocosa).* The first is probably the most popular bird in India and a prized cage bird because of its song and its vivacity as well as the ease with which it is tamed. It is often used as a fighting bird and large amounts are wagered on its contests. Sometimes great numbers of these bulbuls gather to pilfer the fruits of banyan trees or to capture winged termites preparing to begin their nuptial flight. The white-cheeked bulbul descends only as far south as central India but ranges north into the Himalayas, especially to Kashmir, where it is a familiar visitor in houses and on houseboats. The red-whiskered bulbul is found all over India and as far south as the Andaman Islands, where it fills the niche that the domestic sparrow would occupy.

A relative of the bulbuls, the black-winged or common iora *(Aegithina tiphia),* is also frequently found in gardens. The size of a sparrow, it has a greenish-gray back and black wings with white bars, while the lower part of its body is bright yellow. Found, like the other ioras, throughout tropical Asia, this little bird is notable for its nuptial display. The male soars into the air and then lets itself fall in a spiral, ruffling its feather until it resembles a ball. As it descends, it emits a strange little song, more like that of a cricket or a cicada. When it regains its perch, it fans out its tail like a peacock and lets its wings fall while continuing its song.

Although the bulbul's song brightens Indian gardens from morning to night, it does not match that of the dyal *(Copsychus saularis).* A black and white bird of the thrush family, the dyal, also called a magpie robin, prefers well-kept lawns where it hops about like a robin. The warm air of sunrise and sunset vibrates with its clear, whistling song, into which this talented mimic sometimes blends such familiar sounds as the creaking of a door or the meowing of a cat.

The Indian robin *(Saxicoloides fulicata),* akin to the dyal, has nothing in common with the European robin. It gained its name because it, too, is marked by a mixture of boldness and

An adult male gaur with its bison-like dorsal hump is an imposing animal that may stand almost six feet high at the shoulder and weigh nearly a ton. (M. Krishnan)

timidity, hopping on people's feet if no attention is paid it, but disappearing at the slightest approach. Its song is not comparable to the dyal's and adds up to a feeble melody offered by the male during courtship.

The song of the oriole *(Oriolus oriolus),* by contrast, is resonant and tuneful, but one gets few chances to see this golden-feathered bird since it remains in the tallest garden trees, rarely descending to the ground or to low branches. Although it is widely distributed in Europe, Africa and Asia, it is mentioned here because it is so common in Indian gardens. It arrives when the mangos begin to ripen and since it likes these trees, Indians often call it the "mango bird." Its nest is a skillfully woven ball, usually placed so that no climbing animals, with the possible exception of tree snakes, may reach it.

Another garden guest, also widely distributed and represented in India by both a migratory and a sedentary race, is the hoopoe *(Upupa epops).* Recognizable by its long, curved beak and a fan-shaped crest that it raises and lowers as does the cockatoo, it is also remarkable for its cry, a flutelike *hoo— poo—poop.* In spite of its short legs, the hoopoe runs rapidly along the ground, turning over leaves and vegetable detritus

with its beak in its search for worms and caterpillars. It sets up its nest in a hole in a tree and since, unlike other birds, the female never cleans it even while rearing the young birds, the nest soon gives off a most unpleasant odor.

Pigeons and turtledoves also flock to the gardens to nest. The most common of these is the rock pigeon *(Columba livia),* also found in Europe and the Middle East, the ancestor of all domesticated races. It occurs everywhere in India that buildings or rocky cliffs provide nesting places. Most Indians respect these birds and in many large cities there are places where people may bring offerings of grain to the birds in the hope of having a wish come true. Consequently, they sometimes multiply rapidly and do great damage in the fields.

The most familiar turtledoves are the little, brown dove *(Streptopelia senegalensis),* the collared dove *(S. decaocto),* and the spotted dove *(S. chinensis).* The brown dove is the boldest and does not hesitate to enter houses in the hope of gleaning a few grains of rice or crumbs of bread. Its nest is a simple platform of interlaced twigs, occasionally covered with a few blades of grass and some feathers.

Thus far we have mentioned only the most showy birds, but a host of timid little species fidget about in the trees and

191

bushes of India's gardens. Because of Kipling's tales, one of the most popular is the tailor-bird *(Orthotomus sutorius)*, a small, restless bird, greenish-olive on top, whitish below, and with two long tail feathers carried high. Its cry is a gay *tweet-tweet-tweet*, uttered at short intervals as it chases insects in the low bushes. The nest that gives these birds their name is placed less than forty inches from the ground. It is a cup of thin cotton or wool fibers, placed in a funnel made of two or three large leaves folded upon each other and carefully stitched together along the edges.

FIELD BIRDS

Around the villages and farms and on grassy plains with a scattering of palm and kapok trees, the visitor's attention is drawn to dozens of artfully woven peglike structures hanging neck downward from the trees. These are the nests of baya weavers *(Ploceus philippinus)*. It is one of the most familiar field birds throughout most of tropical Asia, but many people confuse it with the sparrow. For, like many birds of its family, this weaver shows two sorts of plumage: the dull mantle ordinarily worn by both sexes and the brilliant golden yellow, with a black mask on the sides of its head and breast, acquired by the male during the rainy season and as the courting period approaches.

This nuptial plumage depends on the pituitary secretions which are related to the duration of daylight. Male weavers exposed to the long days and short nights of summer rapidly change into their brilliant plumage.

The nest of a weaver is made of grasses and leaves, chiefly those of the banana or palm tree. Nothing is more interesting than the way this bird prepares its building material. The bird first slashes the edge of a leaf; then, holding this edge in its beak, it flits up and back along the leaf, detaching a long ribbon that floats in the wind behind it.

The establishment of a colony of weavers is hardly haphazard. The Indian ornithologist Salim Ali has given us a vivid description of the process. First, each of the "bachelor" males, arriving in nuptial plumage, chooses a branch and constructs a nest. The females then visit all the nests without paying the slightest attention to the wooing of the males. Astonishingly, it is only after she has chosen a nest that the female accepts the male who built it, which seems to indicate that she is marrying him only for his apartment. As soon as the female is ready to hatch the two or three eggs she normally lays, the male begins to build another nest; and if that one is chosen by another female, he may very well build a third.

The manyar weavers *(Ploceus manyar)* found all over India, Ceylon and Java, and the Bengal weavers, found only in the northern half of the Indian peninsula, have almost the same habits as the baya weavers. However, their colonies are smaller, usually only half a dozen nests set up along streams bordered with reeds and tall grasses. Their nests are heavier than those of the bayas and, instead of being attached to the branch at only one point, are fastened by many grassy fibers spreading out in all directions.

The sambar (Cervus unicolor) *is the largest tropical Asian deer. Its horns, which may be over four feet long, are prized trophies. (M. Krishnan)*

The giant squirrels of India, Indochina and Malaya measure nearly forty inches in overall length. The Indian race (Ratufa indica) *is usually brown on the back and cream underneath. (M. Krishnan)*

All the weavers normally feed on grass seeds and sometimes do considerable damage to rice or millet crops. However, they compensate for this by their huge consumption of caterpillars and insects during the breeding period, for, like most seed-eaters, the young must be nourished with insect foods.

In the fields and the grassy savannas, one often sees flocks of very small birds with conical beaks and variable plumage. Of the same family as the weavers, these are mannikins and avadavats, captured in droves with nets and exported all over the world under various fanciful names, in France the name *bengalis* being often used for the birds from Africa as well as India.

The insect-eaters found in the unsheltered regions are chiefly the pipits, chats, flycatchers, bee-eaters, drongos, warblers and

shrikes of all sorts—birds that are so much a part of the tropical Asian landscape that we shall have occasion to mention them repeatedly.

The wealth of birds, hares, ground-squirrels, rodents and reptiles of all kinds in the open spaces attracts many birds of prey: buzzards, harriers, falcons, kestrels and owls, including both sedentary species and winter migrants from Central Asia and Siberia. Along the streams, one may see, aside from the eternal fishing kites, occasional ospreys and, at night, great horned owls.

JUNGLE BIRDS

After seeing the swarms of birds in India's open spaces, an observer will be surprised by the stillness of the forests. This absence of life is only apparent for in number and variety of birds the Indian jungle is one of the richest in the world. The birds are simply not so uniformly distributed through the forest as on the savannas and in farm areas. The density of the forest populations depends on such factors as available food, type of soil, vegetable cover, presence of water and natural clearings, the flowering and fruiting of certain plants and the hatching or invasion of insects.

Thus one may cross vast stretches of forest without seeing a single bird and then suddenly come upon quantities of them. The best way to observe such birds is to sit quietly on the edge of the jungle or in a cleared place, preferably early in the morning or fairly late in the afternoon. Soon whistling and chirping bands of little birds will be seen passing from one tree to another, examining leaves and bark in a hunt for caterpillars and insects. The "hunting parties" may be composed of birds of one species, like the babblers who travel about in groups of a dozen, or they may be made up of various species. Such mixed groups may include as many as fifty birds belonging to such markedly different species as tits, warblers, creepers, nuthatches, flycatchers, drongos, minivets, hunting cissas and even woodpeckers. Far from being rivals, the members of these strange associations assist each other like hunters beating the brush together. Insects set flying by the warblers and tits are captured in flight by flycatchers and drongos, while those dislodged by woodpeckers and nuthatches are seized by tree creepers or tits. Each species tends to specialize in its prey, some preferring smooth caterpillars, some hairy ones, others seeking flies or small beetles, or perhaps ants and larvae living under bark.

Left: This curious tandem formation of striped palm squirrels (Funambulus palmarum) *is one of a series of equally unusual groupings photographed near Delhi. (E. Hanumantha Rao)*

Right above: The rose-winged parakeet (Psittacula torquata) *lives in large flocks in forests, in fields, where it does much damage, and in cities. Captive birds become tame but do not talk. Right: The baya weaver-bird* (Ploceus philippinus), *common in tropical Asia, lives on plains or cultivated fields and hangs its long, purse-shaped grass nest from tree branches. Far right: The Indian tree-pie* (Dendrocitta vagabunda) *lives everywhere south of the Himalayas. It comes down to earth only to drink and to hunt caterpillars and lizards. (All, E. Hanumantha Rao)*

194

Flowering trees, especially the erythrine or coral tree *(Erythrina)*, the tulip tree *(Bombax)*, the "forest flame" *(Blutea frondosa)* and the *Grevillea*, also attract many birds to their sugary nectar and to the insects found around their flowers. We have already met most of these birds, and we will meet the others in Indochina and Malaysia. One of them, however, the talking myna, is worth a moment's notice for it is exported to Europe and America as a fairly expensive pet. The size of a large thrush, jet black except for a bright yellow beak, legs, and a bare fold of skin on the head, the myna is highly regarded for its powers of imitation. Not only can it imitate human speech better than most parrots, but it can also reproduce such different sounds as the meowing of a cat and the ringing of a telephone.

When certain wild fig trees bear fruit, they become gathering places for a great variety of birds, especially green pigeons, fruit pigeons and barbets. Many types of green pigeons are found in tropical Asia; usually small or medium-sized, they have predominantly pastel green plumage often set off with pinks, yellows and soft grays. This plumage and their habit of remaining perfectly still camouflages them, and a hunter who fires a gun is often astonished at the dozens of birds that take flight. Fruit pigeons are very large birds with ash gray plumage and metallic green wings. Throughout tropical Asia, forests resound to their raucous cooing in the evenings. Their weight, about two pounds, and their delicate flesh make them excellent game, but they remain in the tops of the tallest trees and are usually difficult to approach.

With their thick strong beaks, barbets faintly resemble woodpeckers, but they are not members of the same family and they eat fruit rather than insects. They range in size from that of a sparrow to that of a thrush, and their plumage is almost entirely green, sometimes enlivened with red, yellow or blue on the head. Their cry is a familiar sound in tropical Asian forests, and that of the "coppersmith" *(Xantholaema haemacephala)*, reminiscent of a hammer striking an anvil, is almost as piercing as that of the "brain-fever bird" *(Hierococcyx varius)*, the hawk cuckoo of India and Ceylon, which even sings at night.

As we said of the Himalayas, the eastern region is particularly rich in gallinaceous birds. The most popular representatives of this family in the central Indian jungle are jungle fowl, peacocks, wood partridges and quail. Of jungle fowl, the gray jungle fowl *(Gallus sonnerati)* lives only in southern and western India, while the red jungle fowl *(Gallus gallus)* is also found in Indochina and the larger Sunda Islands except Borneo. The male of the first species is usually gray, spotted with white and yellow on the neck, while the second is red, resembling the domestic "bantam" in every way. It is, more-

Left above: The lion-tailed macaque (Macaca silenus) *of the Nilgiri Hills in southwest India is little known, but it seems to be as terrestrial as other macaques. (M. Krishnan)   Left: The gray mongoose* (Herpestes edwardsi) *feeds mainly on insects, rodents and small reptiles. Although more resistant to venom than man, it relies on agility to avoid snake bites. (Max Hemple)*

Right: The large brown flying squirrel (Petaurista petaurista) *of India can be forty inches in overall length and glide more than fifty yards. (M. Krishnan)*

over, generally agreed the red jungle fowl is the ancestor of our domestic poultry. Ancient seals prove that the people of the Indus Valley raised these birds about 2700 to 2500 years B.C. Tradition has it that the Chinese imported the cock "from the West," that is from the Indo-Burmese region in about 1400 B.C. A cock is also represented in Tutankhamen's tomb, and it is probable that these fowl reached Egypt and Greece by way of Persia, for Aristophanes calls them "Persian birds."

India's wild peacock is similarly the ancestor of the domesticated ornamental peacock found all over the world. It inhabits hills covered with thick jungles and watered by small streams, living in small groups and seeking its food on the ground but sleeping in the trees. Although ordinarily it flees at the slightest alarm, in those parts of India where it is the object of great veneration it has become very friendly and may be seen perched in trees in the center of a village.

Francolins *(Francolinus francolinus)* are wood partridges that differ from European partridges only in that their plumage is dark and speckled with white. A great variety of partridges and quail is found in the eastern region, all well adapted to life in the tropical and equatorial forest. But they are particularly difficult to observe since they are very distrustful and their exceptionally acute vision quickly warns them of the approach of intruders. They generally flee on foot and only take flight when surprised; then their cry of alarm gives them away and is a warning signal to other jungle animals.

SPECTACLED SNAKES AND KING COBRAS

The Indian peninsula is famous for its many snakes. According to official statistics, of the twenty-five thousand people killed by animals, twenty thousand each year are victims of venomous snakes, while only five thousand, it is claimed, are slain by tigers, leopards, bears and other beasts.

The most famous, as much for their deadly venom as their sacred status, are the cobra or najas, named for the seven-headed snake of Hindu mythology. They are known for their habit, when aroused by an enemy, of spreading out a hood that may reach the diameter of a small plate. This hood consists of dilated skin supported by elongated ribs. In the common cobra, the back of the hood is uniformly black, while the "spectacled" variety wears a design rather like eye-glasses with rims.

Because of their appearance and the respect they inspire, cobras are favored by snake-charmers. It is often claimed that the charmers remove the venomous fangs of the snakes they handle. This is true of a few charlatans but genuine snake-charmers never extract the fangs, for without their fangs the cobras soon die. I have several times examined the mouths of such cobras and I have always found their teeth intact.

The king cobra, whose scientific name *Ophiophagus* indi-

cates its special diet, eats only snakes, whereas other cobras of the genus *Naja* catch small mammals and birds. In addition, the king cobra is the only one to build a nest at breeding time. The female scrapes the ground with the rear part of her body and uses dead leaves and other detritus to form a nest of two cavities, a lower cavity for the eggs and an upper one mainly for the female, who guards the eggs until they are hatched. The latter habit is probably the origin of the king cobra's reputation for aggressiveness. Although, like other snakes, it ordinarily flees before man, it does not hesitate to attack anyone who passes near its nest. I have even heard of an officer of the Indian Army who was chased into a river by a king cobra, finally, in despair, he held out his campaign hat and the cobra bit it several times.

It must be admitted that a snake that rears up, hood spread, to a height of at least forty inches can be quite intimidating. Actually, this is more a gesture of intimidation than a prelude to deliberate attack, for even a newly hatched baby cobra spreads its hood as soon as anyone approaches and tries to strike like an adult.

PIT VIPERS AND CROCODILES

Various other snakes in India in the same family as the cobras are equally dangerous. One of these, the banded krait *(Bungarus fasciatus)*, whose black body is ringed with yellow, prefers to circulate at dusk, often in the dust of roads. Another group, Asiatic coral snakes of the genus *Maticora*, are even more brilliantly colored, a red or yellow belly and yellow or blue stripes on a black or dark-brown back. When threatened, these snakes put on a strange display: they hide their heads under the coils of their bodies and raise their tails, waving them aggressively. Their poison glands are extremely well-developed and extend along almost a third of the length of their bodies.

The venom of kraits and cobras consists mainly of neurotoxins that act on the central nervous system, hemolysins that destroy red corpuscles, and anti-coagulants that help spread the poison through the organism. Also, the venom of both vipers and rattlesnakes contains substances that destroy the lining of blood vessels and the thrombin that produces blood clots and, finally, cytolysin that destroy white corpuscles and tissue cells.

One of India's most deadly vipers, Russell's viper, may grow to a length of five feet and the diameter of a man's arm. It feeds mainly on small mammals that it catches at night. It is generally at that time that, its black-spotted brown coloration blending into the earth, people step on it and are bitten. In the driest regions, the saw-scaled viper *(Echis carinatus)*, although it grows no longer than twenty-four inches, is also responsible for a great many accidents. It has a particularly deadly venom and is quick and aggressive, which may be explained by its habit of remaining out in full sunlight at which time its body temperature may become very high.

The rattlesnake family *(Crotalidae)*, unfortunately well-known in America, is represented in Asia by pit vipers of the genus *Trimeresurus*. The name pit viper results from a small opening or pit in the upper jaw between the eye and the nostril. This pit is separated from a larger cavity by a membrane well supplied with nerve endings. For more than a century, zoologists speculated about the purpose of this unique organ. Finally, experiments undertaken before World War II

Left above: Apis florea *is one of several species of wild bees in India that furnish honey much enjoyed by wild animals and human beings.   Far left: Small coppers* (Lycaenidae) *are as frequent in clearings and along the road in India as in North America or in Europe. (Both, E. S. Ross)   Left: Like many of the tropical insect species, this painted grasshopper nymph* (Poccilocerus pictus) *is brightly colored. (Harry Miller)*

showed that the pit is a true "sixth sense." Even when blinded and deprived of the use of nostrils and of tongue, which serves in most reptiles for touch and taste, pit vipers can still strike illuminated electric bulbs set up around them. This organ permits the viper to feel heat and consequently the infrared rays emitted by a living body. It is easy to imagine the usefulness of this astonishing means of perception for a snake that hunts warm-blooded prey in the dark.

The reader must not conclude from the preceding survey that only venomous snakes live in India, for there, as elsewhere, the harmless snakes are much more abundant. Aquatic snakes of the genus *Natrix* are very well represented, of the seventy-five species in the world, twenty-five are Indian. These snakes, which may reach a length of about six and a half feet and are generally somber in hue, show a decided preference for water. They are found principally along rivers or in swampy areas, for they all swim well and can remain underwater for a long period. They eat cold-blooded animals, batrachians, fish and earthworms. When they are seized, their only means of defense is to eject a foul liquid from the anal orifice. It is only in India and Ceylon that we find the primitive burrowing snakes belonging to the *Uropeltidae* family. These snakes have a flattened scale at the end of their tail that forms a shovel or else a large rough shield with which it is believed they close off the opening of their burrows.

Other diggers, the blind snakes, are very small and are completely harmless, having only tiny mouths adapted to the capture of insects and worms. The most common is the *Typhlops braminus,* four or five inches long and often discovered under flowerpots that have remained standing on the ground for a while. Its eyes, like those of other blind snakes, are completely atrophied because of its burrowing life and it has at the end of its tail a sharp scale that is not a "sting," but a tool with which it pushes its way along underground.

Also found in India is the egg-eater *(Elachistodon westermanni),* a snake astonishingly well adapted to its diet, since it can stretch its mouth and throat to the point where it can swallow almost any egg. In addition, the neck vertebrae have long, sharp ventral projections that pierce the esophagus walls and form a kind of saw inside the throat. When the snake swallows an egg, this saw cuts through the eggshell as the throat contracts.

Before turning our attention from central India, we should mention the marsh crocodile *(Crocodylus palustris),* which fills an important role in the life of the jungle. About ten feet long, this crocodile is found in the streams and in small forest marshes. Those found in the forest apparently make their way there during the rainy season only to be isolated when the waters subside. The crocodiles that remain in the rivers feed mainly on fish but those living in small swamps attack all animals who have no other watering places in the dry season. Dunbar Brander's list of the stomach contents of crocodiles he has killed includes human beings, leopards, wild dogs, hyenas, boars, spotted deer, young sambar and blue bulls, four-horned antelopes, muntjacs, monkeys, domesticated animals and all kinds of aquatic birds.

Left above: A tree-dwelling viper, Trimeresurus popeorum, *is found in virtually all the hot forests of Asia. They are related to American rattlesnakes but do not have so dangerous a venom. (John H. Tashjian) Far left: The active brown arboreal snake* (Boiga ochracea walli) *is one of the colubrids or rear-fanged snakes which are only slightly venomous. Left: Banded kraits* (Bungarus fasciatus), *related to cobras, have a powerful venom and are especially dangerous to those who walk barefoot at night. (Both, E. Ross)*

Land of Floods and Open Forests

Indochina

11 Indochina is a vast peninsula bounded on the north by the mountains of Szechwan, on the west by the Bay of Bengal and on the east by the South China Sea. To the south, this ample landmass, 1,785 miles long by 1,010 miles wide, tapers into the slender Malay Peninsula, which has more faunal affinities with the Malay Archipelago than with the mainland, especially south of the narrow Isthmus of Kra.

Whereas Asia's two other peninsulas, Arabia and India, are of an ancient table-like structure, the surface of Indochina is rugged and, geologically speaking, youthful. It is essentially a succession of narrow ranges, rarely rising above 6,500 feet, separated by valleys, all running from northwest to southeast. On the west we find the Arakan Yoma chain, extending into the Indian Ocean near Cape Negrais and including the Preparis Isles and the Andaman and Nicobar archipelagos. To the east is the Irrawaddy Valley; then the Pegu Yoma chain, the Salween River Valley, the Chan Yoma chain, extending into the Malay Peninsula, the Ménam basin, the Bassac Mountains, the Mekong basin, and finally, farthest east, the Annam Cordillera fringed by a narrow coastal plain.

RIVERS: SOURCE OF LIFE

All of Indochina's rivers have their source in Central Asia—either in Tibet or in China's Yunnan province. Fed by melting snows and especially by the monsoon rains, they all show great fluctuation in flow, and even at their fullest they are scarcely navigable because of countless rapids and falls. In places, these rivers rush through steep and narrow gorges; elsewhere they wander lazily across undulating plains. The Mekong, for example, which rises in Tibet as the Lants'ang, wanders down the entire axis of the peninsula. After leaving Yunnan, it follows the Burmese border, crosses Laos, Thailand and Cambodia and finally ends in a vast delta in the

Large male elephants such as this are rare in Thailand because overhunted, but are still numerous in Cambodia where protective measures are more effective. (E. S. Ross)

202

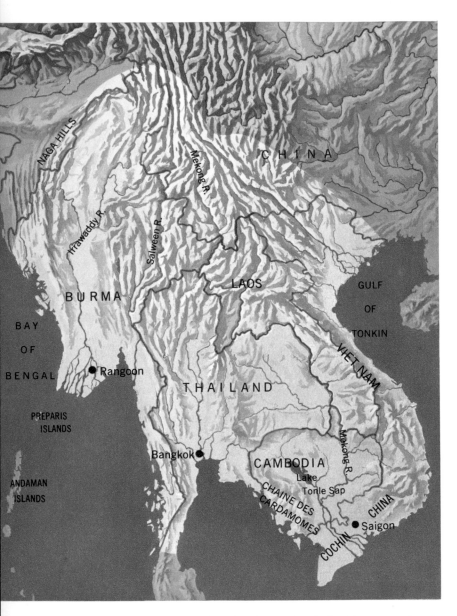

Nearly two thousand miles long, the Indochinese peninsula has a geologically young and very irregular topography with high points generally below 6,500 feet.

Cochin China region at the very tip of the peninsula. Before this, in the vicinity of the city of Phnom Penh, the capital of Cambodia, the Mekong divides into three branches: two of these flow south to the South China Sea and the third, the Tonle Sap, enters the central Cambodian plains and empties into a vast lake, called the Great Lake, that is surrounded by a network of secondary lakes. The Tonle Sap is unique in that it reverses its course twice a year: during the rainy season from June to October its overflow runs from the Mekong into the Great Lake, while from November to May it flows in the opposite direction, that is, toward the Mekong.

During the rainy season the Great Lake overflows its banks and floods the surrounding areas. At this time, the central plains of Cambodia are an amazing spectacle: seen from the air the entire countryside is one vast shallow body of water leaving uncovered only the rows of treetops that line submerged roadways or river beds. Hills are transformed into islands and the only means of travel is by pirogue. What might be taken for a disaster, however, is actually a source of

great wealth, for the receding waters leave large deposits of the most fertile silt, making the central plain the rice granary of all Cambodia. Rice fields cover most of this plain but in some areas a primitive, stunted forest, often mixed with scrub, is able to survive the few months of inundation each year. Rich in organic matter and plankton, these "drowned forests" offer ideal conditions for a great profusion of fish—Cambodia's second largest source of wealth. At time of flood, hordes of fish from the Mekong River invade the undergrowth of the drowned forests for a feast of animal and vegetable life. They gorge themselves for five or six months and thus fattened try to make their way back to the river once the waters subside in November and December. The Cambodians use large wooden barriers to channel this bounty into huge bamboo bow-nets. They catch immense quantities of fish along with giant green fresh-water prawns, some the size of a lobster but with a much more succulent meat.

The subsiding of the waters each year is a time of great festivity in Cambodia and a rare spectacle for the naturalist. The receding lakes and rivers leave behind many temporary ponds teeming with aquatic life. The saying goes in Cambodia, "Wherever there is water, there are fish," and I have seen enormous fish swimming about in puddles so shallow that their dorsal fins could be seen above the surface. More pathetic was the sight of a school of fish flopping about helplessly in an inch of water across a road, desperately trying to return to the river. At this time of the year each family spends the early morning hours fishing for breakfast from atop their houses, which stand on stilts. It would be difficult to estimate just how much fish is caught as winter comes on. The only figures available are for the state fisheries—100,000 tons per season destined for Cambodia's cities or exported to Saigon via junks with special built-in fish wells. This quantity is probably matched by the fish hauled in by the villagers; for months they live almost exclusively on grilled fish or a delicious fish soup simmered with mint and fennel.

These are also times of feast in the barnyard: dogs, cats, pigs and fowl all join in the general pursuit of the fish caught napping by the disappearing floodwaters. Thus a fish diet reigns, adopted as well by many wild creatures—a mongoose pet of mine seemed to prefer fish over any meat. All the wild cats—tigers, panthers and especially the fishing cat *(Felis viverrina)*—seek the larger fish in shallow waters, clutching them with one deadly thrust of the paw, while the civets and palm civets gorge themselves on the whole gamut of aquatic creatures left high and dry—fish, crustaceans, insects and mollusks.

PELICANS, EGRETS AND DUCKS

Wherever there is a profusion of fish, birds are the first to claim their share. Hordes of pelicans, cormorants, darters, adjutant storks and a variety of herons flock to every last body of water for active fishing, paying no heed to man. And man is too busy with his own nets and lines to heed the birds.

Pelicans, both the white *(Pelecanus onocrotalus)* and the

The sparse forests of central Indochina offer animals abundant grass and sheltering trees and are ideal for large bantengs, gaurs (above) and several species of deer. (M. Krishnam)

spotted-billed *(P. philippensis)*, have an ingenious way of catching their prey. The whole colony, which often comprises quite a number of birds, forms a large semicircle and then swims toward the shore, beating the fish into shallow waters where they are easy to catch. Parents feed their young by disgorging the fish right into their beaks and what falls to the ground is simply left there—but not wasted: crows are always on hand in great number, cawing impatiently as they await their turn. Pelicans build their nests on the ground on a small mound of mud.

Cormorants, on the other hand, are perchers, usually choosing the branches of a large tree for their nests. Their remarkable fishing dives are legendary—a skill utilized by fishermen in Asia. The men tame the birds and put an ivory or bamboo ring around the bird's neck to prevent it from swallowing what it catches. An odd fact about the cormorant is that whereas most other water fowl waterproof their plumage by means of an oily secretion of the uropygial gland, just above the tail, the cormorant becomes soaked through after several dives and must take time to dry off. A common sight along Asian watercourses is these birds perched in the trees, wings spread wide, basking in the warmth of the sun. Three species are represented in Indochina: the great cormorant *(Phalacrocorax carbo)*, the brown-necked cormorant *(P. fuscicollis)* and the lesser or pygmy cormorant *(P. niger)*, which, like the great cormorant is totally black and is a familiar bird near all bodies of water in town and village.

Whereas the cormorant seizes its dinner in its mandibles, another diver, the darter or snakebird *(Anhinga melanogaster)*, pierces the fish with its fine, pointed beak. It then comes to the surface, tosses its catch in the air and adroitly gobbles it up as it drops back. Like the cormorant, the darter nests in trees along the banks and is often seen drying itself. It owes the name snakebird to its unusually long and agile neck, slender head and probably also the tiny, piercing yellow eyes.

The heron family is represented in Indochina and the rest of Southeast Asia by about a dozen species ranging from the large gray heron *(Ardea cinerea)* to the tiny Chinese bittern. Not nearly so sociable as its European cousins, the large gray heron is seen either alone or in pairs and when several find themselves in the same rice field or pond, they keep a cautious distance from each other. Somewhat smaller in size is the purple heron *(Ardea purpurea)* but both share the same diet: fish, frogs, insects, mollusks as well as tiny birds. But the latter is more of a twilight creature and it is usually at dawn

Left: Many species of otters are found in Indochina. Some live along the seacoast while others haunt inland streams where fish abound. (E. Hanumantha Rao)

Right above: The Mekong River rises in Tibet and crosses the entire Indochinese peninsula. Its upper reaches follow irregular gorges and are cut by dangerous rapids; its lower part, divided into three arms at Phnom Penh, is navigable. (Henri Hymans) Right: The Bengal roller (Coracias bengalensis), often called the blue jay, is one of the most common birds in cleared zones and sparse forests. (E. Hanumantha Rao) Far right: The white-breasted kingfisher (Halcyon smyrnensis) frequents river banks and plains. Its large red beak, handsome plumage, and noisy movements attract attention to it. (Livna Yigael)

or dusk that one catches sight of its familiar silhouette—perching on one leg with its neck nestled deep in the shoulder, but ever alert to pounce upon passing prey.

The egret, more delicately proportioned than the heron, became popular in the world of fashion because of the long, decorative feathers that appear on its head, back and breast during the mating season. Hunters have nearly exterminated these beautiful birds in several regions. Luckily, however, times and fashions have changed and three species are to be found both at the heart of Indochina and in all of Southeast Asia: the greater egret *(Egretta alba),* the lesser egret *(E. intermedia)* and the little egret *(E. garzetta).* All three keep the same white feathers throughout the year, in contrast to its cousin, the reef heron *(Demigretta sacra),* a coastal species. The reef heron has both a white and a deep slate-gray wardrobe, although such variations in color have never been explained. All, with the exception of the solitary great egret, are very gregarious creatures and nest in trees along river banks, often in the company of herons and cormorants. Feeding on insects and all kinds of tiny animals, they are often seen in the vicinity of cattle herds, joining the cattle egret *(Bubulcus ibis).* Except during the mating season, the cattle egret is also dressed in pristine white but in its courting dress it makes a striking display with long golden feathers adorning the head, neck and breast.

Marshes, flooded plains and rice fields are also the choice habitat for a host of waders of every size, many of which we have already encountered in India: squacco herons, night herons, bitterns, spoonbills, ibises, white-necked storks, white-bellied storks, adjutant storks, painted storks and open-bill storks.

On the larger rivers one often has occasion to see the Asiatic skimmer *(Rhynchops albicollis).* This strange bird is a cousin of the terns but it has an especially curious and useful beak: since the lower mandible is longer than the upper, it is able to glide over the water's surface without diving, scooping up its dinner of fish and crustaceans. Black kites and flocks of pied kingfishers *(Ceryle rudis)* in great numbers also make their dwelling near the larger rivers. I well remember the sight of about a dozen of these kingfishers perched in lower tree branches along the banks of the Mekong, with about a half a dozen black kites keeping watch over them from the treetops. Every once in a while a kingfisher would swoop over the water, beat its wings for several seconds as it hovered over the surface, and then suddenly plunge. When it would reappear with a fish in its beak, one of the black kites would promptly dive down on it like a fighter plane and whirl around it until the kingfisher dropped its catch.

In the same vicinity I have also seen great flocks of gallinules *(Porphyrio porphyrio)* like a cloud over the river. These magnificent birds are closely related to the moorhen *(Gallinula choloropus),* also an inhabitant of Indochina, but they are larger in size and have a much livelier dress—a green plumage with bronze highlights and a bright red beak and frontal shield.

When the floodwaters recede, Indochina, and especially the central plains are a sportsman's paradise. The whole countryside is littered with wild fowl. I have vivid memories of thousands of ducks soaring over the Mekong. Most common is the whistling duck *(Dendrocygna javanica),* netted in great numbers by the Cambodians and sold under the name of "teal" in markets everywhere. Unlike most members of this family, the

whistling duck perches in trees where it often makes its nest either in a hole or the fork of a large branch. Another web-footed inhabitant of tropical Asia is the cotton teal *(Nettapus coromandelianus),* ranging from Southern China, where Père David discovered it nesting under pagoda roofs, to India and Indochina. This tiny, toylike bird, owes its name to its soft and downy plumage. Unfortunately, it is as delicate in constitution as in appearance and does not take to captivity. Both these species are sedentary birds, except for local migrations in rhythm with the monsoon rains. The same is true of the spotted-billed duck *(Anas poecilorhyncha)*—its black beak is tipped with yellow—as well as the knob-billed goose *(Sarkidiornis melanotos),* easily recognized by the horny helmet-shaped casque atop the bill. Although it is not a migrant, the knob-billed goose is also found in India, Madagascar and almost all of Africa.

The majority, however, of the aquatic birds congregating at this time of the year are migrants. Nesting in the northern regions of Asia—Siberia, Mongolia, China and Japan—they take their winter vacations in the tropics—in India, Indochina and Malaysia. Most of these species are familiar not only because we encountered them during our journey across the tundra and the lakes of Siberia, but because a great number of them also winter in Africa and make stopovers in Europe either on the way south or on the return trip. Curiously enough the only exception is the most common of the European wild ducks, the mallard, which has never been observed in Indochina. But on the whole, the European sportsman would be pleasantly surprised to find the whole gamut of his habitual game: greylag geese, shelducks, teal, shovelers, pochards, scaups, tufted ducks and wigeons, as well as the whole range of waders: curlews, godwits, redshanks, stints, snipes and plovers.

THE OPEN FOREST

Apart from the inundated lowlands and the montane forests, a great portion of Indochina has an impoverished, sandy soil covered with what botanists call "open forest." This is a kind of savanna of tall grasses, strewn with stunted trees of the Dipterocarp family, the leaves of which are large and wrinkled. Occasionally, however, one sees an acacia, a jujube tree, a ficus or a palmyra palm. But all these trees are spaced at intervals of about thirty feet, so that one constantly has the impression of passing through a clearing before coming to the real forest. But as the traveler hopefully crosses this monotonous landscape, the trees thin out again as though he had come to another clearing. It is only along the banks of streams or rivers that one finds denser stands of fig trees, latanas and rattans.

During the rainy season the undergrowth of this open forest flourishes so vigorously that grasses grow as tall as a man. Then, in the dry season either natural or man-made fires sweep the landscape, transforming it into a lifeless, smoking expanse. But with the first drops of rain, tender green shoots sprout from the charred soil and animals reappear.

Indeed, from an ecological point of view, the open forest is

The collared scops-owl (Scops bakkamoena) *is active at dusk and at night, when it hunts large insects. (M. Krishnan)*

forests lure the whole gamut of grass-eating mammals, from the hare and the tiny mouse-deer to the elephant, and including the wild boar, the barking-deer, the thamin or Eld's deer, the sambar—here called Aristotle's deer—the banteng or wild ox, the water buffalo, the gaur and the mysterious kouprey. Some of these, such as the Eld's deer, the banteng and especially the kouprey, will be totally new to us.

The Eld's deer *(Cervus eldi)* is by far the most handsome deer of the Indochinese forest. Resembling the fallow deer, it has a fine gray-brown coat spotted with white in the young which deepens to a solid dark-brown after the fourth year. The adults may attain a weight of 220 pounds for a height of about three feet to the shoulder. The antlers, delicate and with jagged edges like those of a fallow deer, form a lyre with a long tine pointing forward while the main branch points backward. Although once found in many areas, excessive hunting, especially at night by lamplight, has made the Eld's deer a rarity in many regions of Indochina.

Of all wild cattle, the banteng or wild ox *(Bos banteng)* bears the strongest resemblance to the domestic cow. The species has, in fact, contributed to several varieties of domestic cattle, especially in Indonesia. The female and the young have a brick-red coat which turns to chocolate-brown and then black in the adult males, great imposing beasts sometimes weighing as much as 2,000 pounds. Capable of living in dense forest, the banteng nevertheless prefers to make its home in clearings or at the forest's edge. A typical Southeast Asian ungulate, the banteng has been found in Assam and Burma (where it goes by the name *tsaïne),* Indochina, Malaya, Borneo, Java and Bali. Oddly enough, it is not found in Sumatra although this island forms a link between Malaya and Java.

There was a time when the banteng abounded throughout its whole range but in some regions it is now almost extinct. Slaughtered mainly for its excellent meat, which is as good as the finest prime beef, it is nevertheless well armed against hunters. It is an extremely cautious creature with an acute sense of hearing and smell. It is not, however, aggressive and even a wounded animal will not attack a man, although some hunters claim to have been charged by these beasts.

THE KOUPREY—A ZOOLOGICAL PUZZLE

Strangest member of the wild cattle family of this region is the kouprey *(Bibos sauveli),* not officially known until it was discovered in 1937 by a French veterinarian and hunter, Dr. R. Sauvel. The fact that a creature of this size could remain a secret from Europeans is in itself an oddity. As for the kouprey's origin, that is still a subject of debate. It resembles the gaur in size, although it is not quite as imposing, and has a gray-brown or gray-black fur and the white stockings of the gaur, the banteng and certain Asian buffalo. The horns form a widespreading lyre; in the adult male the point of the horn has a crown of horny fibers. Zoologists have attached a special significance to this last peculiarity, but I have seen such horny tips in old buffalo bulls in the Sunda Islands and believe they result from the habit these creatures have of digging with their horns during mating time. A far more important feature is the presence in both sexes of a well-developed dewlap; the only other creatures having this so well-developed are the hump-backed zebus, domestic cattle of India.

The kouprey thus has something of the gaur, the gayal, the

The tailor-bird (Orthotomus sutorius), *made famous by Kipling's stories, sews leaves edge to edge to make a funnel for its nest of cotton fibers, horsehair and down. (Loke Wan Tho)*

an ideal habitat for the large ungulates, offering them the shelter of trees as well as all the grass they can eat. It is also thought to be the most suitable biotope for the hunting of game in a rational and useful manner. Unsuitable for agriculture, incapable of yielding more than mediocre timber, this area could become a key center for the production of high-quality meat, in the form of wild animals, with a minimum of investment and preparation. What the Russians have accomplished with the saiga in the arid steppes of Kazakh could certainly be repeated here with still more fruitful results, considering the greater water supply, the superior quality of the grasses and the possibility of more efficient consumption by a more diversified range of animals. Indeed, these open

banteng and the zebu, not to mention a color which is more like that of the buffalo. On the basis of these multiple correspondences, some zoologists have maintained that the kouprey is not a distinct species but merely a hybrid. But the fact that the kouprey shares a number of anatomical and even skeletal traits with several other species is not significant for the bovines are an extremely homogeneous group. Second, these species are not known to crossbreed in the natural state and if they occasionally did so, the offspring would most probably be sterile. Even if they were not sterile, the hybrids would have no reason to isolate themselves from the rest of the herd; they would remain with the mother, grow up with the herd and the hybrid traits would disappear after a few generations. But let us suppose by some stretch of the imagination that these "mongrels" did leave the herd and form a new community. According to the laws of heredity their offspring would be totally heterogeneous, some conserving the hybrid traits, some harking back to the traits of one of the parents. It is a known fact, however, that the kouprey is invariable in its traits. I was lucky enough to meet several herds of these rare and elusive creatures in 1968 and may affirm that they demonstrate no greater variability than do the buffalo or the banteng.

Meanwhile, heedless of these debates, the kouprey continues to roam the open forests of northern and eastern Cambodia. The population has been considerably reduced, however, and according to Mr. Ou Kim San, Supervisor of Wildlife, there are currently only about 200 koupreys left. Luckily, they are now strictly protected. So little is known about the kouprey that great efforts should be made to save it from extinction.

WILD DOGS AND CROCODILES

Man is, of course, the greatest enemy of the ungulates of the open forest and he has succeeded in destroying many of them. The other enemies are the tiger, panther and wild dog or dhole *(Cuon alpinus)*. The dhole, which ranges from Altai to Manchuria and from Central Asia to Java, looks like a medium-sized domestic dog, with a russet coat varying in thickness according to the region, small erect ears and a rather bushy, hanging tail. The main features that distinguish these creatures from the true dogs are the six lower molars instead of seven, some of the details of the skull and the twelve to fourteen teats instead of ten.

Like all gregarious canines, however, they travel in groups of about a dozen, including several families. They hunt by day, generally stalking their prey and then pressing the chase with a frightening chorus of piercing yelps. Once the prey is at bay, they usually make their kill by seizing the ears, eyes, nose and mouth and hanging on with all their weight until the poor creature succumbs. If the victim should try to escape by diving into the water, as stags often do, the dholes, which are good swimmers, soon grab it and sometimes even scramble upon its back. The dhole's preferred victims are wild boar and deer, but a large pack of them would not hesitate to attack bantengs, gaurs or even buffalo. In such cases their strategy is to spread havoc amidst the herd and then cunningly make off with a calf that has strayed from its mother in the confusion. Their only enemies are the tiger and especially the panther, although there are stories of a pack attacking one of these great felines. Thus, only the elephant and the rhino are

The yellow-breasted sunbird (Anthreptes malaccensis) *is one of many tropical Asian sunbirds, counterpart of American hummingbirds. Like hummingbirds, they can suck up nectar with their long tongues. (F. G. H. Allen)*

exempt from their fierce appetites—that is, in addition to man, for whom they have a particular respect, unlike wolves who, in time of famine, have been known to attack a lone traveler.

When they are not actually hunting, the presence of dholes in the jungle does not seem to spread panic: those familiar shrieking signals relayed across the forest by monkeys, jungle fowl and other birds at the approach of the larger beasts are never heard for the dhole. Even deer make little effort to avoid them at such a time as if they sensed the momentary suspension of danger.

The reaction of dholes to domestic dogs is amusing: pursued

by a pack of courageous, sturdy-sized dogs they immediately take to the hills but they approach smaller dogs, such as the fox terrier, with playful interest and start romping with them. Dhole pups are easily tamed. I kept one as a pet for several months before sending it to the Zoological Gardens in Paris: it was as playful as any dog and would frisk about my heels, yapping and wagging its tail in its eagerness to be scratched and petted.

BIRD WATCHING IN THE OPEN FOREST

One of the most interesting trips I have taken was through the open forest in the company of some of my Cambodian friends. It was toward the end of November and the ground was still damp from the last monsoon rains. High on the backs of three docile elephants we followed tracks left in the mud by bantengs, Eld's deer, wild boar and wild elephants, plainly followed by the enormous rosette-shaped prints of a tiger.

At the feet of our great mounts, a host of birds scattered in flight: colonies of manakins *(Uroloncha punctulata)*, larks *(Mirafra assamica)*, pipits *(Anthus richardi, A. hodgsoni)*, and especially buntings *(Emberiza aureola)*. One of my companions explained that the latter were winter migrants from Siberia and Mongolia and appear only at this season in Indochina: there many of them are netted and sold as the delicacy called ortolans. In one spot we came across three hoopoes busily foraging for worms at the foot of a tree. They flew off as we approached, displaying the black and white zebra stripes of their wings. Often earth-colored nightjars *(Caprimulgus monticola)*, relatives of the European goatsuckers, rose, almost from under the feet of our elephants, showing a patch of black and white on the wing. Nocturnal birds, they capture insects in the manner of the swallow. The story that they suck milk from goats—hence their name—is an old wives' tale. In Indochina, and in India as well, nightjars are at times incredibly numerous at night, especially near roads, their eyes glowing in the gleam of headlights.

There was also a profusion of starlings, always congregating around larger animals and serving to rid them of their parasites. I found three species: the crested myna *(Acridotheres cristatellus)*, known in Indochina as "buffalo blackbird," because of its habit of alighting on the backs of these great creatures; the great myna *(A. grandis)*, which has the same habit; and the black-necked myna *(A. nigricollis)*, particularly noteworthy because it has a large repertoire of imitations of other birds as well as a very comical greeting of its own.

As we continued through the forest, a stone curlew *(Burhinus oedicnemus)* suddenly took flight, its long yellow feet dangling awkwardly, and then landed hastily in order to hide. From my lofty perch I was able to see how it concealed itself: with its body flattened on the ground and its dull brown feathers spotted with black and white it achieved a perfect camouflage. Farther on we noticed the coppery glint of a jungle cock *(Gallus gallus)* as it threaded its way through the tall grasses followed by three drab-colored hens. These jungle cocks are agile flyers and are numerous in Indochina, where they are considered attractive game. The same is true of francolins *(Francolinus pintadeanus)*, known as partridges, another bird common in the open forests and treeless zones. Quail of the species *Coturnix coturnix* are winter visitors from the northern parts of Asia, and button quails *(Turnix tanki)*,

sedentary birds, are found throughout Indochina and are quite common on the plains.

We next raised a bustard-like bird, the floriken *(Houbaropsis bengalensis)* and a flock of Indian lapwings *(Lobivanellus indicus)*. The latter often exasperate hunters and photographers by a piping call of alarm that warns all animals of man's approach.

Soon afterward an oriental sarus crane *(Antigone sharpii)*, ash gray with a crimson neck, sprang from the grasses and dashed away with great strides. Along the banks we spotted a running bird, the painted snipe *(Rostratula benghalensis)*, unusual because it is the female that has the more brilliant wardrobe. Here and there we caught sight of small, black and white birds—stone chats *(Saxicola torquata)*, visitors from Siberia and Japan, come to spend the winter in a milder clime. Tailor birds of the same species as those found in India were also numerous here, as were the small, quarrelsome flowerpeckers *(Dicaeum cruentatum)*.

Sunbirds, the Old World equivalent of the American hummingbird, were represented by at least three species: the crimson sunbird *(Aethopyga siparaja)*, with the upper parts yellow, the head and the underparts carmine and the forehead a beautiful, shimmering green; the purple sunbird *(Cinnyris asiaticus)*, dressed in a metallic blue washed with violet and green; and the yellow-breasted sunbird *(C. jugularis)*, with purple throat outlined against a yellow breast and yellow underparts.

Before we had finished our unusual journey we had seen a fantail flycatcher *(Rhipidura aureola)*, a migrant shrike *(Lanius cristatus)*, a group of bee-eaters *(Merops orientalis)*, and a roller *(Coracias benghalensis)*. Since they are very shy, we were particularly fortunate to catch sight of three giant ibises *(Thaumatibis gigantea)* perched in a palm. About the size of a turkey, they are clothed in a brown-gray plumage with a long, naked neck, small, naked head and a long, curved beak. Like other ibises, they feed on frogs, worms, mollusks and crustaceans.

Although we did not see them, other birds common in this area include cuckoo-shrikes *(Coracina javensis)*, velvet-fronted nuthatches *(Sitta frontalis)*, minivets *(Pericrocotus flammeus)*, shy black-headed orioles *(Oriolus xanthornus)*, white-breasted kingfishers *(Halcyon smyrnensis)*, leafbirds *(Cloropsis cochinchinensis)* and all kinds of bulbuls *(Pycnonotus cafer, P. finlaysoni)*, mustache parakeets *(Psittacula alexandri)*, and hanging parakeets *(Coryllis vernalis)*.

MOUNTAIN FORESTS

A rich, dense vegetation covers the parallel mountain ranges extending across the entire Indochinese peninsula. The highest altitudes, about 6,500 feet, are clad in a surprisingly untropical kind of flora—tall heather. A little lower, between 5,000 and 6,500 feet, there are some magnificent pine forests *(Pinus mercusi, P. khasya)*, recalling those in Europe and North America. Health resorts in the heart of these cool forests have become a haven for Europeans seeking escape from the dank

A moist tropical forest with variegated plants grows below 5,000 feet on the slopes and in the mountain valleys of Indochina, here seen in North Vietnam. (H. G. Petzold)

heat of lower regions. The weather is pleasant and dry except in the monsoon season, from September to November, which brings mists and endless fine rains.

Below five thousand feet, both on slopes and in valleys, one finally finds the typical rain forest, perpetually verdant and moist—a kind of forest that covers great stretches of Malaysia and the Sunda Islands. In Indochina this forest has a special character because the taller trees and ends of creeping palms project above the upper forest canopy. This canopy, moreover, does not have any one dominant species. (In the southern part of the Yunnan province, for example, the Chinese botanist Chi-Wu Wang noted that the sixty-nine tree species found belong to a range of sixty different genera and thirty-two families.) At 130 to 160 feet above the ground, the treetops form a compact roof interlaced with myriads of vines and climbing bamboo, all thrusting upward toward the light. This dense tangle of vines and epiphytic plants, is a unique characteristic of this type of rain forest. Most are orchids and bird's nest ferns, which form thick clusters one hundred feet above the ground, but there are hundreds of others. Another curious aspect of tropical or equatorial forests is the fact that many fruits or flowers sprout directly from the trunks or the larger branches, rather than from the tips of the smaller twigs.

With just a thin layer of humus and an abundance of moisture, the roots of the trees grow above rather than beneath the soil, often forming buttresses or props around the base of the trunk. These help to anchor the great giants of the forest which are often like massive marble columns on a weak base of clay, and can be overthrown by the slightest storm.

Beneath the largest trees, whose main branches are located as much as 65 to 100 feet above the ground, two distinct strata are found. The middle layer is composed of delicate-leafed and smooth-trunked trees, mainly of the Araliaceae or ginseng family, forming a leafy crown just beneath the main canopy. In fact, the leaves in the uppermost strata, which are in direct contact with sunlight, are small, thick, tough and glossy. On the other hand, trees in the strata below this bear leaves more typical of wet tropical forest: broad, paper-thin and lustreless, for they live in moisture and are sheltered from intense sunlight. The lowest stratum is composed of shrubby trees, 10 to 15 feet in height, mingled with small palms, young rattan palms and bamboo, *Pandanus* (or screwpines) with their ribbon-like leaves, wild banana trees and tree ferns.

The undergrowth is comparatively sparse and there is a striking absence of the brilliant blossoms so characteristic of spring days in forests of the temperate region. Tropical undergrowth,

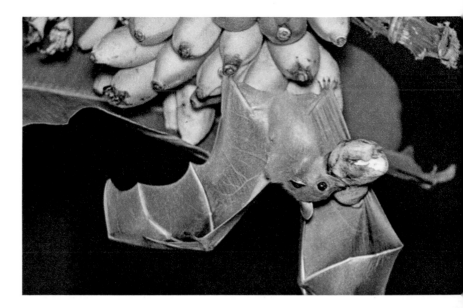

Left: In the jungle encroaching on the ruins of the famous temples of Angkor Vat, a sambar deer browses in brush growing between ancient stones. (Pierre Pfeffer)

Right above: Some fruit bats are mouse-sized (here, a Cynopterus*), but other species may have wing spreads of more than four feet. They spend the day in trees and fly out at dusk to find fruit. (T. S. Lal: Pip Photos Inc). Center: The mangrove snake* (Boiga dendrophila) *is common throughout Southeast Asia. It is harmless and feeds on rats and birds. (E. Sochurek) Right: The red jungle fowl* (Gallus gallus) *of tropical Asia is the direct ancestor of our domestic fowl. Some domestic races, particularly bantams, resemble the ancestral stock. (F. G. H. Allen)*

The green pit viper (Trimeresurus wagleri) *dwells in trees and hunts small animals whose warmth it can detect in complete darkness through nerve-endings in pits behind the nostrils. (Lim Boo-Liat)*

although rich, is composed mainly of ferns, liverwort and humidity-loving plants with papery leaves and few flowers.

There is, however, one fascinating flower found from Assam to the tip of the peninsula, the *Sapria himalayana.* Purplish-pink in color, its cup is about six inches in diameter, fringed by ten to twelve "petals" which are actually the outer rim of the perianth. Of the same family as the giant *Rafflesia* of Borneo, which reaches three feet in diameter, it is leafless and sprouts directly from the ground. It lives parasitically on vines, starting as a swelling on the root of the vine, and then develops into a bud that thrusts above the soil and finally attains the size of a fist. Often partly filled with water, the *Sapria* doubles as an insect trap and one often sees dead ants lining the center. It is not, however, carnivorous like the pitcher plants *(Nepenthes),* which are also found in this region but are more typical of Malaysia. Nor do the insects play any role in pollinization: and strangely enough no seed has ever been found.

HIDDEN TEMPLES AND CELESTIAL DANCERS

Although rain forest covers most mountainous regions on the peninsula, the plains have for the most part been cleared for cultivation. But in places abandoned by man it takes only a few years for the original vegetation to reclaim its former territory; I have seen a stretch of paved road overwhelmed by forest growth after being neglected for a mere two years. A

striking example of this power of the jungle is the ancient city of Angkor, capital of the Khmer Empire between the ninth and the fourteenth centuries. When French travelers rediscovered this city eighty years ago, what had once been the most important center of Southeast Asia was totally engulfed in dense forest. Most of the city has since been cleared but luckily much of the natural setting has been left intact; the very splendor of Angkor comes from this marriage of natural and man-made wonders.

Several of the temples, particularly the Ta-Prohm, have been allowed to remain exactly as they were when first discovered. There is nothing more eerie and fascinating than the sight of these vast, stony ruins and statues bathed in the moisture and the sea-green lushness of the forest. Trunks of giant fig trees thrust from the very roofs of the monuments, forcing aside the ancient arches and colonnades. Their roots, some of them sixty feet long, climb rankly about the chiselled stone blocks or writhe around the grotesque, scaly figures of the nagas. The warty coils of these serpents are wrapped in deadly embrace around the apsaras, celestial dancers whose faces continue to shine with ethereal radiance.

The life of the forest invades every corner of the ruins. Copper-banded millipedes *(Iula)* the size of a pencil crawl on the paths. Muddy puddles of water attract a host of brilliant butterflies, creating a kaleidoscope of color as sun filters through the dense canopy of trees. In fact, most of the large groups of insects which we will find in Malaysia are represented in Indochina by the same or very similar species.

In the same way, many reptiles are similar to those already encountered in India. In bushes or upon tree trunks one often sees a small, iguana-like lizard, the *Calotes,* common throughout Southeast Asia. With a dorsal crest of pointy scales and a brightly colored pouch at the throat, it looks like a miniature dragon. The male may attain a length of about eighteen inches. Living exclusively in trees, the *Calotes* descends to the ground only to lay five or six parchment-like eggs, which the female then buries. On the ground it loses much of its agility, hopping on its hind legs toward the nearest vertical object. In the trees, however, it is a marvelous acrobat and pounces like a cat on the most rapid butterflies. Each male defends its preferred hunting ground from intruders by means of a menacing display: its crest bristling, the throat pouch spread wide, baring its sawlike teeth. If this does not frighten off a rival, a fierce battle ensues and it is not unusual to see the two adversaries remaining locked in a deadly grip on each other's spine. When attacked, they rapidly change color like chameleons, going from green to red-brown, thus leading to the belief that they drink the blood of their adversary; hence their English name "bloodsucker."

The vine-covered stony ruins of the temples are an ideal habitat for many other snakes and lizards. Cobras who live in some of the temples are revered by the local inhabitants and are propitiated with offerings. Several Burmese villages still practice the strange custom known as the kiss of the cobra, which claims a few victims each year. In this ceremony, a maiden offers a jar of milk to a royal cobra, and in a kind of strange dance, the cobra, hissing angrily, sways back and

Bamboos are really Gramineae, very tall grasses. They grow in clumps and often cover vast stretches, especially where primitive forest has been cut down or burned. (M. Krishnan)

forth, the hood opened wide, and the girl sways with it, trying to kiss it without being bitten.

Most of the snakes living in the ruins are more peaceable. I saw a brilliant green and yellow tree snake *(Dryophis)* in one of the bas reliefs of the Angkor Vat Temple where it spent most of its time hunting gekkos, especially at dusk.

During the daytime, forest life moves at a slower pace and a hushed silence hovers about the ruins. The only sounds heard are the hammering calls of the barbet *(Megalaema heamacephala),* the occasional "miaowing" of a black-headed oriole, or the combination of soft tinkles and harsh grating noises that reveal the presence of the black drongo. Particularly common, especially in the mountain forests are gallinaceous birds such as peacocks, pheasants and partridges. It is very possible that a few undiscovered species still lurk in these forests, notably in the Chaîne de Cardamomes of western Cambodia, where the fauna has remained remarkably untouched.

TEMPLE BATS AND ACROBATIC GIBBONS

As in all forests, birds are more easily observed than are mammals. Tigers and leopards do, however, appear in the Angkor National Park and wild elephants occasionally come to trample the outer walls of the Banteay-Srey temple. Once, while visiting the ruins of another temple, the Banteay Prey, I suddenly looked up and saw a superb Aristotle's deer followed by two does; it came toward me and stood waiting for a reward. I gave it a few cigarettes, knowing that most grass-eaters are extremely fond of tobacco!

In the same temple I was struck by the oppressive stench in the galleries and underneath the arches and discovered that it came from a thick layer of droppings from tens or hundreds of thousands of various bats clinging to the ceiling. But it was at Angkor Vat that I had my most unnerving experience. I happened to be standing at the entry of the temple precisely at the hour of sunset and was suddenly overwhelmed by a storm of bats leaving their daytime shelters. With their usual agility they brushed by without touching me although the rush lasted a good ten minutes.

I later discovered that this ritual was well known to the local inhabitants and that they wave a stick about their heads as the hordes of bats fly by and knock a few down—not for sport but for food. I was also surprised to see people in the streets of Phnom Penh gathered around the street lights in the evening to "fish" for bats attracted by the swarming insects. The "fishermen" used a pole, a nylon line and a fish hook with the head of a gekko as bait. Each man was able to angle about ten bats per evening, in other words less than two ounces of meat, since each bat weighs no more than about half an ounce, skin, bones and wings included.

In the larger trees at Angkor I also detected a few red squirrels *(Callosciurus ferrugineus),* identical in appearance with their European cousins except for a ring of yellow fur around the tail. A glimpse of silvery fur and a sudden stir of the branches was all that I saw of a troop of dusky leaf monkeys

The slow loris (Nycticebus coucang) *is, as its large eyes indicate, a nocturnal animal. It moves about trees with extreme slowness, looking for fruit, insects or nestling birds. (W. Suschitzky)*

Very familiar in India and Indochina is the kite (Milvus migrans), *a bold scavenger. Large numbers perch on roofs and trees waiting for scraps or a fish put out to dry. (E. Hanumantha Rao)*

(Trachypithecus germani), close relatives of the sacred langurs of India.

At dusk, when the sun's rays barely graze the tops of the tallest trees, a chorus of hoots spread through the forest, the evening chant of a troop of lar gibbons *(Hylobates lar)* retiring for the night to the uppermost branches. This chorus of rising and falling notes ended with a burst of shrill laughter, the characteristic sound of this curious group of apes.

Classed with the anthropoid apes, not with monkeys, because of their well-developed arms, the ability to assume an upright position and the lack of a tail, gibbons seem nevertheless to be below the gorillas, orangutans and chimpanzees in mental powers. In no way do they possess the uncanny intelligence of the larger anthropoids. According to Pierre Dandelot who has specialized in the study of primates, their behavior is more emotional—expressing anger, joy or excitement—than rational. In agility, however, they surpass all other primates. These born acrobats spend most of their time in the highest

treetops, although I have occasionally seen them on the ground hunting for insects or munching the brackish soil near a spring. Even when they come down for water they usually hang by their feet and one arm from a low-hanging branch while using their free hand as a scoop.

With unbelievably long arms, equal almost to their height, gibbons are truly grotesque-looking when they stand upright. But in the trees these long, dangling arms permit them to perform the acrobatic feats that make them the true celestial dancers of the Indochinese forest. Unlike the other apes who make use of all fours, the gibbons travel by brachiation—hanging from one arm and swinging to the next branch with the other. They can thus make leaps as great as thirty feet, and they often choose dead naked branches high above the forest canopy for their aerial ballets. But they also occasionally miss their target and take sensational spills. I once witnessed such a vertical dive, the hapless creature plunging from one of the loftiest trees. It finally caught hold of a branch just above my head, remained stunned for a second and then began to climb painfully, using its legs and one arm, the other hanging limply at its side. Accidents of this kind are far from rare: A. H. Schultz, who examined the skeletons of 233 wild gibbons, found the sign of fractures in a few young, in 28 percent of the adults and in 50 percent of the older animals, some of them bearing the scars of as many as seven accidents. The gibbon's agility is thus not as infallible as it would seem and it probably diminishes with age.

Troops are composed of from fifteen to twenty individuals, several families living in harmony. The wet forest is their chosen habitat, both in the lower regions and as high as 8,000 feet. The gibbons' diet consists chiefly of fruits but they do not disdain insects, birds' eggs or even nestlings and lizards.

The female carries for a period of about six and one-half to seven months and gives birth to one infant. She carries it on her side for two years. Gibbons reach adulthood after the fifth or sixth year and live, at least in captivity, as long as thirty years.

Only the genus *Hylobates* is found in Indochina and is represented by three species and a variety of races. The most northern is the hoolock *(H. hoolock),* found in Assam, Upper Burma and western Yunnan province; the adult male is black with a white headband while the female is a deep, tawny color. Its more southern cousin is the plain black gibbon *(H. concolor),* which lives in the southern parts of Yunnan province, in the province of Tonkin and on Hainan Island. The lar, or white-handed gibbon *(H. lar),* is found in Cambodia, Siam, southern Burma, the Malaysian peninsula and Sumatra, all races having four white hands with a somewhat darker color in the palm.

Until recent times gibbons were common throughout Southeast Asia, but their number has decreased tragically with the clearing of forests in some regions and especially at the hands of hunters, although in most places such hunting is officially forbidden. One of the main causes for their decline is the popularity of these acrobatic performers in zoological gardens. A local hunter who catches a gibbon alive will always get a high price for it in the nearest city. The usual strategy—used, alas, for all the larger monkeys and apes both in Africa and Asia—is to capture the baby by killing the mother. Usually, however, the infant has little chance of surviving the first few days of captivity in a local village where, instead of milk, it is fed a bowl of rice or at best a banana. It is hardly an exaggeration to say that for every gibbon that arrives safely in a zoological garden at least one hundred die before they get there.

A dark-handed gibbon (Hylobates agilis) *in Malaya, among the most acrobatic and the noisiest of Old World apes. (F. G. H. Allen)*

Ten Thousand Islands

The Malay Archipelago

12 South of Indochina, the Asian continent crumbles, so to speak, into fragments: almost ten thousand islands are strewn through the Indian and Pacific Oceans between Indochina and Australia and New Guinea—a surface as vast as the whole of the United States. Many of these are deserted and remain nameless even upon sea charts but others rank among the largest islands on our planet.

Borneo, third largest island after Greenland and New Guinea, is one and one-half times the size of France. In the

Right: The Philippine archipelago is divided into 7,100 islands with eleven of them accounting for 95 percent of the total land surface. (Ted Spiegel: Rapho Guillumette) Below: The redtailed tropic-bird (Phaëthon rubicauda), *found all over the Indian Ocean, is a bird of the open sea that feeds mainly on small fish. (F. G. H. Allen)*

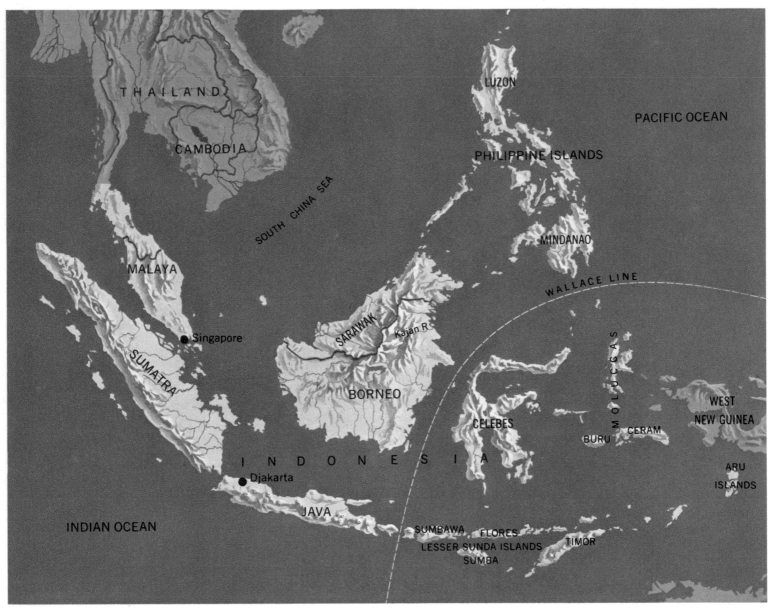

Since the Malay Archipelago was part of Asia until a recent geologic epoch, its plants and animals are largely those of the tropical part of the continent. It is still mostly covered with great rain forests.

words of the great nineteenth-century naturalist and traveler, Alfred Russel Wallace, Borneo could easily engulf all the British Isles in an ocean of forest. Sumatra is larger than England and Ireland combined. Java, Celebes, Mindanao and Luzon are each as large as Cuba, and at least twenty others range between the size of Puerto Rico and that of Formosa. Taken together, the total land area of the Malay Archipelago amounts to about 770,000 square miles.

Flanked by two continents, Asia and Australia, the archipelago is of particular interest not only to naturalists and anthropologists but to geologists as well. For where we would expect the flora, fauna and human populations in the westerly islands to have much in common with Asia, those in the east to resemble Australia, and those in the middle to be a mixture of the two, there are many strange exceptions. For example, studies of these regions made by the American botanist Elmer D. Merrill reveal that the flora of the Philippines is much closer to that of far-off Australia than to the neighboring islands of Borneo or Formosa. As for the fauna, most Asiatic species have readily colonized the archipelago as far as the

Greater Sunda Islands but a mysterious barrier seems to have prevented most of them from going any farther. Similarly, most Australian species seem to have stopped at Tasmania and New Guinea. Another curious fact is that those islands lying midway between the two continents, instead of reaping the benefits of their crossroads position, are relatively poor in animal life.

The only explanation for these anomalies is that definite barriers do exist. Indeed, a study of the submarine topography of this region reveals that two vast continental plateaus lurk beneath the ocean's surface, each covered by very shallow waters but separated from each other by deep trenches. One of these, the Sunda shelf, joins Sumatra, Java and Borneo to the Asian continent, while the other, known as the Sahul shelf, joins New Guinea to Australia and Tasmania. Were the

In estuaries of Malaysian rivers, short-trunked nipa palms back up coastal mangroves. Tall coco palms are planted or sprout from coconuts swept in by the tide. (Pierre Pfeffer)

224

seas to drop a mere hundred feet or so, each set of island outposts would become part of the neighboring continent. According to geologists, these connections were once a reality: before the great glaciations at the end of the Tertiary Period, the Sunda shelf formed what is called Sundaland while the Sahul shelf formed Papualand.

As the continental glaciers melted at the beginning of the Quaternary Period, the seas rose and the Sunda Islands were thus isolated from Asia while New Guinea was cut off from Australia. Celebes, the Philippines and the Moluccas acquired their jagged outlines as the seas invaded former river valleys. One proof of such a change in sea level is the presence of a coral barrier reef, three hundred miles long, southeast of Borneo; this could have been formed only in shallow waters.

Study of the relief of the ocean floor provided another proof. This is the presence of traces of a hydrographic system that flowed toward the South China Sea and drained a large valley whose sides are now eastern Sumatra and western Borneo. The same species of fresh-water fish still swim in the rivers of both countries. Another river, with tributaries flowing from northeastern Java and southern Borneo, flowed eastward into a valley now covered by the Java Sea.

On the basis of these speculations and the affinities in flora and especially in fauna, Alfred Russel Wallace traced a line of demarcation between what he called the Indo-Malaysian and the Austro-Malaysian regions. Going from south to north, the Wallace Line passes between Bali and Lombok, traverses the Makassar Strait and then the Celebes Sea, curving above the island of Celebes. This line thus sets off the Greater Sunda Islands and the Philippines from the rest of the archipelago: the Lesser Sunda Islands, Celebes and the Moluccas. This biographical distinction has a good deal of validity and will be used in this chapter, treating on the one hand Malaysia in the broad sense (the Malay Peninsula, the Greater Sunda Islands and the Philippines) and on the other hand everything else that falls between Wallace Line and New Guinea, often called Wallacea in honor of this great naturalist.

RAIN, HEAT AND WINDLESS CALM

The Malay Archipelago lies squarely in the heart of the tropics and most of its islands are either directly on the equator or not more than 10° to the north or south of it. Heat, humidity and windless calm—the typical equatorial climate—reign both on the islands and in the seas. Average temperatures in the lower regions hover around 77° F with a difference of not more than two degrees between the coldest and warmest months. The higher regions enjoy a cooler climate and I remember feeling chilled at night in the mountains of Borneo. Above 6,000 feet in both Borneo and Java, frost has occasionally been recorded at night.

The sky is often darkened by clouds. The sun does shine at least six to eight hours per day and to the uninitiated European it may seem weak and hazy but it can be dangerous. When we first arrived in Djakarta European friends there advised us to wear pajamas on the beach and even in the water. This seemed absurd, and we wore bathing suits when we set out the following day for a small coral isle off the coast of Java. That evening the two blond members of our crew returned huddled at the bottom of our boat with a very bad case of sunstroke and sunburn.

Regions directly on the equator enjoy abundant and almost daily rainfall with only one short, dry period. Only once during a stay of over a year in the heart of Borneo did I count ten consecutive days without rain. Local populations anticipate these annual "droughts," which coincide with the equinox, and use them to clear and burn the forests for the cultivation of mountain dry rice. Periods of maximum rainfall, on the other hand, occur twice a year, when the sun is at its zenith.

The farther from the equator the greater the influence of the monsoons, but weather conditions are complicated in the archipelago by the proximity of the two continental landmasses, Asia (in the boreal hemisphere) and Australia (in the austral hemisphere). The summer monsoon—which coincides in the northern hemisphere with our summer and in the southern hemisphere with our winter—normally brings rain whereas the winter monsoon, bearing winds from the continents, is usually dry. But if the latter picks up moisture during a long trip across the ocean, it may cause much precipitation as soon as it meets an obstacle.

As a result, some areas may have heavy rainfall while others, on the same island but sheltered by a chain of mountains, may be in the midst of their dry season. This contrast is particularly true of Celebes and the Moluccas but it can also be observed in eastern Java: during the month of August —the austral winter—the city of Pakudo, south of Idjen volcano, gets almost sixteen inches of rainfall from the monsoon blowing from the southeast while the region of Baluran just on the other side of the massif gets no more than a tiny fraction of an inch. The same dichotomy is true of many of the Lesser Sundas, Bali, Lombok, Sumbawa, Sumba, Flores and Timor— intense dryness in the north while the south enjoys a few rains. In spite of such local variations, lands north of the equator generally face a dry season in winter and a rainy season in summer; south of the equator it is just the opposite.

On the whole, the Malay Archipelago boasts of an extremely abundant and regular rainfall. The norm is somewhere above 80 inches, generally between 130 and 170 inches. Rains in the tropics are far more torrential than those in Europe but the interminable drizzles that in many parts of Europe persist grimly for days in autumn and winter are unknown. Even during the rainy season the mornings are usually sunny; clouds begin to gather around ten o'clock but it is not until early afternoon that the downpour begins. Then, sheets of rain transform paths into gulleys, roads into torrents and streets into rivers. After two hours the cataract ends just as abruptly as it began, the clouds disperse and the sun shines until nightfall, usually followed by mild, clear evenings.

ACTIVE AND DORMANT VOLCANOES

Squalls and hurricanes are almost unheard of except in the northern parts of the Philippines and on the island of Timor. The air is calm and windless, the waters as smooth as glass. This can be an inconvenience for sailors: out at sea in an

Right above and below: Thousands of orchids grow on trees in the equatorial forest, but species sought by orchid fanciers are rare. (Both, Lu Ming Sheng) Far right: Many wild banana trees (Musa sp.) bearing small fruits filled with black seeds grow in the damp forests, especially in clearings. (E. S. Ross)

outrigger pirogue we would often find ourselves forced to spend endless hours rowing to shore because our raffia sail had suddenly slackened and collapsed. The earth itself in the Malay Archipelago is unfortunately not as tranquil as the air: During one of my first nights in Java I was suddenly thrown out of bed by a series of minor quakes. The entire archipelago is girded by a belt of almost five hundred volcanoes, a hundred of which are still active and have erupted at least once in the last few centuries.

The eruption of Krakatau was one of the most famous in recent history. The whole island, located between Sumatra and Java, literally exploded, shaking the entire archipelago and filling the air with falling ash for almost two years. A gigantic tidal wave swept over the neighboring islands, engulfing villages and claiming at least forty thousand lives. In 1919, the Kalud volcano of eastern Java violently hurled forth its crater lake—fifty million cubic yards of water laden with solid matter, taking a toll of 5,500 lives. During its last eruption at the end of the eighteenth century, Papandajan volcano of western Java destroyed forty villages. To this day ominous rumbles still surge from its depths. In 1962, almost thirty thousand people were annihilated by the sudden eruption of Bali's Agun volcano. Ironically, they had gathered on the flanks of this sacred volcano to present the customary offerings—an event that takes place but once a century! Just a month before the catastrophe I had visited the island and admired a lush countryside surrounding the mountain. One year later I saw nothing but dust and ashes.

The Malay Archipelago offers an ideal field of study to the geographer—almost every type of volcano can be studied in this region. Most typical are those with a perfect cone, nesting in a sea of mist with a wreath of smoke trailing from the summit. Mayon volcano in the southwest portion of Luzon is one of the most regular in shape and is considered the equal even of Japan's famous Fuji in majesty. Papandajan represents another type; the crater is more complex and constantly spews forth clouds of sulfurous gases. These settle as golden crystals on its slopes, and children of the neighboring villages often come to gather basketfuls to offer as gifts to visitors on the island. In some cases there is a double crater, as on western Java's Tangkuban Prahu. Or, there may be a series of secondary cones around the main cone, as on Lamongan in eastern Java, Bonthain in Celebes and Tambora in Sumbawa.

Other volcanoes stand together in groups, often in the center of a vast caldera—a huge crater flanked by steep walls of lava, some several hundred feet high as those of Tengger volcano in Java. From the edge of the main crater the visitor looks down into a yawning gulf almost six miles in diameter, where, amidst a sea of sand and dunes rise the craters of smaller volcanoes: Widodaren, Batok and Bromo. The crest of Batok is an almost perfect cone, its flanks cut by deep ravines. Streams of pilgrims pay yearly visits to the sacred Bromo; they come laden with chickens and goats which they sacrifice alive to its fuming crater to appease the angry gods.

The presence of both active and dormant volcanoes has left its stamp on the entire topography of the region. The vision of lowlands clad in marsh and forest as the typical equatorial landscape is true only of some of the lower regions of the Malay Peninsula, Sumatra and Borneo. Elsewhere the terrain is rugged. The highest peak, at 13,455 feet, is Mount Kinabalu in Borneo. The highest summits on Sumatra and Java are Kerintji (12,484 feet) and Semeru (12,060 feet) but many others

on these islands and on the Philippines range between 9,000 and 10,500 feet. Whereas most lofty peaks in continental Asia slope gradually to their maximum heights, here the steep mountains rise almost vertically from the sea. From what I have heard from climbers who have scaled the Himalayas I would think that it is far easier to climb to fifteen thousand feet in the Himalayas than to 9,000 feet in Java or 4,500 feet in the Lesser Sundas and the Moluccas.

FORESTS ON THE MOVE

On some islands, especially Java, the familiar silhouettes of the volcanoes lend a special beauty to the landscape. From any point on this island there rises on the horizon a somber mountain with a halo of white cloud, looming over low or terraced rice fields. On the islands that are geologically more ancient, such as Sumatra and Borneo, the features of the terrain have been blurred beneath the lush vegetation.

One of the most interesting of these zones, which greets the traveler arriving by sea, is the mangrove, a growth typical of tropical regions in Africa, America and Australia. Adapted to living with its "feet in the water," this forest thrives on the islands as an outer fringe from seventy feet to ten miles wide and along the interior estuaries. They are found as far inland as the ebb and flow of the tides have an effect—for mangrove roots require this alternating rhythm of submersion and exposure. There are three genera with a variety of species, each occupying a distinct place according to the strength of the tide and the salinity of the water. Most mangrove trees are of medium stature but some species, especially of *Bruguiera*, may grow as tall as a hundred feet. All bear small, leathery leaves and dainty white flowers. The easiest way to identify a particular species is by the root system.

Growing nearest to the sea are the *Rhizophora (R. mucronata, R. apiculata)*. The Greek name, meaning "root carrier," is an accurate description of the wild profusion of aerial roots of all sizes springing both from branches and trunk. This baroque array of arches and flying buttresses forms an impenetrable tangle breached only by the river estuaries. Sparse stands of *Rhizophora* are able to take hold in sandy or coral beaches but true forests need muddy soil to flourish.

The place behind the *Rhizophora* is reserved for the *Bruguiera (B. conjugata, B. sexangula)*. Here, the roots are not aerial, but crawl as long snakes just above or below the ground. After these come the *Sonneratia (S. caseolaris, S. alba)*; growing in the mud, the roots have long points jutting above the surface like the spikes on a fakir's bed of nails. Some botanists assign a respiratory role to these points but since they are submerged in water much of the time they may have

Right above: All the muddy coasts of tropical Asia are fringed with mangroves of the genera Rhizophora, Bruguiera *and* Sonneratia *(above). (Ivan Polunin) Right: Fiddler crabs of the genus* Uca *live in all mangrove swamps of the Old and New Worlds. During high tide they hide in burrows closed with corks of pressed sand. (Pierre Pfeffer) Far right: Mud skippers (the large are* Boleophtalmus *and the small are* Periophtalmus), *strange denizens of mangrove swamps, hop on the mud or climb over tree roots, entering the water only when pursued. (Ivan Polunin)*

By retaining mud at high tide, mangrove trees build up land and thus constantly encroach on the sea, meanwhile disappearing from the interior as the soil dries out. (Peter Ward)

some other function as yet undiscovered. Whatever their role, it is certain that they help the tree stand firm, and brace it against the onslaught of waves, especially at high tide.

Both species of *Sonneratia* noted above prefer waters low in salinity. They are found quite far inland, where they mingle with nipa palms *(Nipa fruticans)* that are so short in stem that the palms seem to spring out of the mud. A third species, *Sonneratia griffithii,* takes to much stronger salinity and is often found where the tides retreat the farthest, braving the elements in front of the *Rhizophora* outposts.

Mangroves perform a vital geological function: in the words of Dillon Ripley, American naturalist and specialist on tropical Asia, these trees wage a valiant battle against the sea by draining the shores. The aerial root system allows muddy sediment to build up instead of being swept back out to sea. As layers of these sediments accumulate, other mangroves

take root; in this way these strange forests on stilts slowly but surely conquer the shoreline.

Reproduction in the mangrove is not the least of its feats. The seeds risk being carried out to sea or scattered on firm ground. But the mangrove tree takes the precaution of germinating the seed on the spot and then planting it in the surrounding narrow muddy fringe. Growing at the tip of a branch, the seed develops a long, smooth and pointy root. The tiny plantlet even supplies feathers for its own arrow in the form of a terminal bud surrounded by two small leaves. When ripe it falls—the point headfirst. This is the only stage left to fate: if the parent plant tosses its offspring at high tide the embryo is carried to sea with only the smallest hope of being carried back by the waves. But if the tide is low it has every chance of survival: the point thrusts in the mud like a dagger and within the space of a few hours the plantlet develops tiny roots which anchor it firmly in the soil.

MUD SKIPPERS AND FIDDLER CRABS

The rich fauna lurking in the twilight of the mangrove forest is often heard rather than seen: the plashing of mollusks clapping together their valves, the gurgling of fish in a tangle of roots, the cooings of tiny herons—these are all familiar sounds in this strange forest where the muddy banks merge almost imperceptibly with murky waters.

The traveler new to tropical seas would probably be surprised at the sight of hundreds of tiny fish, about the size of a gudgeon, leaping from the water and crawling over corals and on tree trunks. These are mud skippers. Its Greek name, *Periophthalmus,* meaning "eyes outside," refers to the way the eyes bulge way out of the head, permitting the mud skipper to see above the water's surface while its body is submerged.

In the midst of a chase, mud skippers have been known to make leaps of almost three feet, but they usually get about by propping themselves on their breast fins and moving by brisk flips of the tail, "walking" in this manner at about two miles an hour. As they skip about the mud they pursue small crustaceans—the mainstay of their diet. From time to time mud skippers have the habit of standing up almost vertically on the tip of the tail and then slumping down on the mud. Some say they do this to snatch a passing fly but my guess is that this display is simply a way of attracting the attention of other mud skippers.

Although they take to the water when in danger, these curious fish cannot survive long under water; it has been demonstrated that they actually drown if they are prevented from coming up for air. In clear water, rich in oxygen, this would not be true, but in the brackish slime of the mangrove, air is indispensable. This is not to say that mud skippers have lungs along with gills as do some African and Australian fish, but that their gills are constantly kept moist by water carried in small spongy cavities on each side of the head. Thus, whereas the deep-sea diver uses air-breathing underwater, the mud skipper uses underwater-breathing on land. One

The Malayan small-clawed otter (Amblonyx cinerea) *frequents mangrove swamps, hunting the crustaceans and small fish that swarm there. (Jane Burton: Photo Researchers)*

A portrait of an adult proboscis shows its remarkable nose. (Harrison Forman)

Proboscis monkeys are good swimmers. This large male was picked up on the high seas where it had been carried by the tide. (Hedda Morrison)

species has become so alienated from aquatic life that when pursued, it flees not toward the water but from one bush to the next.

To lay its eggs, the female digs a small hole in the mud and uses her mouth to build a wall about an inch high made of mud mixed with sticky mucus. This tiny reservoir is then connected to the nearest body of water by a small channel several yards in length. In the muddy water of this miniature pond a small number of tiny oblong eggs are deposited for fertilization by the male. Most other fish lay their eggs and leave them to fate; in the few species that linger to keep watch the doting parent is always the male. It is the female mud skipper, however, who stands by until the eggs are hatched. The young then live in the family pool, adapting only gradually to an amphibious way of life.

The proboscis monkey (Nasalis larvatus), found in the mangrove swamps of Borneo, eats only the leaves of Sonneratia and the flowers of nipa palms. The female (left) lacks the long proboscis. (Harrison Forman)

There are other fascinating inhabitants of the mangrove. Millions of small, vividly colored *Uca* crabs, called fiddler crabs, about the size of a large coin, haunt the waters and seem to beckon to the visitor with an uncanny gesture of their long white claws. But as soon as they are approached, these jewel-like creatures vanish almost mysteriously. To observe them one must lie still in the mud, keeping close watch over one of the many tiny burrows. After a while, a cautious eye at the end of a stalklike feeler may peep out. If the coast is clear the owner of the eyes emerges. Actually it has only one long claw, almost as large as itself—a second, stunted claw is used to scoop morsels of mud to the mouth, from which the crab extracts organic matter. Whereas the male is brilliantly colored, the female is a brownish color and has only two small claws. Each male chooses and defends a specific place in the mud and any rivalry leads to a struggle, each male trying to break his adversary's long claw.

In the midst of its territory the crab digs a narrow burrow about fifteen inches long. This it maintains endlessly with repairs, at the same time building up a vertical column, often set at an angle like the leaning Tower of Pisa. With adhesive substances the crab fashions a kind of stopper or cork; when

Rizophora *are mangrove trees whose trunks put out lateral roots that help to anchor the tree in mud.*
(Pierre Pfeffer)

the tide rises the crab takes refuge in its shelter and shuts the door firmly behind it, waiting for the waters to recede. If the crab is hindered in constructing its little lid, it becomes panicky with the coming of the first waves and frantically shapes a ball of mud to shut off the entry.

But the most curious habit of these crustaceans is the motion of the long claw that has earned them the name of fiddler crab. This is a beckoning call to the weaker sex. When a female is passing, all the males in the vicinity stand high on their legs and begin waving their long white or pink claws until the fair creature is charmed by one and joins him in his lair.

Mangroves shelter a great wealth of interesting crabs and shrimp of every size and color. One of the most amusing is the soldier crab *(Dotilla mictyroïdes)*, with long legs and a spherical body. Great troops of these small crabs can be seen trekking to the shore like the hordes of Genghis Khan's horsemen. Another, the gray shrimp, is one of the most useful species, for it breeds in the mangrove and fishermen catch the young shrimp by the millions for use in a very popular seasoning.

THE ARCHER FISH: MASTER MARKSMAN

In the brackish waters of inland estuaries, small yellow fish with five or six large black spots on the side, poke about the tangle of roots. It circles near the water's surface in the shadow of a large tree, keeping a sharp eye on the branches above. Once it sights an insect in the trees, the fish pokes its nose just above the water and fires fine spurts of water at his victim, adjusting its aim with each shot. When it hits its mark it simply waits for the prey to fall and gobbles it up. Because of this habit, it has been dubbed archer fish *(Toxotes jaculator)*.

This profusion of mollusks, fish and crustaceans draws a great many predators. Monitor lizards *(Varanus salvator)*, often as much as seven feet long, are frequent visitors and are so proficient in climbing, running, swimming and diving that few animals can escape them. Sea crocodiles *(Crocodylus porosus)*, more notorious among fishermen than sharks, lie in wait in the murky shadows of the mangrove and nest in small estuaries. In eastern Java I saw one that was well over fifteen feet long, and they have been known on rare occasions to reach a size of thirty feet.

Sea snakes, particularly of the genera *Enhydrina* and *Hydrophis,* are often quite numerous. One night when a companion and I were wading ashore from our pirogue, our flashlights suddenly revealed them on all sides, coiled at the bottom and writhing about the mangrove roots. Normally they are not aggressive creatures and reserve their venom for paralyzing fish, their usual prey. But since this venom is twice as toxic as that of a cobra, the thought of accidentally stepping on one was far from pleasant.

The mangrove fauna is also subject to bird predators. The most common of the latter are fish eagles *(Haliaetus leucogaster)* with their graceful flight and elegant gray and white plumage, the brash and noisy brahminy kites *(Haliastur indus),* who dare to whisk fish away from under the nose of a fisherman, adjutant storks *(Leptoptilos javanicus)* strutting solemnly across the mud with their bald heads drawn down between their hunched shoulders, and a host of herons and kingfishers. Most handsome of the latter is the stork-billed kingfisher *(Pelargopsis capensis),* with its red beak, bright blue back and rust-colored belly standing out like a flower against the drab mangroves.

A few ground-living birds frequent the mangrove. Among these are crows *(Corvus macrorhynchus),* even bolder than the kites and constantly squabbling over dead fish or carcasses washed in by the sea. There are also several varieties of flycatchers, notably the black-naped blue monarch *(Hypothymis azurea)* and the mangrove blue flycatcher *(Muscicapa rufigaster).* Along with the sand martins, these flycatchers live on the myriads of mosquitos and sand flies that swarm in this area. The sand flies are an especial plague, penetrating even the finest mosquito nets and transporting such human diseases as sand fly fever and filariasis.

Among the other insects that make their home in the mangrove are fireflies. They usually flash their light in unison and sometimes the greenish beams make a mangrove glow like a Christmas tree in the dark tropical night.

MERMAIDS AND CRAB-EATING MONKEYS

Wild pigs *(Sus scrofa, S. vittatus)* pay frequent visits to the mangrove for an occasional dinner of crabs and mollusks. Their burrowing for these delicacies leaves deep furrows in the mud and sand. Evidently some pigs make this their exclusive diet: the fat and flesh of one that had been killed were a brilliant salmon color and it had such an overpowering fish taste that no one could eat it.

Otters *(Lutra sumatrana)* are also seen here but mainly in search of fish. The crab's greatest enemy here, the long-tailed macaque *(Macaca irus),* is known as the crab-eating monkey. These macaques, along with other species, are found throughout Southeast Asia. All members of the clan have similar

Above: Limuloids (Limula), *incorrectly called king-crabs or horseshoe crabs, are really archaic arthropods, living fossils or relics of the Mesozoic Era. (F. G. H. Allen) Right: A soldier crab* (Dotilla mictyroides), *so called because it often moves across a beach in legions, builds a mud shelter against the rising tide. (M. W. F. Tweedie)*

Pandanus or screw-pines predominate in coastal forests. In some species, the seeds in the large red fruits are edible after cooking. (M. W. F. Tweedie)

habits and all are considered a great nuisance by the local inhabitants because of their extremely destructive habits. With all their faults, they are extremely entertaining creatures to watch, especially during their crab hunting. They emerge from the woods in Indian file led by one of the older males, and if the coast is clear they all disperse, males in one direction, females and young in the other. As soon as a crab is seen disappearing into its burrow, a monkey stands perfectly motionless near the opening and seizes it as soon as it reappears. The monkey then with very human gestures tears it apart and devours it. Of course things do not always go so smoothly; some crabs put up a fight and the monkey then has trouble handling it.

Macaques are at home not only in mangroves but in a great variety of habitats; less widespread is the proboscis monkey *(Nasalis larvatus)*, which is found exclusively in the mangroves of northern and eastern Borneo. It is a large monkey, the male sometimes reaching a height of four or five feet, but its most extraordinary feature is the nasal appendage of the adult male—so monstrously long that it hangs down over the mouth and chin. These creatures are rare and very little is known about them. I had the good fortune to observe troops of about fifteen or twenty of them, led by the males, in the mangrove forests at the mouth of the Kajan River in eastern Borneo. These forests are really vast marshes clad in mangrove trees and nipa palms. The diet of the monkeys is made up exclusively of the fruits and leaves of the *Sonneratia caseolaris* mangrove and the red flowers of the nipa palm. Vegetarian diet is typical of the whole leaf-eating family of monkeys, all members of it having special digestive adaptations to this kind of food. It is sometimes thought that a proboscis monkey must lift its nose with its hand whenever it eats, but this is not so. It is true, however, that when the animal is angered its nose not only reddens and swells to absurd proportions, but begins to vibrate ridiculously.

These creatures are in many ways grotesque. They amble slowly about and spend endless hours gazing into space, absently scratching their absurd noses. In spite of their large size they are peaceable: they can even be playfully grabbed by the tail without turning in defense. This is probably because humans are rare in their domain. They may of course adapt to local conditions: although those I observed in the Kayan delta were friendly, I later met others among more remote mangroves of Borneo that reacted with great alarm because of persecution by Dayaks armed with blowpipes firing poisoned darts. Their only enemy is the crocodile, which attacks as soon as the monkeys, which are good swimmers and can cross wide rivers, venture into the water. One proboscis monkey, probably carried by the undertow, was even found far out at sea and taken aboard by Chinese fishermen.

A still stranger inhabitant of the mangroves is the dugong *(Dugong dugong)*. It is not limited to Borneo but is also occasionally found throughout the islands of the Indian Ocean and the Pacific from the east coast of Africa to Formosa and Australia. A close relative of the extinct Steller's sea cow, the dugong is a massive, seal-like creature weighing as much as 650 pounds and about six feet long. Unlike the seal, the dugong is a vegetarian, feeding on the leaves of the mangrove and on marine algae *(Zostera, Posidonia* and *Halophila)*.

Although I have seen this elusive creature only twice, I often heard the melancholy sound of its call, which is the origin of its Malayan name *douhong*. This haunting call, along with the fact that the females have almost human breasts and clasp their young to their bosoms, may well have given rise to the legends of the mermaids, half woman, half fish, who called to sailors and lured them to their deep-sea kingdoms. Scientists have thus classified the dugong in an order known as *Sirenia,* along with Steller's sea cow and the manatee, which is found in fresh waters in Africa and tropical America.

The dugong is a quite harmless creature despite the fact that the male has two large incisors, similar to walrus tusks. In fact, these incisors have proved to be more of a handicap than a help because they are prized for their allegedly marvelous powers. In Indonesia it is widely believed that the possessor of a dugong tooth is invulnerable to poison, gunfire and evil spirits. Made of a lovely rosy ivory and sometimes eight inches long, the tusks sell for from twenty-five to fifty dollars on the local market. The animals themselves are hunted for their flesh and for "dugong tears," a viscous substance found in their eyes and made by the Chinese and Indonesians into a love potion that is thought to be infallible.

In spite of the laws protecting them, dugongs are hunted either by harpoon or nets. Fishermen admit that even in the last thirty years the dugong population has decreased considerably and what with their slow rate of reproduction—a single cub about every two years—there is little hope that this curious creature will escape extermination.

WONDERS OF THE SEASHORE

Along some stretches of coast, especially those bathed by the waters of the Indian Ocean, large breakers hinder the deposition of muddy sediment. Here the shore is fringed with gentle sandy beaches, white, gray or even black, depending upon the amount of volcanic matter. In some places the beaches are littered with rough coral rocks.

These shores, among the most beautiful in the world, are a shell collector's delight, especially along certain deserted stretches. Here can be found cowries *(Cypraea)* polished to a soft luster by the waves; cones *(Conus),* white or mottled with brown; murex *(Murex)* bristling with fine spines; the large green turbo; the frosted valves of the pearl oyster *(Pinctada)* and a host of other shellfish, from the tiny pearl-like nucules *(Nucula)* to the giant clam *(Tridacna).* The large tan and white shell of the *Nautilus* occurs here but it is so

fragile that it is rarely found intact. Nor would one find the nautilus itself for it lives in the ocean depths along with other cephalopods—cuttlefish, squids and octopuses.

In some places the beach is littered with violet-colored oval disks covered with tiny holes—the skeletons of sea urchins washed in by the tide. The urchins themselves *(Diadema),* often found in pools in the sand, are dangerous little creatures for they are armed with black spines six inches long which can cause painful wounds. These tide pools also hide a wealth of crabs, many-hued mollusks, brittle stars, feather stars, large azure-blue or bright orange starfish and tiny cuttlefish that emit a cloud of inky fluid as soon as they are approached. Here one occasionally sees hundreds of creatures resembling hazelnut shells with a long pointed tail—horseshoe crabs *(Tachypleus).* In spite of their appearance and name, horseshoe crabs have nothing in common with true crabs and are the last survivors of a group that flourished until the end of the Mesozoic Era, leaving fossil remains throughout the world.

As for the true crabs, two are very popular on all coral and sandy beaches. The first is the fleet and elusive ghost crab *(Ocypode ceratophthalma);* the second is the very familiar creature that would come swarming in the tens or even hundreds around the left-overs of one of our beach picnics.

These at first glance would seem to be empty shells but closer scrutiny would reveal two small crab claws, one of which fits neatly over the opening when the crab withdraws into the shell. Anyone familiar with shore life will recognize this as a description of the hermit crab. Since its abdominal parts are soft, making it vulnerable to predators, this crab borrows the shell of a mollusk to protect itself. In the Malay Archipelago, hermit crabs are represented by two genera: one, the *Pagurus,* quite similar to its European cousin, never strays far from the water, while the other, *Cenobites,* often ventures far inland. Attracted by the light the latter will not hesitate to raid the cottages near the shore, not sparing clothing, specimens or books.

GIANT TURTLES

Some of the sandy beaches are commonly used by the green turtle *(Chelonia mydas)* when it lays its eggs. These giants— an adult female may weigh between 250 and 800 pounds —spend almost their entire lives in the water, where, sole vegetarians among marine turtles, they feed upon the same algae as the dugongs. Mating takes place in the water and only the females come to shore at intervals of about two or three years, always returning to the same site, often more than 600 miles from their undersea pastures. The return to exactly the same egg-laying grounds bears witness to the turtle's powers of memory and the strength of its preferences. The sites are well known to the local inhabitants; from generation to generation they visit certain beaches to gather the eggs, which are considered a great delicacy.

When I last visited the southeastern tip of Java, I spent several nights on one of the green turtle's egg-laying beaches with two natives, expert in egg collecting. Behind us stretched the vast forest of Blambangan, one of Java's few primitive jungles and now set aside as a national reserve. After the ten-mile trek through the jungle during the day I dropped into a deep sleep in spite of stinging sand flies. Suddenly, one of my companions shook me, crying in Javanese, "The turtle! the turtle!" Immediately I heard sounds like heart-rending sighs coming from an enormous turtle very slowly dragging herself onto the beach by means of flippers that marked the sand like the tracks of a tank. The strain seemed to be beyond her capacity and she continued to make those sigh-like sounds. Although I longed to photograph the monster, my companions advised me to wait until the eggs were laid. But when we awoke the next morning she had disappeared, leaving exactly 140 eggs in a small excavation beneath the sand. With their soft shells the eggs looked like dented table tennis balls. Inside, the eggs are largely yellow yolk with only a thin layer of white, which does not harden even after much boiling. The yolk also remains soft and syrupy with a slightly grainy texture and is delicious.

The next few nights brought no other turtles. We did, however, catch sight of a panther circling the camp, probably in search of turtle eggs, which are esteemed by all beasts, including wild dogs and tigers. Besides the animal and human threat, the young turtles, after fifty-three days of incubation, face still another array of enemies before they reach the sea: monitor lizards, wild boars, the smaller carnivorous animals and even birds. Once in the sea they are threatened by birds and a host of fish. According to the American zoologist John Hendrickson, at least 95 percent of the young turtles perish during the first days after hatching. Luckily, the females are astonishingly prolific and are thought to lay between five and six hundred eggs each season and do this five, six or seven times in a lifetime.

The most popular beaches for egg-laying are on the Talang Talang Islands and the Turtle Islands to the north and northeast of Borneo. Altogether they yield between two and four million eggs yearly for export to Singapore, Borneo and the Philippines. Many other islands in the neighboring seas each produce between 100,000 and 250,000 eggs.

In spite of this extensive exploitation, green turtles are still quite common in the Malay Archipelago. Egg collecting is far less of a threat than the killing of the turtles themselves. Fortunately, only in Bali is turtle meat a regular part of the diet; in other areas, for example the south of Java, it is not unusual for zealous collectors literally to kill the hen with the golden eggs—slashing the female's throat to prevent competitors from obtaining the eggs. Cruel as this practice may seem it nevertheless prevails: twice I came across such slaughtered victims in the sand.

In Indonesian waters the hawksbill (Eretmochelys imbricata) is even more widespread than the green turtle. The eggs are collected and the meat highly appreciated in Bali, where it is traditionally served at marriage banquets. The carapace also yields the famous tortoise shell which is used locally for combs and ornaments although it has now been replaced on the international market by plastic imitations. Three other genera of marine turtles are found in this region: Caretta Lepidochelys and Dermochelys. They are similar in habits to the green turtle but the meat is far less prized, probably because their diet is mainly carnivorous and composed mainly of mollusks and dead fish.

COASTAL FORESTS

The sandy beaches and coral coasts of many islands are lined by what botanists call littoral forest. Behind the sands or dunes clad in stiff, bluish grasses (Spinnifex littoralis) there are often impenetrable thickets of screw pine (Pandanus tectorius). These trees branch out into a rosette of thorny, ribbon-like leaves, with a fruit that resembles a pineapple springing from the center. The red fleshy part surrounding the seeds is edible, as is the "heart" of the palm, the terminal bud at the center of the rosette. Tiny gekkos find shelter during the day in the center of the leaves.

In other places, occasionally just bordering the sea, there are delicate trees with rounded leaves like those of the linden and large yellow flowers that are often swept far out to sea by the tides. These are hibiscus (Hibiscus tiliaceus), closely related to a tree with the familiar red flower found in all exotic gardens. Much larger than the hibiscus is the Barringtonia asiatica growing in veritable forests along some shores. The undergrowth is sparse and the ground is carpeted with the leaves, fibrous pink flowers and the pear-sized fruits of the trees. This fruit is often carried to distant islands but they generally take seed in the shadow of their parents, springing from the fruit like a series of potted plants.

Some trees attract attention because of some outstanding characteristic. Such is the ketapang (Terminalia catappa), which bears long sweeping leaves that turn violet as the tree matures. The dadap (Erythrina variegata) is not so large but bursts forth during the dry season with brilliant red flowers which lure a host of insects, birds and, at night, nectar-eating bats. The Sterculia foetida, as its Latin name implies, has foul-smelling flowers as well as inedible fruits.

Forests of cassowary trees (Casuarina equisetifolia) frequently border on the sands, their trunks black and resembling in outline a cypress or pine. Somewhat rarer is the cycas tree (Cycas circinalis), which looks like a palm because its stem is crowned by pinnated leaves, but belongs to a most primitive plant family, prominent back in the Mesozoic Era.

These littoral forests usually have a sparse undergrowth; only in clearings does one find dense thickets of Wedelia biflora or Lantana camara. Animals dislike the foliage of both plants and both are considered a foe to natural pasture. They have been a particular nuisance in the Udjungkulon Reserve in the extreme west of Java. Dutch authorities cleared part of the forest to create vast pasturelands for grass-eating mammals, and in 1956 I remember seeing a goodly number of sturdy bantengs and deer in this reserve, but in 1964 I was shocked to find that after a few years of neglect the grazing lands were overrun by Wedelia and Lantana plants. The few grazing animals that I saw were weak and scrawny.

GIANT SERPENTS AND FLYING DRAGONS

The Udjungkulon Reserve is one of the most interesting in Southeast Asia. Here roam about thirty Javan rhinoceros (Rhinoceros sondaicus), sole known survivors of a species once found from Java to Indochina and probably even in Assam. The Javan rhino shares its tragic fate with all Asiatic members of the group—all victims of age-old beliefs; Chinese doctors have always considered rhino horn the best of aphrodisiacs. In Singapore an ounce of the horn is today worth sixty dollars. The horn of the African rhino is not nearly so dear and costs only about three to five dollars per ounce. In addition, the skin, blood and even the bones, dried and powdered, are considered excellent tonics, the urine and excrement are

The small one-horned or Java rhinoceros (Rhinoceros sondaicus) *is almost as rare as the Sumatran rhinoceros, only about thirty surviving in the jungle in westernmost Java. (A. Hoogerwerf: The World Wildlife Fund)*

supposed to be a cure for eye diseases while a powder obtained from worms in the rhino's intestines is thought to be the best way to fight these parasites in man. In other words, the carcass of a rhino is worth almost its weight in gold and a live animal is considered a walking fortune. Still common throughout western Java in the middle of the last century, the Javan rhino was mercilessly hunted to the verge of extinction. Were it not for the strict laws protecting it since 1921 in the Udjungkulon Reserve, it would surely appear on the long list of vanished creatures.

Among other interesting wildlife sheltered in the reserve are the already familiar bantengs, a small race of sambar deer *(Cervus timorensis)*, a species of boar *(Sus vittatus)* along with mouse-deers or chevrotains *(Tragulus kanchil)*. Although the chevrotain is a ruminant related to the musk deer of China, it bears a striking resemblance to a small South American rodent, the agouti. The only apparent differences are that the chevrotain has hoofs instead of claws and, in the male, two upper canines jutting out like daggers. The pelt is a rust-brown on the upper parts with white on the underparts and at the throat. The chevrotain is a timid creature, living alone or in pairs in the densest thickets and venturing out only at sun-

down to graze in nearby clearings or pastures. During the day it lies motionless like a hare and if approached it scurries away only at the very last moment. In Java, the tiny *kantjil,* as it is called, is the hero of many folktales: like the fox in Western fables it uses cunning to outwit enemies much larger than itself: tiger, python, panther, wild dog and even man.

The Udjungkulon Reserve is also one of the last strongholds of the tiger that once inhabited the entire island. There are also many snakes in the region; when I visited the reserve to photograph the animals it was no small surprise to come across two impressive specimens in the course of our very first day—a cobra and a cat snake *(Boiga)*. It was in this area, too, that a record specimen of the python *(Python reticulatus),* over twenty-eight feet long, was captured. And Panaitan, an islet off the coast of the reserve has even been dubbed the "island of the giant serpents" because of the size of its reptiles.

My curiosity was also aroused by what seemed to be large insects with orange-colored wings flitting from one trunk to the next in the littoral forest. When one of these finally settled near me I was surprised to discover that it was a small lizard about nine inches long, the flying dragon *(Draco volans)*. It is widespread in all Malaysia but I had never seen so many.

Although cycads—here shown in seed, a rare spectacle—resemble palms, they have archaic characteristics and belong to a plant group that flourished in the Paleozoic Era. (M. Krishnan)

Although a member of the Agamidae family, a flying dragon is not able to change color. But the overall hue, gray flecked with brown, blends perfectly with its usual haunts on tree bark. It almost creates the impression of a dazzling butterfly by a pulsating expansion and deflation of a bright yellow throat pouch. The "wings" of the flying dragon are flaps of skin which the lizard normally keeps folded at its side like a closed umbrella. As it takes off for a flight, or rather a glide, the flying dragon opens the folds to an almost perfect circle. Normally, they fly from one tree to the next but I have seen one glide as far as ninety feet. They seem to feed mainly on the red ants that crawl up and down the tree trunks. Male flying dragons are constantly defending their home territory against other males but do not seem to object to females. During displays of rivalry the males put on quite a show, stalking each other around a tree trunk, rapidly expanding and deflating the throat pouch, spreading and folding their "wings" and so forth.

In front of a female, the first stages of the display are the same as those before another male, but the female remains perfectly still. Perhaps this tells the male that he is confronted by a female. He redoubles his efforts, spreading his "wings" to a full circle, trembling and thrusting forward the throat pouch so that from a distance it looks like a long bill. Mating takes place in the trees. Later the female comes to the ground to bury about ten eggs and after about five or six weeks the baby "dragons" are hatched.

COCONUT-EATERS AND ROBBER CRABS

On the more populated islands, the original coastal forest has long since given way to coconut plantations *(Cocos nucifera),* thriving especially in sandy and slightly brackish soil. These palms are not actually native to tropical Asia. Some believe that they were introduced from Mexico in ancient times, certainly before the European discovery of this region. It is also quite possible that the palms traveled from America to the Old World by floating from island to island, for one often sees the huge nuts far at sea, impervious to salt water for long periods of time. Whatever its origins, the coconut palm, with its tall, slender silhouette reaching to a graceful leafy crown is now an integral part of the landscape and useful both to the inhabitants and much of the local animal life.

Macaque monkeys, for example, appreciate these palms. Although these monkeys in the wild state do not feed on the nuts since they cannot crack the shell, they like the buds, and in pillaging these wreak havoc in the plantations. In fact, I was called upon to aid the people of one Indonesian village where macaque monkeys were systematically raiding plantations, stealing from clothes lines, plundering cornfields and even biting children who tried to chase them away. My strategy was to wait for a troop of the bandits to invade the palms in the center of the village, and then attack them, killing one before they fled. From that day on I was the terror of every monkey in the region; but they continued to show the same defiance toward the villagers.

It is only fair to point out that these monkeys can be of great help to the plantation owners. In Sumatra and Malaysia the pig-tailed macaque *(Macaca nemestrina)* has been trained to gather nuts. With a long cord tied around its waist, it scrambles to the top of the tree. As it moves from one nut to the next, its master tugs at the cord when it arrives at the ripe ones. At this signal the monkey winds the nut around its stem until it breaks off. At the end of a hard day's work it receives a stalk of corn or a few bananas as its reward.

Coconuts are considered a delicacy by wild boars; they are able to break the tough shell, drink the milk and eat the meat. Often, too, the shells split by themselves when the ripe nuts fall to the ground. One of my favorite pastimes was to prowl through the forest at night around the plantations with an unlit miner's lamp around my forehead, walking cautiously to avoid the crunching of the dry palm leaves and trying to keep the wind ahead of me, for most animals, and especially boars, have a keen sense of sound and smell. At the familiar clicking

Bantengs (Bibos sondaicus) *are found from Indochina to Malaysia. Adult males are darker than females and in the Javan race, shown here, may even be sooty black. (Pierre Pfeffer)*

240

sound that boars make with their jaws when they open a nut I would turn on the lamp and try to flash it in the right direction hoping to sight the creature, which I rarely did because of the dense screen of palms and tall grasses.

Such prowls were full of surprises. Often one crossed the path of a panther lurking about the village in search of a dog. Sometimes one came upon wild or domestic buffalos, which often seemed to be enraged by the lamp and charged directly at it. More than once the rays of my lamp revealed the presence of a monstrous robber crab *(Birgus latro)*. This crab, which may reach one and one-half feet in diameter, feeds almost exclusively on coconuts; in fact, a chemical analysis of the crab's fat showed that it has the same composition as coconut oil and does not resemble the fatty substances in other marine creatures. The fat accumulates mainly in the abdomen and as much as one quart may be drawn from a single crab. This diet has made zoologists wonder what the crab's ancestors ate before the palm was introduced in this region. The probable answer is that in those times the fruits of various other palms such as the *Borassus* or the *Pandanus* were abundant.

Before reaching adulthood the robber crab, like its close cousin the hermit crab, protects its vulnerable abdominal parts by means of a borrowed shell. Once it develops a calcified abdominal shield it abandons this burdensome shelter and can then adopt a terrestrial way of life. But since, like all crustaceans, it breathes through gills, it has a crucial need for moisture and often bathes in the sea at night, spending the day on land in a deep burrow thickly lined with coconut fibers. It is also at night that large bands of these crabs visit the coconut plantations. According to the natives, they readily scramble to the top of the palm and select the choice fruit. As for opening the shell, Darwin reported that a British resident of the Coco Islands said that the crab strips the shell fiber by fiber and then uses the large pincers as a hammer to shatter the thinnest part at the tip of the shell. It then uses its smaller pincers to extract the meat.

Other crabs forage in the littoral forest. When we set rodent traps using a biscuit or pieces of cassava we often found the claws and pincers of a land crab *(Cardisoma carnifex)*, another adaptable scavenger that is at home on land, in water and in trees and spares nothing edible that it finds in its path. Once, when four of us were camping on a deserted island in Indonesia along with our mascot, a macaque monkey, we discovered that our soap, towels and sundry other items were disappearing no matter where we hid them. The mystery was finally solved when one morning I rose to light the fire and discovered that a land crab had made its burrow in the dead ashes. Suddenly, a white object caught my eye—it turned out to be one of our towels, intact. Digging further I found all the other missing objects. It is hard to imagine just what use the land crab could make of such inedible articles.

Palmyra palms (Borassus flabellifer), *which yield a sap used to make wine or sugar, usually grow on hot coastal savannas.* (M. Krishnan)

243

Mountain Cats and Grassland Buffalos

Forests and Savannas of Malaysia

13 Between the coastal vegetation and the foothills of the inland mountain chains stretches the true rain forest—that mysterious "jungle" a child imagines in tales of exotic adventure. At first sight the forest is almost disappointing; instead of the impenetrable tangle he had imagined, the traveler is surprised to find himself treading freely among gigantic trees that resemble the pillars of a vast temple. The air is relatively cool and, 130 to 150 feet above the ground, the leafy canopy of the tallest trees closes out the sunlight. In the eternal shade below, where every plant reaches up toward the dim light above, the tree trunks are perfectly straight and bare of branches—a far cry from the scenes in jungle films. Even the stories about carnivorous plants and "strangling" vines are much exaggerated. Actually, the largest victim of the most carnivorous of tropical plants, the Nepenthes, is a fly and the only growths worthy of the name strangler are certain parasitic figs which may eventually smother their tree hosts.

However, once the virgin forest is cleared by man or destroyed by natural fires, the secondary growth is much closer to the popular image of dense jungle. Oddly enough, this secondary forest is composed not of the young saplings of the primary forest species but those of completely different species. The explanation of this is simple: species of the primary rain forest are adapted to lack of sunlight and, unlike most plants, the seeds and saplings thrive only in shadow. When the virgin forest is destroyed, the seeds of the original shade-loving species are unable to germinate on the bare ground and trees that thrive in open forest take over. The secondary forest will thus have an entirely different appearance, even to the uninitiated. The same changes take place in the fauna—species characteristic of open spaces eagerly colonize this new habitat.

But nothing is static in nature. When trees of the secondary forest finally grow tall enough to spread sufficient shadow, seeds scattered from neighboring virgin forests take root and in turn eventually smother the young plants of the secondary forest in darkness. After a century or two the virgin forest is restored to its original splendor.

Although undergrowth in the mature rain forest is relatively sparse, this is not to say that walking through it is easy. Beneath a thin carpet of dead leaves the soil always remains muddy and slippery from the constant rain storms. And, since the ground is uneven and hilly, the hiker may suddenly find himself taking a spill. If one does start to skid the instinctive reaction of reaching out for support should be avoided. Chances are it will be some rattan palm with stinging thorns, a poisonous shrub *(Semecarpus gluta),* an arborescent nettle *(Laportea)* or a bush covered with caterpillars that have stinging hairs. One of my Dayak guides once had the misfortune of grabbing one of these poisonous vines, and for an entire week his back was covered with huge lumps and he writhed with pain in spite of all remedies. Another time I reached out and found myself holding an almost invisible lizard. This was a stroke of luck for it was a species known as the fringed gekko *(Ptychozoon kühli),* usually impossible to find because of its astonishing camouflage. The entire body, legs and tail of this lizard are fringed with a delicate lacelike border of skin, totally obscuring both the contours and shadows of the animal. Its overall brownish color adorned with irregular spots is an almost perfect rendering of tree bark covered with lichens, and the lizard can vary the hues at will.

When it begins to rain, travel through the forest becomes still more difficult. Virtual cataracts pierce the forest canopy, and since there are no low branches there is no shelter. To avoid chills the best thing is to continue walking—ploughing through the tacky mud in spite of the rain.

Leeches abound in dry weather but during these downpours they are in their element. At almost every other step one passes one of these creatures poised at attention on the ground, weaving its body around and ready to fix upon anything that crosses its path. When we stopped our marching even for a second, all the leeches within a ten-foot radius would close in on us just as rapidly as their wormlike creeping would permit. In this region there are two kinds of leeches, both of the genus *Haemodipsa:* the first makes its home on the ground and is earth-colored; the second lives in shrubby trees about the height of a man and wears a greenish garb. About the size of the small finger, they fix themselves on any part of the body without being noticed. When they fill themselves to bursting with blood they drop to the ground and complacently digest the meal until the next occasion to feed arises. In some places, especially in Sumatra and Borneo, they are almost unbelievably abundant. One day, just to get an idea of how many were collecting on my body, I began at eight in the morning to count those I pulled off. After three hours I had reached the startling figure of 175!

To burn each leech with a cigarette—the traditional remedy in movies with a tropical setting—would require carrying lit cigarettes all the time. One solution is simply to walk barelegged, stopping from time to time to scrape the leeches off with a knife. Another remedy popular amongst the Dayaks of Borneo is to touch the leeches with a bit of *Derris* vine; the sap seems to burn the leeches. This sap, which also yields a substance called *tuba,* used by local inhabitants to stun fish in the rivers in order to catch them, can also serve as protection against leeches if it is rubbed on the legs and feet. Unfor-

A membrane that joins all four paws and tail of the flying-lemur (Cynocephalus variegatus) *permits it to glide as much as fifty yards. (Peter Ward)*

tunately, the protection is short-lived because one is obliged to wade through countless streams in any trek through the rain forest.

The drenched soil in the heart of the forest is porous and spongy and the roots of the larger trees interlace above the ground, having no need to penetrate the ground in search of water. In spite of the impressive buttresses flanking the base of the trunk, the slightest storm brings the oldest giants crashing down, felling others in their path like a series of bowling pins. In some cases, the trees collapse by themselves. That is why Dayaks will never sleep near a huge tree.

Such fallen trees are a constant obstacle to passage through the forest. But they disintegrate rather rapidly through the action of termites, the larvae of wood-eating insects, mushrooms, mildew and saprophytic bacteria. Another result of the fall of these trees is that a small clearing is created which is soon occupied by young saplings that would be unable to reach sunlight in the shadow of their elders. But even in this new phase, some grow faster than others and out of a hundred young trees only two or three are able to reach up to the forest canopy after having smothered all their rivals. In this way, the still quiet depths of the forest are the scene of a constant struggle in which the losers are mercilessly condemned to death by suffocation.

STRANGLER FIGS AND GIANT FLOWERS

As in the wet forests of Indochina and southern China, the rain forests of this region are made up of three distinct strata: the largest trees forming the forest canopy, trees of medium stature occupying a middle level, and, near the ground, a sparse undergrowth consisting mainly of saplings of taller species. These levels are particularly distinct in zones where there is a sharp alternation of wet and dry seasons. But, on the equator, where rains are abundant and constant, the middle level tends to disappear, leaving only the tall trees of the canopy and tiny saplings mixed with stunted plants.

The uppermost story is always composed of a great diversity of species, recognizable only by their bark or the fallen fruits and leaves. In some regions, however, especially in the Sunda Islands, the Philippines and on Celebes, one typically Indo-Malaysian family plays a leading role: the Dipterocarpaceae. Occasionally, as much as 50 percent of the great trees belong to this family, represented by a host of species which are distributed amongst the genera *Dipterocarpus, Anisoptera, Driobalanops, Shorea, Hopea* and *Vatica*. This family lends a special stamp to the forest, especially in an aerial view where one sees the lofty, pale-colored trunks surging above the deep-

Left above: Permanent shade and humidity in a Singapore forest create ideal living conditions for a variety of flat worms like this Turbellaria. (Peter Ward) Left: The Mabuya *of Java, one of the most common forest skinks, preys on butterflies and grasshoppers. (Pierre Pfeffer) Right above: Heat and moisture in the equatorial forest prompt the growth of such exotic plants as the cup-fungus* (Cookeina sp.), *one of which is albino. (Betty Allen) · Right: A cluster of gaudy mushrooms grows on the soggy floor of a Bornean forest. (Michael Fogden) Far right: This stinkhorn fungus* (Dictyophora duplicata) *is found in the lowland forests. (E. S. Ross)*

green forest roof. Most of these trees grow to about 180 to 200 feet, and branches on the thick, buttressed trunk only begin at about 100 to 130 feet above the ground.

The fruits of these trees are winged (the name of the principal genus, *Dipterocarpus,* means "fruit with two wings") and when they fall they spin to the ground like a shuttlecock in a game of badminton. In some species, particularly those of the genus *Anisoptera,* the fruit are tiny and surrounded by delicate membranous wings which enable them to glide over considerable distances. From afar they could easily be taken for some insect with an irregular flight.

Other trees play an important role in the forest because their fruit provides food for much of the fauna. First of these are the fig trees *(Ficus),* represented in the region by almost six hundred species. Most resemble other trees except for their small, round fruit, filled with tiny seeds in a sweet, rosy pulp. Others, of which the most famous is the banyan fig, send a multitude of aerial roots from branches down to the soil; a single tree becomes so enlarged by all these props that it is transformed almost into a grove. Every Indonesian village has its *beringin,* which sometimes covers an area of several hundred square yards. The most curious member of this group are the strangler figs, of which there are many species both in Africa and tropical Asia. The seed, carried by a bird or other animal, and then left on the trunk or the branch of a tree, germinates on the spot and develops two small leaves that permit it to breathe and a root that grows toward the ground. Once rooted, it grows rapidly, wrapping itself around its host and eventually strangling it completely. Just as common as the fig trees are the *jambu (Syzygium);* the fragrant and watery fruit ranges from the size of a pea to a small apple.

Some of the fruit nestled in the dead leaves of the forest floor will bring nostalgic reminders of his native forests to the traveler from Europe or North America. Here he will perhaps be surprised to find acorns, usually somewhat larger than those at home. But the leaves of the trees that bear them *(Lithocarpus),* close relative of the European oak, are usually smaller and are never lobed. Spiky shells, exactly like those of the European chestnut, are also found here, belonging to trees of the genus *Castanopsis* and related to our *Castanea.*

Much of the fruit produced by trees of medium height are appreciated both by birds and mammals of the region. Some of these are also relished by the human population, notably the *mata-kutjing* or cat's eyes *(Nephelium),* tiny yellow balls striped with brown, related to the Chinese litchi nuts; the *langsat (Langsium domesticum);* the *rambutans (Nephelium lappaceum);* various species of *manguistans (Garcinia)* and the famous *durians (Durio zibethinus)* whose enormous prickly fruit with its repugnant fecal odor lures all the forest dwellers, especially the orangutan.

The forest undergrowth, as we have noted, is usually sparse. In some places, however, especially in clearings or along watercourses, there are dense stands of wild ginger, sago palms *(Metroxylon),* rattan palms *(Dendrocalamus),* the screw pines and ferns.

It is also on the ground that one may be lucky enough to find the giant flower of the *Rafflesia,* over three feet in width, a parasitic blossom that lives on the underground parts of certain vines. A close cousin of the *Sapria* of Indochina, this flower is unmistakable because of its purplish-blue color and its size, and also because of its overwhelming odor of decaying matter. In the Sunda Islands there are other giant flowers,

closely related to the calla lily of florist shops. The largest is Sumatra's *Amorphophallus titanum,* attaining a height of over eight feet. All humid zones are the domain of an amazing plant with sweeping leaves, the elephant ears *(Allocasia macrorhiza),* often used by the natives as umbrellas.

But, to the newcomer, the most striking aspect of the rich forest flora is the profusion and length of the lianas. Especially at the edge of a clearing, these contribute to that impression of chaotic exuberance so characteristic of the middle level of the rain forest. Often, they are braided together in twos and threes, forming cables that seem to be lowered from the heavens. On rare occasions, the leaves thrust above the forest canopy itself. Rarer still is the sight of the flowers, usually small and lustreless. In vines of the leguminous genera *Bauhinia* and *Mucuna,* however, the flowers are brilliant splashes of red and yellow.

This profusion of vines is rivaled by that of the epiphytes. These latter may grow upon other plants or especially upon trees but the association is in no way parasitic, the host serving merely as support. They are represented by a wide variety of mosses and selaginella but especially by ferns and orchids.

One of the most common epiphytic ferns, the bird's nest fern *(Asplenium nidus),* with huge, glossy and even fronds, usually grows in the fork or on the branches of the large trees. In the same places one also sees a larger fern *(Polypodium heracleum),* which by comparison, should merit the name "eagle's nest fern" so huge is its mass of pennate fronds. Indeed, the names of most of the popular ferns are descriptive of the particular outline of the frond, amongst these the staghorn fern *(Platycerium),* the oak-leaf fern *(Drynaria quercifolium)* and the adder's-tongue fern *(Ophioglossum pendulum).*

The wealth of orchids, including almost five thousand species, lacing the trees is as great as that of the ferns. Often, however, the blossoms are unobtrusive and dull compared to what one might expect from an orchid, and the traveler generally passes without ever noticing them. As for the species that bear huge flowers, there is little chance of finding these near inhabited areas. As the American botanist Elmer D. Merrill hats observed, the orchid cult is an ancient one and practically all of the world's tropical forests have been ransacked for rare forms by generations of orchid hunters.

In the forests in the heart of Borneo and the islands of Molucca I often came across orchids that would make a collector's heart leap. Naturally, I left them untouched. And both in Java's Udjungkulon Reserve and on Komodo in the Lesser Sunda Islands I saw that unique spectacle—a tree totally clad in the white flowers of the *Dendrobium,* one of the most typical genera of Asiatic orchids. Other genera widespread in this region are *Phalaenopsis, Vanda* and *Cymbidium*—all much sought after by collectors.

Not all flowers that grow on tree trunks are necessarily

Right above: Caterpillars of the moth Thosea vetusta *(family* Lymacodidae) *are armed with stinging spines that raise huge blisters on anyone who touches them. (Michael Fogden) Right: Newly hatched stinkbug nymphs surround neatly placed eggs. Members of the odoriferous* Pentatomidae *family do great damage to crops and are a nuisance. Far right: Widely projecting wing cases give these* Cassiniidae *the name of tortoise beetles. Many are brightly colored, but the color disappears after the insect's death. (Both, E. S. Ross)*

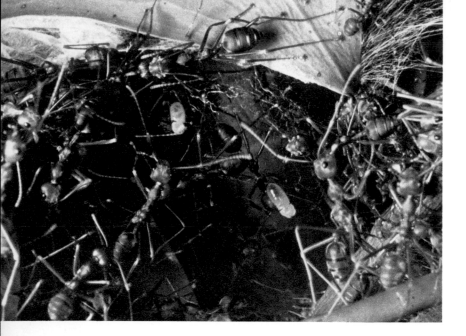

epiphytes. Even experienced naturalists have described as "parasitic" various plants that are not at all parasitic. As in Indochina, many blossoms and plants form on the bark of a tree's trunk or main branches. This phenomenon, known as cauliflory, occurs in *langsat (Lansium)*, trees of the fig family, in the *jambu (Syzygium)* and others. Cauliflory is less frequent among the trees of a second-growth forest and occurs only in the breadfruits. Other species characteristic of the secondary forest are the teak *(Tectonia)*; the *Colona*, close cousin of the European linden; a host of fig trees; the Asiatic elm *(Trema)*; and the *Litsea*, of the laurel family.

Bushes and shrubby trees *(Antidesma, Mallotus, Melanolepis*, etc.) compose most of the understory, along with palms, bamboo trees and an array of lianas. This tangled skein combined with the low-hanging branches of trees makes penetration of the secondary forest difficult. Here rattan palms thrive in great profusion, their thorns and brambles a constant annoyance. They may grow to the astonishing length of several hundred or even one thousand feet so that it is often impossible to tell where they begin or end.

AN ENTOMOLOGIST'S PARADISE

We have not yet even touched on one of the richest forms of life in the jungle: the insects and their close relatives, the scorpions, centipedes and spiders. Along with tropical America, the Indo-Malaysian region contains the greatest variety of these groups and is thus an entomologist's paradise. Of course, for anyone who has journeyed days on end up a torrential river, the only means of travel in the jungle, the word insect evokes the memory of a plague of mosquitos, sand flies and sweat bees and the sting of certain caterpillars or biting ants and wasps. He also remembers gigantic butterflies, huge walking-stick insects with pink or orange wings, cicadas announcing the break and close of day with the precision of a clock, massive scarab beetles dive-bombing his gas lamp, golden chafers and metallic word-boring beetles, leaf-insects, flower-insects, stick-insects and a hundred others.

The danger of mosquitos and sand flies *(Ceratopogon)* should not be minimized. Aside from being troublesome they transmit some deadly diseases: malaria, sand-fly fever and filariasis. The *Stomoxys* and horseflies are simply annoying because of their stings; others transmit such diseases as amebiasis and trachoma. But some are useful; they deposit their maggots on the bodies of other insects which the larvae devour; thus each species of tachinid fly has its preferred host and plays an important role in the fight against agricultural pests. I saw an example of this on the sugar cane plantations of Madagascar and the Reunion and Mauritius islands. A borer caterpillar had been accidentally introduced from Java in the last century and multiplied in such profusion that it was destroying as much as 30 percent of the annual harvest. Oddly enough, in its native habitat this caterpillar is in no way

Left above: Weaving ants (Oecophylla smaragdina) *use their own silk-producing larvae to weave and to repair their nests. Center: Workers pull leaves together to close a breach. Left: Weaving ants "execute" members of the colony handled by man and then returned to the nest. (All, M. W. F. Tweedie)*

remarkable and the damage it does is insignificant. It was found that a certain species of tachinid fly attacked this caterpillar, so I undertook to capture these flies by the thousands and ship them to Madagascar and the two neighboring islands. After a year's work with a team of entomologists, I found that the tachinid fly seemed to have adjusted to the new habitat and will, it is hoped, curb the undesirable borers.

There is, of course, a danger in such a procedure. It is known that an animal or plant in its native land may be kept in check by predators or competitors, but when introduced into a new habitat may proliferate to such an extent that it becomes a serious menace. It follows that when a natural enemy is introduced to combat a menacing species, great care should be taken not to introduce the enemy's parasites in the process, lest the cure prove worse than the affliction. Worse still, the newly introduced species may take a liking to a new prey—a useful creature perhaps—and lose all interest in the one on which it originally preyed.

Tachinids have many ways of destroying their caterpillar victims. The simplest is the laying of their eggs or larvae directly on the caterpillar's skin. The method used by the tachinid of Java leaves more to chance: the young larvae are laid at the entry of galleries hollowed out by the caterpillars and are left to track down the host themselves. In a third procedure the female tachinid hovers above the caterpillar's favorite plants and bombards these with hundreds of eggs so small they can be swallowed whole by the caterpillar. The most ingenious technique is that of certain tachinids that live on beetles. Encased in a horny sheel, the host's only vulnerable spot is beneath the elytra or wing cover; the fly succeeds in depositing its eggs on the beetle's back while it is on the wing—a remarkable feat of synchronization since the beetle's wings vibrate at an exceedingly rapid rate.

Wasps and hornets also abound in the rain forest and several species will attack an intruder without the slightest provocation. The tiger wasp (Vespa tropica), with a wingspan of as much as four inches, has the most deadly sting. Dillon Ripley has pointed out the extent to which these hornets have influenced the pattern of native footpaths in the heart of the jungle. Many detours are apparently made just to avoid the hornets' nests. I have often seen my Dayak guide in the forests of Borneo give wide berth to a tree from which came an ominous buzzing. I was stung on several occasions and rank these hornets as only slightly less of a jungle menace than mosquitos and sand flies.

Fortunately, other tropical wasps are harmless or even useful: parasitic wasps, for example, play the same role in the balance of nature as tachinid flies. The habits of the potter wasp (Eumenes) are of special interest for they fashion delicate juglike nests of clay which are attached to tree branches, the roofs of houses and often in the most unlikely places. Once, when camping in a grass hut, I left a shirt hanging for several weeks and when I went to put it on I found hundreds of these tiny clay structures inside the sleeves and in every fold. Potter wasps lay a single egg inside these receptacles along with a storage of provisions in the form of caterpillars, stung and paralyzed, to serve as food for the young larva.

The stingless or sweat bees (Meliponidae) are small, harmless bees but they do have the disagreeable habit of clinging to the back and the face to lick the salt of perspiration or tear secretions. In spite of this I have fond memories of these insects: their deep, syrupy honey is delicious and the plump

Such spiders as Gasterocantha ascuata *of Borneo have bodies covered with a thick hard cuticle, often brightly colored and ornamented with long spines. (F. G. H. Allen)*

larvae cooked along with their wax honeycombs make an excellent pudding.

Giant honeybees (Apis dorsata), which are true bees, are found throughout the forest regions of Southern Asia. They build their honeycombs, which are often enormous, on the branches of the largest trees, notably those of the genus Terminalia. Some of these trees are so laden with honeycombs that natives from miles around visit them regularly to collect the honey. Since the stinging bees vehemently defend their property, honey collectors begin by overcoming them with smoke from torches burning the resin of conifers of the genus Agathis.

Knowing of my interest in these subjects, Dayak children would constantly come to me with tiny creatures that they had found. Among these was a kind of huge metallic blue bee captured in the tunnels bored by the insects in the stilts supporting all the houses of Borneo. It was a carpenter bee (Xylocopa), a larger relative of the European variety.

Ants abound in Southeast Asia and are represented by a good many species. Most striking are the giant ants (Camponotus) over an inch in length, that wander by themselves on the forest floor. In spite of their size and their fearsome jaws, they bite feebly and only if attacked.

It is difficult to avoid the deceptive nests of tailor ants

251

(Oecophylla smaragdina) that are hung in bushes and stunted trees. But an encounter does provide an opportunity to observe this ant's ingenious devices for repairing its nest, which is made of huge leaves glued together. The workers line up at the edge of a leaf, grasp another leaf in their jaws and bring it flush with the first. A second band of workers arrive, bearing in their jaws the larvae, which secrete a sticky substance that hardens when it dries. Using the larvae as a kind of thread, the workers rapidly move along the edges of the two leaves, stitching a perfect and durable seam.

Other insects of the forest are noteworthy because of their curious associations with plant species. Black ants and epiphytes of the genera *Myrmecodia* and *Hydnophytum* are classic examples of this symbiosis. The plants, a cluster of leaves on a short, swollen, tuberous stem, are riddled with countless galleries that are inhabited by thousands of minute black ants. The plant is in no way harmed by these tenants but can also get along very well without them.

White ants or termites have little in common with true ants and belong to an entirely different zoological order: the Isoptera. Their termitaries are often quite large and termites do considerable damage to plantation and houses. Although termites are everywhere in the rain forest, they shun light and are therefore rarely seen, the only clues to their presence being ribbons of soil festooning trees or small mushroom-shaped mounds on the forest floor. Occasionally, when a seemingly sturdy tree stump or trunk is broken it reveals swarms of tiny, whitish, larva-like bodies scurrying into a maze of burrows in the wood, which is usually beginning to crumble. Termites live almost exclusively on wood and are able to digest the cellulose through the aid of thousands of ciliated protozoa lining the digestive tube. Because of this diet termites play a crucial role in the life cycle of those untouched forests. Trees felled by a storm disintegrate rapidly on contact with the dank soil, saprophytic plants and insects rapidly changing them to humus. But those remaining upright simply dry up and may stand for years, hindering the growth of other trees and adding in no way to the formation of humus. The activity of termites greatly speeds up the natural process of decomposition, transforming the wood to decaying debris easily permeated by humidity and all forms of mildew.

GIANT BUTTERFLIES

Aside from insects that are annoying to man or have fascinating habits, there are many that are noteworthy for their beauty or stunning coloration. The most brilliantly colored are the butterflies, and of these the most prized by collectors are the bird-winged butterflies *(Ornithoptera)*, which surpass their rivals in size as well as beauty. Each island, moreover, possesses its own local variety. Some particularly rare bird-wings bring astonishing prices on the international market. One was bought in an auction in Paris, in 1967, for more than $2,500 by an amateur American collector. The males of these butterflies are dressed in black and shimmering green flecked with gold, while the females are dull brown highlighted by a few eyelike spots. The females more justly merit the name "bird-wing," for they have a wingspan of as much as ten inches compared to the eight inches of their more handsome mates. Since females are always rarer in collections, it was long believed that there were also a greater proportion of males in

nature. Actually, there are about the same number of each sex but the males often alight on the ground to suck the mud fringing a puddle, while the females sequester themselves on the upper levels of the forest and are rarely captured.

Some of the *Papilios*, close cousins of our swallow-tails, are almost exactly like the *Ornithoptera*, while others are predominantly black and pale yellow. There are a great variety of these in the forest but they are difficult to catch because they soar swiftly and high above the ground. Occasionally, however, they congregate at the water's edge to sip the liquid from decaying animal and vegetable matter. In fact, the best means of luring either the *Papilios* or the *Ornithoptera* is either by leaving a rotting fish or other decaying matter in a clearing. Such bait, as well as patches of mud, are also effective lures for various butterflies related to our cabbage butterfly. Of these, the genera *Dilas* and *Appias*, common on all the islands, are of special interest to collectors, as is also *Hebomoia*, a large butterfly with bright orange spots at the tip of the wings.

One of the most common butterflies of the forest is the *Hestia idea*, related to the monarch, the North American butterfly famous for its migrations. Rather large, and with translucent wings veined with black, the *Hestia idea* has been dubbed *kupu kertas*, paper butterfly, in the Malay tongue because of its delicate appearance and a flight that recalls a scrap of paper fluttering in the breeze. Although it flies high, it is easily captured by a rather amusing trick; the hunter simply waves a handkerchief or butterfly net, and the *Hestia* invariably folds its wings and spirals right to the waving object. It is always the males that are enticed, probably mistaking the white fabric for a female flitting above the ground.

European and American collectors may be surprised to learn that wood nymphs *(Satyridae)* are as common in this region as in the western world. Most numerous are those of the genus *Mycalesis*, their brownish or yellowish wings adorned with the eyelike spots typical of this family. They avoid dense forest and prefer clearings or river banks. The tiny blue and copper butterflies of the *Lycaenidae* family are represented here by a great many species, as are skippers *(Hesperidae)*, recognizable by their hooked antennae and rapid, zigzagging flight.

It would be impossible to list the wealth of daytime butterflies in the Malaysian region but we cannot omit mentioning the dead-leaf butterfly *(Doleschallia)*. When it lights on a branch with folded wings it is impossible to distinguish it from a dead leaf, including every last detail of veins, spots of mildew and even tiny leaf-stalk.

Moths are even more numerous than butterflies and the best way to appreciate their abundance and diversity is to attract them to an artificial light on a moonless night. We hung a gas lamp in front of a white sheet between two young trees and on a good night would find hordes of moths bombarding the lamp and the sheet, scarcely giving us a chance to collect them. Most of the moths were of dull varieties just as common in the west, including the *Noctuidae*, *Geometridae*, *Lymantridae*, *Drepanidae* and *Arctiidae*. Occasionally one catches a glimpse of the swift hawk moth or the *Brahmoph-*

The enormous eyes of the tarsier (Tarsius spectrum), *a primitive primate found on Sumatra, Borneo and the southern Philippines, reveal that it is a noctural animal. (Michael Fogden)*

The noisy flight and trumpet-like call of this hornbill, Anthracoceros undulatus, *is one of the most common sounds in Borneo's forests.* (Georges Bourdelon)

talma with dark, eyelike markings on its wings. Members of the emperor moth family *(Saturnidae)* are quite numerous. One of these, the famous *Attacus atlas* rivals the female bird-wing butterfly in size and closely resembles the luna moth, which originated in China and is now widespread in the United States. Two other species of *Attacus* are found in the Malaysian region, each island having its characteristic races. Some of the emperor moths, particularly those of the genus *Argema*, can be identified by long extensions on the posterior wings that float like ribbons behind the moth.

FLYING JEWELS

During our moth hunts, many beetles would collide with our lamp and drop to the ground—metallic may beetles *(Melolontha)*, sacred scarabs *(Scarabaeus)* or rhinoceros beetles *(Oryctes)*—all familiar to Western collectors. Other common

beetles were the stag beetle *(Lucanidae)* and the rose chafers *(Cetonidae)*, represented by a great many species in iridescent shades and with bizarre "horns" on the head and thorax. Rose chafers are among the most beautiful insects and, as with hummingbirds, a student of this group becomes almost more of an aesthete than an entomologist. They are avid nectar-lovers and are ever in pursuit of flowers and sweet fruits. But these jewels are not easily captured—not only are flowers generally rare and inaccessible in tropical forests but, like many beetles, the rose chafer's hatching cycle is spread over a period of several years. But if one chances upon the right spot at the right time, the reward would fill any collector with envy.

Once in the heart of Borneo, I came across a stunning metallic-green rose chafer with a long, recurving horn sprouting from the head, and recognized the *Theodosia westwoodi*, a coveted species. Showing it to various villagers, I promised a handsome reward to anyone who could bring me others. After many months ten villagers appeared, all bearing bamboo tubes brimming with the precious chafers. Hatching had just taken place and the Malaysian pink rhododendrons *(Melastoma)* that grow like weeds on the outskirts of every village were swarming with these insects. The feast lasted only two days but my harvest was enough to astonish the specialists when I returned to Paris.

Wood-boring beetles *(Buprestidae)* are almost as beautiful as rose chafers, making up for a smaller range of shapes with a rich variety of colors, with golden, purplish-blue or green hues predominating. Wood-boring beetles inhabit primary forests and although they are also found in vast temperate forests, they flourish in the tropics. In the Malaysian region alone, almost eight hundred species are known, and many others remain to be discovered. The larvae live in the bark or even in wood, boring long galleries. The adults are diurnal and can often be seen sunbathing on the bark and showing off their shimmering colors, an effect produced, as with all beetles, by light rays refracted by the chitinous cuticle. They warm themselves lazily in the sun, but they are not so easy to capture as would seem for they can take flight with the utmost despatch.

The beauty of these beetles has long been appreciated not only by collectors but by local populations and by artisans and jewelers around the world. In India, ladies of fashion use a species of *Chrysochroa* in place of sequins, studding their gowns with the live insects, and in Java a *Cyphogastra* is sometimes mounted in silver brooches. Before World War II the latter species was exported in great quantities to Europe where the elytra were made into shimmering inlays on jewel cases.

Long-horned beetles *(Cerambycidae)* lack metallic sheen but are prized for their elegance of outline and their coloring. Like the wood-boring beetles, the larvae live in wood and the adults are generally awkward enough to let themselves be caught on the bark. Their long, jointed antennae give them a goatlike look and some of the family are thus called capricorn beetles.

The pangolin or scaly anteater (Manis javanica) *can roll up into a tight ball. It uses its powerful hind claws to break open termite nests and its sticky tongue to gather the termites.* (Ivan Polunin)

Although scarcely noticeable because of their speckled barklike dress, long-horned beetles, with six thousand species, are even more plentiful in the forests of tropical Asia than the wood-boring beetles. Studies by Alfred Russel Wallace in the last century indicated this profusion: he gathered 130 new species in just two months in a wooded district of Singapore, no more than one square mile in area. The specimens ranged in size from under an inch to over four inches, but some of these beetles may reach a length of six inches.

A particularly interesting group of beetles in Oriental forests, known as the bess beetles *(Passalidae),* have the unusual habit of caring for the young, a rare instinct in insects, with the exception of course of the so-called social insects—bees, ants and termites. Adults of the genus Passalus not only protect the eggs but chew up wood and feed it to the larvae. The entire "family"—larvae, pupae and adults—gathers in the same burrow, additional evidence of their communal tendencies.

The great variety of tropical beetles would require a chapter in itself: we can but name the ground beetle *(Carabidae)* and the tiger beetle *(Cicindelidae).* All are brilliant, elusive and difficult to catch, especially the tiger beetles, often seen hovering above steep, sand, river banks. Among the ground beetles, the fiddle beetles *(Mormolyce)* are highly esteemed and, in the Sunda Islands, make their home in tree bark. At the beginning of the nineteenth century a specimen of this violin-shaped insect was purchased by the Paris Museum of Natural History for the astronomical sum of one thousand gold francs. Needless to say, as more specimens became available, the value has lowered.

CICADAS AND DAMSELFLIES

The diversity of the beetles of tropical Asia is matched only by the wealth of other insects: wood bugs, dragonflies, katydids, walking sticks, praying mantids and cicadas. As in other parts of the world, dragonflies and damselflies prefer clearings or places near water. They closely resemble their European cousins, although some wear brilliant colors, particularly those of the widespread genus *Neurothemis,* the body and wings being either a golden-brown or deep red color.

Katydids and praying mantids are even more various and in some the dress mimics the surroundings. Certain katydids of the genus *Seliquoferella,* for example, bear a close resemblance to a green or brown leaf. As for praying mantids, some could easily be mistaken for a jagged leaf, others for a dry twig and still others for a flower. In such instances the insect always crouches on the leaf or flower that it resembles, thus eluding its enemies.

Mimicry is even more remarkable in the walking sticks *(Phasmidae)* with their twiglike appearance. The group is here represented by a host of species, many of which qualify as giants, wingless females reaching a length of sixteen inches. The males, with their multicolored wings, are no more than a third of the size of their mates. The leaf insects are by far the most astonishing members of this family for, unless they move, they cannot be detected. Reproduction takes place by

The slow loris (Nycticebus coucang), *a nocturnal animal, is very clumsy on the ground, but an excellent, if slow-moving, climber in trees. (W. Suschitzky)*

Leaves of certain epiphytes, like this stag-horn fern (Platycerium), *may reach a length of six or seven feet. (Chan Bing Fai)*

means of parthenogenesis; that is, without participation by the male. The female simply drops hundreds of tough-shelled eggs from the treetops and after several months the young are hatched. At birth they are replicas in appearance and size of their elders.

Close relatives of the katydids and walking sticks are the enormous cockroaches, the terror of all Western women who come to live in the tropics. They creep into every nook and cranny and will devour anything. I remember my amazement the first time I entered a Dayak house in Borneo: the entire wooden panel above the hearth was covered by a tapestry of swarming cockroaches, their bronze bodies gleaming in the firelight.

More pleasant traveling companions are the cicadas. In Borneo when one of these lovely lavender-colored insects poured forth its call from the trees we could be sure that it was a quarter to six and time to arise. At twilight, a melancholy trumpet-like sound from the forest depths was a signal to stop and make camp for it was exactly five minutes to six and night would fall in fifteen minutes. I longed to catch sight of this vespers cicada belonging to another species than the morning one; finally one evening in the forest I suddenly heard the piercing trumpeting sound just behind me. Turning, I spotted a very beautiful green cicada perched on a tree. Other cicadas would sing in the middle of the day, each species doing so for only a moment and always at precisely the same time.

There are a number of other small creatures that have acquired a notorious reputation: spiders, centipedes and scorpions, rarely seen but everpresent in equatorial forests. Their harmfulness is greatly exaggerated: they bite only if one disturbs them. The pain of a bite may last from two hours to two days, occasionally accompanied by a high fever, especially after the bite of a scorpion or one of the large centipedes (Scolopendra).

I had first-hand contact with only one spider of the region, the wolf spider. It lives in the branches and the bite can be rather severe. Its close cousin, the leaping spider (Menemurus), known to pursue its prey stealthily and then pounce like a cat, is quite common throughout the region.

Nephilia is a much larger spider but it is perfectly harmless. It weaves a huge geometrical web, more than three feet in diameter. The silk fibers of the web are so sturdy and fine that they are in great demand for use as cross-hairs in high-powered telescopic sights. The spiny-backed spider (Gasteracantha), living at the center of a smaller geometrical web, has a hard, colorful body and long, menacing spines.

The giant millipedes, quite common in the forest, are harmless, whereas several of the centipedes have, as we have noted, a dangerous sting. As for scorpions, the giant of this group, the Heterometrus, is as large as a crayfish but it keeps out of sight, rarely bites and its venom is not harmful. The tiny yellow or brown scorpions of the genus Hormurus can be more dangerous for they lurk in epiphytic fronds or beneath the bark and it is possible to be stung as one climbs a tree or even sleeps beneath one.

In Asia and many other regions it is believed that when a scorpion is caught in a circle of fire it commits suicide. It is true that when a scorpion finds itself trapped by flames it panics. As it struggles, it may accidentally jab itself with the stinger at the tip of its tail and then suddenly slump as if stung by its own poison. Actually, its immobility is due to a sudden dehydration of the branchiae or gills. Indeed, all one has to do to revive the victim miraculously is to immerse it briefly in water!

HORNBILLS, BULBULS AND SUNBIRDS

The visitor is often disappointed by the apparent lack of birds in the virgin forest. Only if he has slept under the trees and awakened at dawn will he see small, sharply twittering birds chasing each other high in the treetops. During the day he may walk for hours without glimpsing anything other than the azure flash of the fairy bluebird (Irena puella), one of the most beautiful creatures of Southeast Asian forests, or perhaps the gliding flight of one of the malkohas (Phoenicophaeus, Rhinortha), gray or brown birds with a very long tail, akin to the cuckoo but without its parasitic habits. Occasionally there is the flapping of wings of the red and black oriole (Oriolus cruentus) or of the green-winged ground dove (Chalcophaps indicus), taking flight when danger is near.

Most often the presence of birds may be detected only by their cries. One of the most characteristic in these forests is the nasal trumpeting of the hornbill, often accompanied by the peculiarly grating sound of its flapping wings. Many species of hornbills, belonging to various genera (Buceros, Rhinoplax, Aceros, Anthracoceros) inhabit the Indo-Malaysian region, all huge and all with monstrous toucan beaks topped by variously formed casques. They feed principally on fruit, including Strychnos, source of strychnine; although they are reputed to be immune to this deadly poison, they actually digest only the harmless pulp and discard the nut containing the toxic substance.

The unique nest-building habit of the hornbill is well known. At nesting time, the male encloses the female in a hole in a tree, almost completely stopping up the opening with clay. During the entire period of the incubation and raising of the fledglings, he feeds his family through the narrow opening, and not until the young birds are ready to fly does he free them by breaking the seal.

While the raucous cooing of the very large imperial pigeons (Ducula aenea) reverberates through the forest, the sound of the green and pink fruit dove is very sweet and more like a lamentation. Another green pigeon, the Treron vernans, sounds like a childish voice heard over the telephone, while T. olax whistles a melodious little tune. The jewel-thrushes (Pitta) utter a sweet rising and falling whistle, particularly at sunset. About the size of a thrush, the pittas move about on the ground turning over dead leaves in search of worms and small mollusks. In spite of their brilliant color, their cautious behavior makes them difficult to detect.

Sometimes a succession of harsh cries, "koo-wye! koo-wye!" rings out. This is the call of the great argus pheasant (Argusianus argus), the mysterious bird that all travelers to Sumatra and Borneo hear but rarely see. The first time that an argus slipped away in front of me in the underbrush, I thought momentarily of a panther because of the bird's peacock size and its gray-brown plumage starred with small pale eyes. I had the opportunity to watch the male in his nuptial circle, an area about seven feet in diameter that he clears of every twig and dead leaf. On this dance floor, he parades, hopping up and down, beating his wings, nodding his head and uttering sharp cries to which the female replies from a distance. The bird will not suffer any foreign body on the cleared space and the Dayaks take advantage of this by placing a snare in the circle. The argus hastens to remove it and is automatically caught. His long feathers with their glistening eyes garnish the ritual headdresses of tribal chiefs.

A dug-out is perhaps a slow means of transportation, but it is particularly good in this region for watching the birds

Insects caught in this pitcher-plant (Nepenthes ampullaria) *in Borneo drown in a liquid secretion and are then digested.* (B. E. Smythies)

that seek out the waterways. One of the most common and most beautiful is the black and red broadbill *(Cymbirhynchus macrorhynchus)* which perches on low branches overlooking the river. More modest in brown livery, the yellow-crowned bulbul *(Pycnonotus zeylanicus)* is the river troubador, and his song, similar to that of our blackbird, accompanies the voyager all along the stream. Kingfishers abound also, especially the stork-billed kingfisher *(Pelargopsis capensis)* of the great, orange beak and, in winter, the black-capped kingfisher *(Halcyon pileata)* from continental Asia.

Around the villages, where the vegetation has been burned off for planting crops, normally less common birds have replaced the forest species. These are primarily bulbuls, of the family of Pycnonotidae, represented in Malaysia by about thirty species. Bulbuls are medium-sized birds, usually of dull plumage, but their pleasant trills and roulades announce from a great distance a cleared area and a village. One of the most popular is the yellow-vented bulbul, the *kutilang* of Java, where its melodious trills symbolize the joy of living, like the song of the lark in Europe.

Among other species in this area are the flowerpeckers *(Dicaeidae)*, very small birds, brightly colored on a generally olive ground. Sometimes even smaller than the flowerpeckers are the sunbirds *(Nectariniidae)*, in a sense the counterparts of the hummingbirds of tropical America. Like hummingbirds, their plumage has a metallic shimmer, they feed principally on nectar and have a thin, curved beak with a tubular, protrusive tongue adapted to this special diet. Unlike hummingbirds, they do not gather nectar while in flight, and can hover only for an instant in one spot.

The spiderhunters of the genus *Arachnothera* are allied to sunbirds but are larger in size, have olive-hued plumage without the sheen, and extraordinarily long, curved beaks. Their diet is definitely more insectivorous than that of their smaller relatives.

In Borneo, the Dayaks consider them prophets, never undertaking a voyage, a head-hunt or any essential agricultural task without observing the flight of this bird. We were forced to remain in one village an extra week because each time we were about to leave we had the ill luck to see an "issit" cross our path from right to left, a bad omen.

One of the noisiest birds here is the magpie robin *(Copsychus saularis)*. A born mimic, from morning on it treats the neighborhood to a serenade in which the most mellifluous refrains are mingled with the most discordant sounds. A slightly different species, the black and russet shama bird *(Copsychus malabaricus)*, is well known to Western fanciers, its song making it one of the most valuable cage birds.

Swarming in all the cultivated zones are doves *(Streptopelia chinensis)* and the little weavers of the *Lonchura* genus, called "rice stealers" because of their depredations in the rice paddies. Finally, on the few trees spared by the clearing of land, one may fairly often see many sorts of woodpeckers or leafbirds in their soft green plumage.

ORANGUTANS AND FLYING ANIMALS

Mammals generally expose themselves even less than birds. The most noticeable are the gibbons whose strident ululations salute the rising and the setting sun. At such times on the Malay Peninsula and in Sumatra one can also hear the even more impressive howls of the siamang *(Hylobates syndactylus)*, a kind of gibbon with a resonating throat sac that amplifies its powerful cries.

Macaques are more numerous at the edge of water or in partially cleared zones whereas in the forest, one meets leaf-monkeys of several species gathered into the genus *Presbytis*. Those in Sumatra are a bright reddish-brown, those in Borneo fawn color and the many Javanese breeds are cinder gray or black. These monkeys are hunted in Borneo for the gallstones often found in their bile ducts. Horribly bitter to the taste, these "stones" are very much in demand by Chinese pharmacists to dispel fevers.

The most famous ape of the region is the orangutan, whose name means "man of the forest" in Malayan. He lives only in Sumatra and Borneo and his absence from the Malay Peninsula and from Java is difficult to explain. A legend of ferocity surrounds this huge anthropoid but he is actually peaceful and shy. He is so discreet in his living habits that he frequently is unobserved even in the places where he is still commonly found. He spends the nights in nests of branches that he builds half-way up in trees. During the morning he feeds on shoots and fruits, especially that of the malodorous durian tree. Then he rests in one of his nests until afternoon. Orangutans normally lead a family life, although sub-adult males often form separate groups of bachelors.

Despite official protection, these interesting animals are very near extinction. The high prices offered by zoos that consider it essential to exhibit an orangutan is the main cause of the destruction of the species. According to Barbara Harrisson, the first to study orangutans in their native habitat, very conservative estimates are that for each ape that reaches a zoo alive, three die either during capture or in transit. And no one knows how many orangutans die in Dayak villages or on the sampans of smugglers taking the animals to Singapore. Mrs. Harrisson points out that to maintain the 250 orangutans in the world's zoos for ten years, it would be necessary to kill or capture 2,400 animals, which is perhaps greater than the number of orangutans surviving in the jungles of both islands.

One of the most unusual animals of these forests is the so-called flying-lemur, which is not a lemur at all. You can imagine my surprise when I spied in a tree an animal vaguely resembling a rabbit and busily eating fruit that suddenly launched itself into the air and glided along for nearly fifty yards! I realized then that it was a flying-lemur *(Cynocephalus variegatus)* whose four paws and tail are connected by a membrane that allows it to glide through the air.

Malaya is the land of gliding animals. Among the reptiles we have already noted the flying-dragon and the fringed gekko, which uses membranes around his body like a parachute and leaps from the tops of the tallest trees. The colorful

Right above: The crab-eating monkey (Macaca irus) *of the Malaysian islands is found mostly on the ground, often in mangrove swamps or among coastal rocks. (Ivan Polunin) Right: Nepenthes mirabilis, found in Malaysian forests, illustrates another of the many shapes characteristic of pitcher plants. (Michael Fogden) Far right: This member of the ginger family* (Zingiberaceae) *has a waist-high stalk and bracts that form rain-catching cups in which mosquitos may breed. (E.S.Ross)*

The otter-civet (Cynogale bennetti), *a very rare mammal of Malaysia, Sumatra and Borneo, has adapted to an aquatic life and is a clever fisherman. (F. G. H. Allen)*

Ordinary squirrels, from giant species like the almost three-foot-long *Ratufa* to the mouse-sized *Nannosciurus,* also abound. Some, like the *Ratufa,* live mainly in the treetops, coming down only to drink or lick the mud of salt springs. All the *Calliosciurus* live in the middle strata of low or thick trees of either virgin or secondary forests. Others remain on the ground, rarely mounting as much as three feet above it. Most of the ground-squirrels, medium-sized and with three of four black stripes on their backs, belong to the genus *Lariscus.* Some of them, however, are quite large and I was once surprised by the sight of a *Rheithrosciurus,* the giant ground-squirrel of Borneo, whose long-tufted ears make it look like a bobcat. We also find on the ground a long-nosed squirrel *(Rhinosciurus)* with teeth and tongue adapted to an insectivorous diet. His short, very bushy tail distinguishes him immediately from the tree-shrews *(Tupaia),* which are considered true insect-eaters.

Tree-shrews look like squirrels; they have pointed snouts, astonishingly human ears, and long tails covered with short hairs. Although one species lives in the south of India and another in Indochina, the real home of tree-shrews is Malaysia and their Malayan name "tupaia" is the source of their scientific name. These astonishing little animals seem to be extremely nervous, often ascending and descending a branch twenty times at a dizzy speed, pausing only to stand shaking on one spot like mechanical toys. Then they suddenly start off again. Some species of tree-shrews are also terrestrial, diurnal as well as nocturnal, insectivorous as well as fruit-eating. When taken while young, they become comparatively tame. Dayak children use blow-pipes loaded with soft clay pellets to stun such small animals or birds, and capture them usually unharmed.

The greatest enemies of tree-shrews and squirrels are the yellow-throated marten *(Martes flavigula),* which will chase a tree-shrew in spirals around a huge trunk at a furious speed, and the very rare monkey-eating eagle of the Philippines, which pursues its victims into the tops of the tallest trees.

Most small forest mammals lead a cautious nocturnal existence and the best way to collect them is to hunt by night wearing a miner's lamp. The most numerous victims of such hunts are civets *(Viverra, Viverricula)* and palm-civets *(Paradoxurus, Paguma),* pretty animals that range from the size of a cat to that of a fox, and have pointed muzzles, spotted or striped black fur, and long, ringed tails. They are common in the forest, in cultivated areas and villages, where they are often accused of stealing chickens, and even in the largest cities, where one of them, the "musang" *(Paradoxurus hermaphroditus),* frequently betrays his presence by his noisy gallop across the tin roofs of bungalows. Taken young, he becomes as friendly as a cat and adores playing with children. Tamed and carried about by the Malays from time immemorial, this species is found on almost all the islands of the archipelago and as far as Madagascar.

Another interesting civet is the binturong or bear-cat *(Arctitis binturong),* which is the size of a large dog and has silvery-

paradise-snake *(Chrysopelea paradisi),* using its long and mobile ribs to increase the surface of his body and hollowing out its belly like a trough, sails through the air like a boomerang.

Even frogs seek to leave the mire and launch themselves into space! One of them, the beautifully colored red or orange rhacophore or flying frog has very long, webbed toes that serve as a parachute. It is so well adapted to living in trees that it no longer even lays its eggs in ponds, but makes nests of leaves or resin in the treetops, the tadpoles living in the rainwater that accumulates there.

Even better adapted for aerial locomotion are nearly 150 species of bats, ranging from the little *Miniopterus* to the giant flying-foxes, some with a four-foot wing span. Flying squirrels are numerous and varied throughout the area; their sizes range from that of a mouse *(Petaurillus)* to that of a fox *(Petaurista)* and their coats from gray to reddish-brown or black spotted with white. Like flying-lemurs, flying squirrels have their paws joined on each side by a membrane, but their long, bushy tail is free and acts like a rudder.

The orangutan (Pongo pygmaeus), *now found only in Sumatra and Borneo, may grow to well over four feet and weigh 150 pounds. Contrary to report, it is peaceable. (Hedda Morrison)*

Leaf-insects (Pulchrephyllium *sp.*), *here shown in Singapore, imitate almost perfectly the leaves of the plant they live and feed on. (M. W. F. Tweedie)*

black fur. Essentially a tree-dweller, the binturong's prehensile tail enables it to hang with its paws free so that it can pull toward it the branches laden with the fruit that is its food.

Also in the civet family are several species of mongooses (Herpestes), Kipling's celebrated Riki-tiki-tavi, very easily tamed and rendering great service by its destruction of all household and garden pests. I have raised several, none more domesticated than the one I had in central Borneo (H. hosei), which followed my footsteps like a dog.

Hunting by night also affords the best opportunities for meeting wary members of the cat family. The most common is the Bengal or leopard-cat (Felis bengalensis), found from southern China to Bali and on the large Sunda Islands and the Philippines. As large as a domestic cat and with spotted fur like a cheetah, this hunter attacks anything from large insects and frogs to mammals the size of the mouse-deer. The rarest is the bay-cat (F. badia) of Borneo, approximately the size of the leopard-cat but with unpatterned mahogany-red or blackish-gray fur.

The rare and comparatively unknown marbled cat (F. mar-

morata) and the golden cat (F. temmincki), both about as large as a medium-sized dog, are found from Southern China to Borneo, with the latter also found in Sumatra. In the same regions and in Formosa lives the clouded leopard (F. nebulosa). A little smaller than the common panther, it has gray-brown fur with large grayish spots, lives in the great forest, has many more tree-dwelling habits than most felines and a very long tail. It also has exceptionally developed canine teeth, which the Dayaks of Borneo like to wear in their earlobes. At one time, only warriors who had cut off at least one human head had the right to wear these ornaments; today the teeth are merely a sign of wealth, exchangeable during times of scarcity for rice or other valuable commodities. As for the real leopard (F. pardus) and the tiger, outside of the peninsula the first is found only in Java and the Kanga Islands, and the second only in Sumatra, Java and Bali.

One of the least known of nocturnal animals is the teledu or Malay badger (Mydaus javanensis) of Sumatra, Java and Borneo. It is small, covered with long, black-tipped fur and has a white dorsal stripe. Although classed among the badgers, it is like the American skunk in its ability to spurt a fearfully nauseating liquid for a considerable distance. The ferret badger (Helictis orientalis), found from south China and Formosa to Java and Borneo, resembles a skunk even more, but has no liquid defense. Only the hog-nosed badger (Arctonyx collaris), which ranges all over Indochina and Sumatra, resembles the badger of the West.

Hunting at night is rich in surprises. Once when I flashed my light at two yellow eyes in a treetop, the eyes vanished, but immediately reappeared. When I drew close enough to see the entire animal I realized that it was a tarsier (Tarsius), a primate that first appeared on earth some seventy million years ago. Its frog-sized body is topped by a very large head with two enormous globular eyes. One zoologist has calculated that proportionately large human eyes would measure at least a foot in diameter! Its mouth is large and has small, pointed teeth, indicating an insect diet. Its paws are slender, terminating in true hands with very long delicate fingers, each ending with a nail and small pad at the tip. Its tail, at least twice as long as its body, ends in a little pompom of tawny hairs. Beneath their toylike aspect, tarsiers harbor ferocious instincts. Rejecting all vegetable food, they feed on insects captured during nocturnal roamings, probably adding a few eggs and young birds snatched from the nest, and perhaps small lizards and frogs. Malays call the tarsier "hantu" or demon, and misconceptions about it abound. In Borneo, at least, the natives make an eye ointment from its eyeballs mixed with boar's grease and other ingredients.

Lemurs are found mainly on the island of Madagascar. Lorises, which are rather similar, are found in parts of Africa and Asia. The only Asiatic representatives are the slender loris

Right above: Attacus atlas *is one of the largest and most beautiful moths of Malaysia. It weaves a rough silk cocoon, sometimes used to make fabric. (F. G. H. Allen)   Right: Mud and rotting plants attract many multicolored forest butterflies such as these* Appias nero, Cepora *sp.,* Catopsilia *sp.,* Graphium everron, *and* Polyaradelphin. *Far right: Along streams and in forest clearings, dragonflies and demoiselles (shown here:* Neurobasis chinensis), *some brightly colored, hunt small insects. (Both, Jane Burton: Photo Researchers)*

The forests of the Malayan Archipelago harbor a variety of walking sticks. The female of some species may be as much as twelve inches long. (Pierre Pfeffer)

Lorises progress clumsily on the ground, falling constantly unless they can cling to a support; in a tree, however, they move slowly but with the ease of monkeys, their more sophisticated cousins. Strictly nocturnal and blinded by light, they spend their days in tree hollows, coming out after sunset to rummage methodically through the foliage and clumps of epiphytes.

THE LAST RHINO AND BOAR HUNTS

Light undergrowth and the near absence of a herbaceous layer make the virgin forest an unfavorable habitat for large animals. The impoverished environment, providing only leaves and shoots of young trees and fallen fruit, precludes a large herbivorous population; thus forest ungulates, contrary to their habits on savannas, form herds that rarely reach fifteen or twenty head. This is true also of primates, both monkey or human. Men living on open farming or grazing land gather in village groups while forest hunters form clans of twenty to thirty individuals. Very strict customs keep these numbers from reaching a level dangerous to communal existence; a clan that expands to more than thirty persons splits up, and the excess group finds new hunting grounds.

Such social animals as the elephant, the buffalo, the banteng, and most of the deer, which normally form herds of as many as several hundred, move about individually or in small groups in the forest. Distribution of these animals in the Malay Archipelago is fairly irregular, elephants being found in their natural state only in the Malay Peninsula and in Sumatra. As for the rhinoceros, beside the one-horned species of Java on the Udjungkulon Reserve, another species is found in this region: the two-horned or Sumatran rhinoceros *(Rhinoceros sumatrensis),* the smallest of all, no more than 106 inches long and with a shoulder height of about 52 inches. It is the only one of the three Asiatic species that has two horns and an unwrinkled hide covered with rough, sparse hair, whence its Malayan name of "badak kerbau" or buffalo-rhinoceros. Found from Assam to Sumatra and Borneo in the last century, it has fallen victim to the qualities attributed to its horns and has been rapidly exterminated in the continental portion of its habitat, except perhaps along the Pahang in Malaya, where a few specimens are seen from time to time. It was not yet rare in the two large Sunda Islands before the last war, travelers reporting that the Dayaks of Borneo often kept young rhinoceroses in captivity. I have myself met several hunters who had grown rich from the sale of horns and skins. But my inquiries in 1957 revealed that scarcely more than ten rhinoceroses remained in an area as large as England.

Although less hunted, the Malay tapir *(Tapirus indicus)* is not much more common and the chances of seeing it are small. This shy animal lives in the remotest parts of the forest and seems endowed not only with exceptional auditory and olfactory senses, but also with vision clearly superior to that of the rhinoceros. The tapir lives in the southern Indochinese peninsula, in Malaysia, and in Sumatra, and is different from

of India *(Loris tardigradus)* and the slow loris that is found in Indochina and the Malaysian region *(Nycticebus coucang).* Lorises resemble plush, fat teddy-bears, with thick, short, soft, ash-gray or brown fur, round heads with tiny ears, great golden eyes, myopic and astonished in expression, and very short tails hidden in the downy fur. Their most striking quality is an extraordinary sluggishness of movement, like that in a slow-motion film. It is almost impossible to believe that these grotesque creatures can seize any live prey, including even small birds. For although lorises enjoy fruit, they are not satisfied with a strictly vegetarian diet, and although as slow as South American sloths, they can capture a small animal with an astonishingly quick thrust.

White-handed gibbons (Hylobates lar), *found from lower Burma and Cambodia to Sumatra, are known for the melancholy wailing and treetop acrobatics with which they salute sunrise and sunset. (Ylla: Rapho Guillumette)*

266

his South American cousin only in his coat, which is blackish-gray with white covering back, hindquarters and belly.

The bearded boar of Sumatra and Borneo *(Sus barbatus)* is covered with a silvery coat forming a hairy beard on either side of its head, making it look like a prize-winning pig, for these animals may weigh from 300 to 400 pounds. They are the basic food of hunting tribes, the Dayaks and Punans in Borneo, the Kubus in Sumatra. For nearly two years our own party ate practically no other meat. In certain parts of the forest, were little "beds" of small branches laid so carefully side by side that I could hardly believe it belonged to an animal until I came on a boar sleeping in one.

At another time, out hunting with two Dayaks armed with spears and followed by a pack of small dogs, we came upon a three-foot-high, six-foot-wide accumulation of ferns, small branches and dry palms. When the dogs approached, a sow burst forth and charged at the nearest dog. The sow rushed back into her vegetable mound when little cries indicated the presence of young ones. The mother renewed her attack two or three times before I persuaded my companions to spare her.

A strange behavior pattern of these boars is that of mass migrations, difficult to explain since they are not undertaken purely for the sake of food. At certain periods, an irresistible urge to move overcomes entire sections of the boar population, whether food is scarce or abundant, the animals young or old. A very old boar with paralyzed hindquarters was seen dragging along trying to follow its fellows, and sows are accompanied by small marcassins destined to perish on the way. They follow routes that become sunken paths under the tramplings of thousands of feet. Their swimming talents are stupendous and they can cross fifty to sixty yards of rough water in a few minutes and then scale a rocky shore with the agility of goats. Borneo villagers find these mass movements a blessing and the entire male population of a village will leap into pirogues to meet the boars in midstream and slaughter them one by one. Often, wounded animals and carcasses are swept downstream by the current to be gathered up by other hunters, women and children. In 1954, the migration on the Kajan River was so huge that the killing lasted for weeks and thousands of carcasses piled up in front of the small city of Tandjungselor, inhabited by Malay Mohammedans to whom the pig is an unclean animal. Furious at their inability to bathe in or drink the polluted water, the Mohammedans declared war on the upstream tribes and it required the intervention of police and soldiers before the Dayaks ceased the slaughter.

THE NIGHTMARE FOREST

As one penetrates the "mid-mountain forest" at altitudes between 3,000 and 6,000 feet, changes in the general character of the vegetation become evident. The tall trees of the low regions give way to smaller species, although some giants persist. The ground is no longer as clear of growth as in the great forest below, and wild ginger, palms and ferns abound. Tree ferns sometimes form forests twelve to fifteen feet high, with some growths reaching thirty-six feet. The typical lowland Diptero-carps disappear or become quite rare, but representatives of the same genera, adapted to the altitude, appear.

Striking features of the highland forests are the intermittent canopy, the comparatively well-lighted undergrowth of ferns, bushes, and shrubs, and a distinct thinning out in climbing plants, epiphytes and mosses. Although generally receiving more rain than the lowland forest, the mountain forest seems drier since its slope allows for drainage and prevents the heavy humidity caused by the constant evaporation of stagnant water.

In some places, however, clouds descend relatively low, and by preventing fogs from being dissipated by the sun, transform the air into a steam bath. The landscape takes on the curious aspect of what is called cloud or "moss forest," the permanent humidity favoring the growth of all epiphytes, mosses and ferns.

Such a forest, in Borneo, has a nightmarish quality. Every open spot on the ground, every rock, trunk and branch is covered with parasitic plants, lichens, ferns and orchids with insignificant flowers. The branches are so overgrown with mosses that every branch appears to be twice as thick as it actually is. Some mosses hang down in long woolly filaments, while others cover even the leaves so that the forest resembles a submarine landscape draped in seaweed.

The ferns are equally variegated, the most typical being the creeping masses of the Gleichenia, the erect fronds of the Oleandra, and the Lecanopteris whose spongy bases shelter thousands of tiny black ants. There are many tropical creepers bearing brightly colored pink or violet flowers. Other flowers such as aristolochia *(Aristolochia)*, generously display corollas whose interiors are death-traps for insects. Equally numerous are pitcher-plants *(Nepenthes)*, shaped like urns topped with little half-open lids ready to close down on the prey. Unlike the aristolochia, pitcher-plants contain a fluid that permits them to digest and assimilate their victims.

As we walked, our feet pressed water out of the mossy carpet covering the ground as if from a soggy bath-mat. Caught by surprise, a pair of muntjac deer bounded off, baying in terror. A group of black gibbons *(Hylobates moloch)* stared at us spellbound for a moment and then disappeared into the unreal landscape.

Birds were more numerous or more visible than in the lower forest. The nasal trumpeting of calaos, the raucous cooing of great fruit-eating pigeons, the mewing of black-headed orioles, and the hammering of barbets were so many signs of life in this exotic environment. Noisy bulbuls abounded, as did gray drongos and minivets in their brilliant red plumage. Cuckoo doves *(Macropygia)* and low-flying malcohas *(Rhinortha)* were more discreet. The fairy bluebird proved much more abundant and friendly than in the lowlands, and the croaking cry of the great bee-eater *(Nyctiornis amicta)* came at times from high in the trees. Once a beautiful green bird passed in front of us, the cruel hunting cissa *(Kitta chinensis)*, scourge of small forest animals.

In this dream-like landscape, I collected two extremely rare birds: Whitehead's broadbill *(Calyptomena whiteheadi)*, thick-set, with a short, widely split beak, and a soft-green plumage marked with small black spots, and a wood partridge *(Haematortyx sanguiniceps)*, completely black except for head, tail and feet of brilliant red. Highland forests are richer in partridges and pheasants than are lowland forests. The argus

The water buffalo (here shown at the foot of Baluran volcano in eastern Java), originally found in lowland swamps, has adapted perfectly to the driest terrains. (Pierre Pfeffer)

pheasant is found on the humid slopes and the crested fire-back pheasant (Lophura ignita) in drier areas. Red-breasted tree partridges (Arborophila hyperythra) seek light places and bamboo thickets, while ferruginous wood partridges (Caloperdix oculea) prefer the darker places. One of my most surprising observations involved the very common crested wood partridge (Rollulus roulroul). One day, while crouching under a Lithocarpus whose acorns littered the ground, a huge silver-coated boar approached, escorted by five partridges, two easily recognizable as males by their red crest. When the boar began to eat, I understood this strange association. Since Lithocarpus acorns are too bulky to be swallowed by the partridges, they let the pig crunch them. Then, crowding about its snout, they not only pick up fallen morsels but even snatch crumbs sticking to the beast's lips.

The vision of these birds is so acute that my least movement did not escape them. Two raised their heads uneasily and uttered a little cackle of alarm. It is probable that as in other such associations—between cattle heron and the grazing mammals, jungle fowl and bantengs, African ox-peckers and

large mammals—the benefit is reciprocal, the partridges feeding on the remains of their companion's meals and on his external parasites and sounding an alert in case of danger, compensating for the boar's myopia by their vigilance.

ASIAN ANIMALS IN AFRICAN LANDSCAPES

The forest does not cover Malaysia. Everywhere it is retreating before the axe and before repeated fires, usually caused by man. In areas exhausted by haphazard agricultural exploitation, the soil sprouts tall grasses in which one usually predominates, a lone species perfectly adapted to resisting fire by means of a deep root system. Repeated too often, brush fires finally destroy all the less resistant but often most useful species, leaving the ground clear for the hardy grasses.

In the valleys and along the streams, wild sugar-cane (Saccharum spontaneum), frequently much taller than a man, forms almost impenetrable thickets of razor-sharp, silica-bearing leaves. On the hills and mountain slopes it is replaced by what the Filipinos call cogon and the Malays alang-alang (Imperata cylindrica), a plant not as hardy and tall as the wild cane. Completely sterile, alang-alang is an index to what abusive farming practices and too frequent fires can do to impoverish the soil. Experts have calculated that nearly 40 percent of the land in Indochina and Indonesia has thus become useless for agriculture.

Nevertheless, this process would not be irreversible if the annual or biennial cycle of fire could be halted for a sufficiently long period. Brushwood and the Malay rhododendron (Melastoma polyanthum), with its beautiful pink flowers, would finally smother the alang-alang and, in the shade thus created, seeds from the forest could sprout and restore the trees. It would require at least a century or two before the original forest could thus be replaced, and it could only take place if man never intervened with his axe or his fires—which is, of course, out of the question in densely populated regions.

Some of the grassy expanses are nevertheless considered natural in origin. These are most likely to be found above the tree line, somewhere between sixty-five hundred and ten thousand feet up. One day, while I was out hunting with two Dayaks in the center of Borneo, we suddenly came upon one of these clearings. Accustomed to being able to see no more than a few yards ahead, it was a great surprise to gaze out over a series of hills covered with tall grass waving in the breeze and extending to the horizon. Great clumps of Malay rhododendrons, covered with pink flowers and little violet fruits, were a meeting-place for hundreds of green and pink pigeons (Treron vernans) and small, multicolored flower-peckers (Dicaeum chrysorrheum). Button-quails (Turnix suscitator), larks (Mirafra javanica), pipits (Anthus novae-zelandiae) and flocks of little white and black weavers (Lonchura ferruginosa) flew up from under our feet, while the resonant song of invisible ground cuckoos (Centropus bengalensis) echoed from all sides. It was clear that this pleasant landscape had not been invaded by a human being in years, for herds of large animals grazed calmly all about, heedless of our presence. Boars, muntjac deer, bantengs and an incredible number of magnificent sambar deer, grazing singly, in families or in small groups, were not disturbed even when we walked among them. Some looked at us with wide, astonished eyes before moving aside slowly as if to let us pass. A doe came to

In Indochina and Malaysia, the Javan peacock (Pavo muticus) replaces the Indian peacock, ancestor of the domesticated bird. Hunted intensively, it has become very rare outside protected areas. (Pierre Pfeffer)

Fan palms (Corypha utan), *shown here in the Udjungkulon Reserve in western Java, are typical of the lower shore forest of Indochina and Malaysia. On savannas they are found in company with jujube and acacia trees. (Pierre Pfeffer)*

sniff at me, so close that I felt her warm breath on my face. Doubtless surprised by my scent, she uttered a shrill little cry, shied away and then began to graze again unconcernedly.

Other natural savannas in this region result from a lack of rainfall, which of course prevents forests from developing. One of the most striking examples of this is in the region of Mount Baluran, an extinct volcano in east Java, where mountain chains intercept the humidity brought by the winds of the southern monsoon. While the rainfall in the west of the island reaches over 200 inches a year and is as great as eighty inches in some eastern localities, it reaches no more than thirty-six inches around Mount Baluran. The traveler, accustomed to the exuberant plant life of Southeast Asia, imagines himself suddenly transported to East Africa. Savanna covered with tall grasses stretches as far as the eye can see. Most fortunately, *alang-alang* is rare and is replaced by grasses—*Andropogon, Themeda, Polytoea*—preferred by animals. Jujube trees *(Zizyphus jujuba)*, gebang palms *(Corypha utan)* and white-barked, spiny acacias *(Acacia tomentosa)* shaped like parasols are

scattered across open spaces scorched by the sun. A very dense monsoon forest of acacias and a few other trees extends around the volcano. The most spectacular tree in the forest in the dry season is the erythrina or coral tree. Although leafless at that time, it is covered with huge, red flowers and attracts animals eager for nectar. Insects of all kinds, birds, including bulbuls, flowerpeckers, barbets, parakeets and crows, and mammals—squirrels, bats, shrews, monkeys—gather about it day and night. Two other prominent trees are the *Sterculia foetida,* which also loses its leaves and yields green fruits the size of an apple, and the tamarind *(Tamarindus indicus)*. The latter is very important for animal life because its long, brown, velvety pods enclose many large, acid seeds eagerly sought by birds, monkeys, boars and humans. The underbrush is a tangle of thick vines and thorny brambles, principally *Calotropia gigantea,* whose sprigs are four-inch spines. The flanks of the volcano are covered with a much more humid forest, similar to those on other mountains of the archipelago. It shelters many interesting animals: boars, pangolins and, among

the birds, three species of hornbills that have disappeared from most of Java because of the excessive cutting down of trees.

Thousands of turtledoves, ring-necked *(Streptopelia bitorquata)* or striped *(S. chinensis)*, warble and coo in the low trees of the savanna and fly above us, while wild chickens *(Gallus varius)* cackling in terror, spring up in front of us. Javan peacocks *(Pavo muticus)* are as numerous, but so cautious that it was only after a stay of two months at Baluran that I managed to photograph them. Their prudence is warranted for, beside being hunted by man for their beautiful plumage, they often fall victim to the spotted or black panthers at Baluran. During my last stay there, we found a litter of three cubs, one black and two spotted, in a cave.

Small carnivores are numerous: musangs *(Paradoxurus hermaphroditus)*, palm civets *(Viverricula malaccensis)* and mongooses. I was once even lucky enough to catch a glimpse in tall grasses of one of the most cautious animals of the jungle, the Bengal or leopard-cat *(Felis bengalensis)*. Among the larger wild animals of the region are the Javanese tiger, of which two or three specimens living here and a few in Udjungkulon are the only survivors on the island, and the so-called wild dog *(Cuon javanicus)*. Packs of these little yellow dogs corner stags and young bantengs with a chorus of yelps audible for several miles. The Baluran region, now a reserve unfortunately little respected by poachers, is a paradise for large, grass-eating animals. It is the only place in Asia where it is possible to see herds of more than fifty bantengs. As for sambar deer, I have myself counted 246 stags, does, and fawns in one group.

Buffalos, doubtless brought from the continent by Indian invaders, also form formidable herds. At the slightest hint of danger, they spread out in an arc, converging on the intruder with head high and nose in the air in an intimidating attitude, males on the outside to protect females and young animals.

Some old males, often weighing a ton and having horns with a spread of more than five feet, live solitary existences. They are generally feared by the inhabitants of the area for they will charge an imprudent stroller unhesitatingly. Nevertheless, I managed to tame one of these old hermits so far that when I spoke to him, he came within two or three paces of me and sometimes remained near me for an hour, while I used my cameras. At other times, he came to our camp seeking water, tapping his hoof impatiently; for water-holes are scarce in Baluran. Having emptied one or two pails, he would settle down in the doubtful shade of an acacia and take a siesta until evening when he went off to graze at the edge of the forest.

Reptiles are comparatively abundant around Mount Baluran. One may meet two species of python *(Python molurus, P. reticulatus)*, cobras, Russell's vipers, banded kraits and harmless whip snakes *(Dendrophis)*. Green, slim and long as vines, whip snakes spend almost all their time in trees where they hunt lizards of all kinds.

The savannas scattered through the forest region attract many species of animals tempted by open spaces with plenty of grass. The abundance of forage supports a dense population of large animals unknown in the forest. The scientific and economic value of these savannas is therefore immense and they should be made available for tourists and limited hunting. At present, all the open spaces are visited by hunters on horseback or in jeeps who slaughter the large animals day and night, most often for commercial purposes. In 1964, the meat of a buffalo or a banteng sold for thirty thousand rupiahs (sixty dollars) in East Java, a sum equivalent to nearly ten months' salary for the average Indonesian government worker. As a result, although Baluran is officially a natural reserve, its stock of large animals has been so depleted by men such as soldiers and policemen, who have weapons, that it will soon be totally wiped out.

The large animals of Java such as this banteng bull have been eliminated except in forests on volcanic slopes and two natural reserves. (Pierre Pfeffer)

Steppingstones to Australia

Islands Beyond the Wallace Line

From Celebes and the Moluccan Archipelago on the north to the Lesser Sunda Islands on the south, a multitude of small islands stretches from Borneo and Java eastward to Australia and New Guinea. The Greater Sunda Islands—Sumatra, Borneo and Java—were, as we have said, linked to continental Asia until the melting of the glaciers caused the sea level to rise. New Guinea and Tasmania in earlier times were similarly joined to Australia to form the Sahul shelf. Animals and, to a lesser extent, plants of the Indo-Malaysian or Oriental regions differ greatly from those of Australia because they developed independently. It is thus not difficult to determine what the stock of islands lying between these two regions owes to each. Nevertheless, for more than a century the location of the frontier between Oriental and Australian animals has been the subject of lively dispute among biogeographers.

The line varies according to the zoological groups being considered and will not have the same position for the specialist in mammals, for instance, as it has for the reptile expert. Alfred Russel Wallace, the great naturalist who developed at the same time as Darwin a similar theory on the origin and evolution of the species, traces this line east of Mindanao in the Philippines, between Borneo and Celebes, and then between Bali and Lombok in the Lesser Sunda chain. Other authors have proposed several modifications. However, the Wallace Line seems to be the true Oriental limit for the great majority of Indo-Malaysian vertebrates. It is valid for fresh-water fish and specially for the large family of Cyprinides: carp, goldfish and other species common on the Eurasian continent. It is not so clear for reptiles because some species have crossed the Makassar Strait and some have reached New Guinea. Very few Australian reptiles have, however, been able to spread westward and only a few snakes and a giant skink (Tiliqua gigas) have reached the Moluccas.

The problem is more complex for birds since they can move more readily than land or fresh-water vertebrates. In general, the number of Indo-Malaysian bird forms diminishes toward the east, but, contrary to the situation of reptiles, the number of Australian forms distinctly increases. Eighty-seven percent of the birds on Bali are Oriental and only 13 percent are Australian, but the islands between Flores and Timor have respectively 57 percent and 42 percent. Typically Indo-Malaysian families like the bulbuls, quite common in the Greater Sundas, are represented east of the Wallace Line by only one or two species, depending on the island. Such distinctly Australian birds as the yellow-crested cockatoo, the whistlers (Pachycephala), a honey-eater called leatherhead (Philemon buceroides), the striped dove (Geopelia striata) and the megapodes have spread through the Lesser Sundas as far as Bali. The striped dove is found even in eastern Java, but the bird was probably introduced voluntarily or accidentally since the Javanese are very fond of it. In the most eastern archipelagos bird life is even more distinctly influenced by the proximity of Australia. Birds of paradise are found on the Aru Islands; cassowaries, megapodes, cockatoos and all sorts of lories on the Moluccas.

The distribution of mammals is more difficult to explain, for man has upset it for centuries by voluntarily or involuntarily transporting many species. Long-tailed macaques, civets, deer, buffalos, wild boars, horses and wild dogs are often descendants of animals brought to most of the islands east of the Wallace Line by Malay sailors. Rats, mice and shrews have been disseminated accidentally. Consequently, except for bats, there is practically no Indo-Malaysian mammal that can be guaranteed to be a natural migrant to these islands. The one exception is the porcupine (Hystrix), which has spread as far as Flores, and even here it is not certain that this expansion was not assisted by natives, who enjoy its delicate flesh. Australian emigration has not really compensated for the lack of Indo-Malaysian species. Among the marsupials, cuscuses or phalangers have spread through Celebes. A kangaroo has managed to colonize the Aru and Kei Islands, which also harbor a bandicoot or marsupial rat (Echymipera), a native of New Guinea.

Birds, often members of the most brilliant species, are more numerous. This is true also of reptiles and of insects. Thus, although poor in comparison to Oriental and Australian, regions, the islands are not without interest to naturalists. They not only share some curious animals with the other regions, but shelter a few vertebrates strange enough to be classified as a special species and genus. Quite unusually, animals of the region, often called Wallacea, are generally represented on each of the islands by highly differentiated geographical races. This may seem normal enough for land vertebates, but is more unusual for birds that can easily fly the narrow bodies of water that separate some of the islands.

SPICES AND MULTICOLORED VOLCANOES

Often volcanic in origin, the islands are all very hilly. Many of them rise from sea level to nearly 22,000 feet within a few miles. Although most of the volcanoes are extinct, a few have awakened abruptly: Agung on Bali claimed nearly 30,000 victims in 1962. Subterranean volcanic activity is revealed in the form of frequent earthquakes. Although these are usually slight tremors, one of them, in 1958, almost entirely destroyed the town of Ende on Flores. That island has one of the most

A chaplet of coral and volcanic islands, once covered with forest, extends from the Greater Sunda Islands to New Guinea. This view shows Ambon. (Pierre Pfeffer)

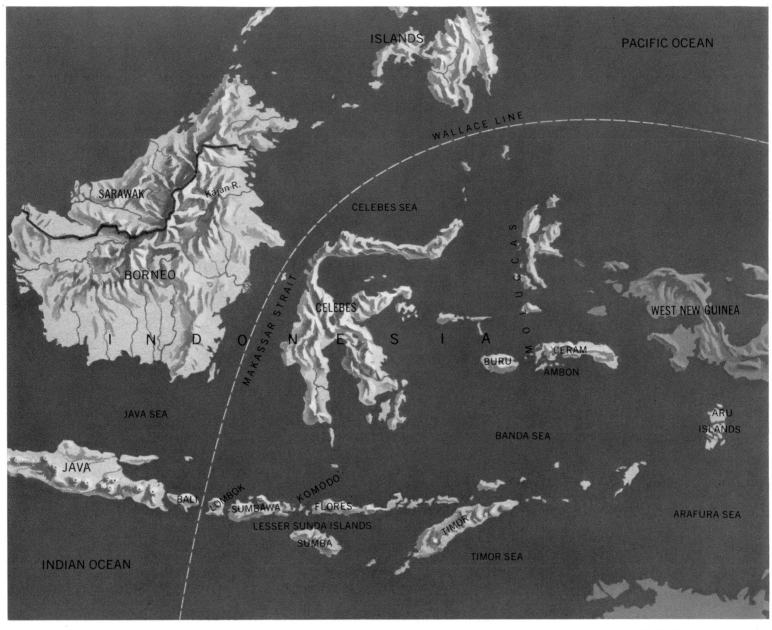

East of the Wallace Line between Borneo and Celebes stretches the biogeographical region called Wallacea. It consists of islands never linked to the Asiatic continent or detached from it very early. Animal life in this region is made up largely of Asiatic or Australian elements, but includes some completely native forms.

beautiful extinct volcanoes in the world, Keli Mutu, with three craters lying side by side, each sheltering a lake of a different color: turquoise blue, blood red and snow white. The incredible colors in the first two craters result from copper and iron salts in the water; in the third, from the activity of sulphur bacteria.

The northern Celebes and Molucca Islands, normally well watered, were originally covered with a primeval forest whose giant trees were as large as those of Borneo or New Guinea. On the Moluccas, this magnificent forest is still almost intact, but on Celebes, where mountain people practice agriculture on burned land, it has been largely cut down. The botanical families are generally those we have already seen on the Greater Sunda Islands. However, certain trees predominate, and one of these is the damar *(Agathis)*, a huge white-trunked conifer with wide pennate leaves, like those of the ash,

instead of needles. The damar is also found in Borneo, but is clearly dominant east of the Makassar Strait and often forms almost pure stands. Resin flowing from holes in the tree dug by certain insects forms large amber-colored blocks of a substance called damar, much sought for certain varnishes, such as those used in oil painting. Curiously enough, the insect's assistance is indispensable, for resin flowing from an artificially made wound never turns into damar.

Since the Wallace Line is the western limit of distribution for certain other trees, they, too, appear for the first time as we voyage eastward. The most typical is the canary *(Cana-*

Sumba, in the Lesser Sunda Islands, is covered with savannas strewn with palmyra palms and spiny jujube trees. Dense forest survives only on the volcanic slopes. (Sven Gillsater)

276

Most volcanoes in the Lesser Sundas, like this one on Sumbawa, are extinct but the chain is still often shaken by violent earthquakes. (Harrison Forman)

rium), a large tree whose nuts are eaten by boars and the largest cockatoos, the only animals with jaws or beaks strong enough to break the thick shells. In the easternmost islands grow several species of Melaleuca whose wood, when distilled, furnishes scented essences used in pharmaceutical preparations. Typical of the Moluccas and source of their wealth and their misfortunes are the nutmeg tree and the clove tree which as early as the fifteenth century became the subject of fierce struggles among the great maritime powers. Until recently, these trees conferred on these islands a world monopoly of these most precious spices. In humid places in swampy valleys and on slopes, the sago palm *(Metroxylon)* forms impenetrable forests. The sago is the most important plant on these islands and in New Guinea, for its pith furnishes a flour that is the staple food of local populations.

The Lesser Sunda Islands are much more arid than the

The wild boars (Sus scrofa) *on most of the islands of Wallacea such as Komodo (left) were probably brought there by man. They can also swim across narrow straits. (Sven Gillsater)*

northern archipelagos. They have a very long dry season, lasting from February to October, and a short season of heavy rains too violent to be entirely absorbed by the soil. Vegetation here is much less luxuriant than in other parts of the Malay Archipelago. On these islands a mangrove belt usually encircles a brushy coastal forest from which a few tall trees *(Ficus, Barringtonia)* grow. The hills and steep slopes of extinct volcanoes are covered with savannas strewn with thorny jujubes and slender palmyra palms *(Borassus).* A thick forest of bamboos and all sorts of fig trees intertwined with lianas and rattan palms grows on the summits.

PARROTS, CASSOWARIES AND BIRDS OF PARADISE

The most beautiful birds in this region are found on Celebes and the Moluccas. That is why, during the nineteenth and early twentieth centuries, these islands were the world centers for gathering the feathers so desired by fashionable women. Each year hundreds of thousands of multicolored skins left clearing-houses in Makassar and Menado on Celebes and in Ambon in the south of the Moluccas destined for Paris and London, the two great international markets of the feather

industry. The caprices of fashion luckily put an end to the massacre more effectively than the severest protective measures.

The island birds do not seem to have suffered permanently from these heavy inroads, and naturalists are pleasantly surprised at the number of birds that may still be seen in the Moluccan forests, even though the number of species on Sumatra or Borneo is greater. Each of the islands of the archipelago has its own few species or subspecies. Since some of the islands lie very close together, it is difficult to explain why, for example, large pink cockatoos, able to fly easily and rapidly, inhabit Ceram but have never settled on Ambon, whose coast is clearly visible across the sea. Lories, fruit- and nectar-eating parrots, whose brilliant, bright red plumage is mixed with green, blue or yellow, are represented by different varieties on each of the islands they inhabit. Much more surprising is the presence on Ceram and a few other islands

Left: Celebes, once covered with a high equatorial forest, has suffered severely from the ancient practice of burning land before farming it. (Luc Bouchage: Rapho Guillumette) Below: The rusa deer on all these islands is a small island race of the sambar deer of tropical Asia and the Greater Sundas. (Pierre Pfeffer)

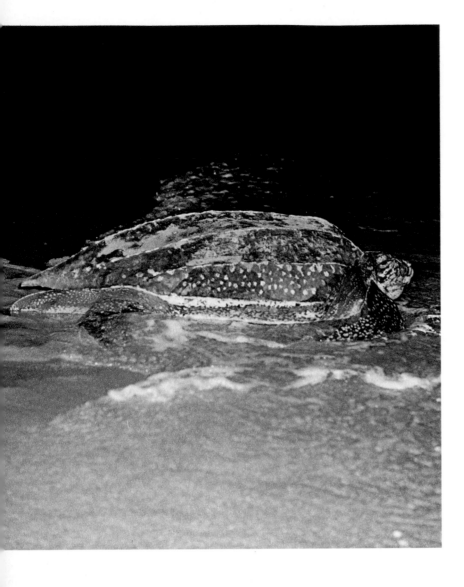

of the completely earthbound cassowary whose native habitat is New Guinea and the wooded part of Northeastern Australia. Unlike other ostriches, this large bird prefers dense, humid forests, where it feeds on fruits and small animals.

Another representative from New Guinea, the greater bird of paradise of the Aru Islands, also lives in damp, thick forests. The golden-yellow shimmer of its long velvety plumes and the fact that the first skins to reach Europe arrived with the feet cut off gave rise to the legend that the birds never perched, even to procreate, and lived on air and sunshine. As early as 1522, however, one of Magellan's companions, Pigafetti, described a pair of birds given him by the Rajah of Batjan in the northern Moluccas and clearly mentioned the feet "as thin as a goose feather." The legend died hard, for in 1766 Linnaeus himself described the bird as *Paradisea apoda*, "the footless paradise-bird."

As long as only the Papuans desired its marvellous plumage, the future of this bird was safe. But when the vogue for feathers reached its height, and skins brought sky-high prices, the Dutch, who governed the Aru Islands, were forced to take protective measures. The demand for bird of paradise feathers has sprung up again in the last few years, and smugglers now ship them to Java where "souvenir" hunters pay large sums for them. Luckily, only the male birds have the bright, trailing plumes. Females are so dull in color and unadorned that even very few natives know that they belong to the same species. In addition, the males don their splendid feathers only at the end of their second or during their third year and the long side trailers pass through a long brownish stage before acquiring the valuable golden sheen. Sexual maturity probably occurs before the feathers turn to gold so that the birds can reproduce at least once and help insure the survival of the species.

INCUBATOR BIRDS AND WILD FOWL

The strangest birds of this region are the megapodes; they look like chickens that have—as their Greek (or scientific) name indicates—large-sized feet. They are basically runners, ground birds, but can fly as well as pheasants. Several species belonging to the genera *Megapodius*, *Eulipoa* and *Megacephalon* dwell on the islands of Wallacea, while others live in the forests of New Guinea. Modestly clad in earthy or purplish brown, these birds developed "artificial incubation" millions of years before man ever thought of it.

In the genus *Megapodius*, ten to twenty females gather at

Left above: The leathery sea turtle (Dermochelys coriacea) *is one of several species of marine tortoises found in warm waters. The eggs it deposits on beaches are prized by islanders. (Jane Burton: Photo Researchers) Left: Several species of sea serpents live in the Malay Archipelago. Some are harmless but others, as this* Laticauda, *have a powerful venom that they use on fish. (Pierre Pittet)*

Right: Komodo Island, between Sumbawa and Flores, attracted attention in 1912 when the Komodo dragon (Varanus komodoensis), *a 10-foot monitor lizard, was found there. (David Attenborough)*

laying time and, using no other tools besides their large feet and their beaks, carefully clear an area of the forest of even the slightest twig. Scratching with their feet, they then build up a pile of humus as much as thirty feet wide and five feet high; the hens dig a small crater at the top of the tumulus, lay their eggs in it, and having covered it, pay no further attention to it. Incubation, lasting forty days, results entirely from the heat given off by the fermentation of humus. When they crack their shells and emerge, the chicks must provide for themselves.

Megapodes of the genus *Eulipoa,* which usually live in high places, have equally unusual breeding habits. The females come down to the beach during the night and lay one egg at a time in the sand. Just like sea turtles, the hens place the eggs where the conditions of humidity and sunshine are best for incubation. When the chick emerges it seems to feel a kind of irresistible attraction to the heights and immediately ascends to altitudes of 1,500 to 6,500 feet.

The inhabitants of islands sheltering megapodes do a lively business in eggs. Since the females always return to exactly the same sites for reproduction, these belong to the same families for generations. The megapodes have disappeared from many islands because of this pillage of their eggs, but they are still abundant on many uninhabited islands.

The southern islands of Wallacea, the Lesser Sundas, have fewer native birds than Celebes and the Moluccas. About sixty species live there permanently, and approximately another sixty migrate from Asia or Australia during their winter seasons. Among the sedentary birds, as we have noted, the number of typically Asiatic genera decreases progressively from west to east and the Australian genera increase. Besides turtle-doves *(Streptopelia chinensis)* and striped-doves *(Geopelia striata)* that literally swarm and make the air vibrate with their constant cooing, the commonest birds are the little yellow-crested white cockatoos and the large fruit-eating pigeons *(Ducula aenea).* Typical of the region, but with definite Australian affinities, the leatherhead *(Philemon buceroides),* a brown bird the size of a thrush, called *koka* by the islanders, fills the forest and the coconut plantations with childlike cries. There are also many gray cuckoo-shrikes *(Coracina floris)* carefully searching each tree and, in the grasses of the savannas, sky-larks *(Mirafra javanica),* pipits *(Anthus novae-zelandiae),* two or three species of mannikins *(Lonchura),* spotted astrilds *(Taeniopygia guttata)* and button quails. Coucals *(Centropus bengalensis)* are common but are so shy that it is useless to try to spot one even when their resonant "coo-coo" seems to spring from beneath one's feet. Megapodes are abundant in both the low and high forests, as are jungle hens *(Gallus varius).* One often sees shrikes of the sedentary species *(Lanius schah)* or of the migrants from Japan *(L. cristata)* on the isolated bushes of the savannas. Bands of bee-eaters *(Merops superciliosus, M. orantus)* flutter about above the tall grasses. Brahminy or eagle kites *(Haliastur indus)* and white-breasted sea eagles *(Haliaeetus leucogaster),* as fond of fish as of dead animals on the savannas, constantly cross the sky over the beach as well as over the interior. In the mangrove swamps, one can watch crows, several species of kingfishers, blue

A solitary dragon paces Letuho beach on Komodo. Behind it are the coastal forest and volcanic hills covered with savannas and palmyra palms (Borassus flabellifer). *(Sven Gillsater)*

flycatchers *(Hypothymis azurea)* and the great tit mouse of Eurasia *(Parus major),* represented here by a race with a light gray belly.

BABIRUSAS AND NATIVE MONKEYS

Mammals are even scarcer than birds on the Lesser Sundas. Including bats, only seventeen genera are represented and two of these were introduced by man but have proliferated to such an extent that they must be included in any discussion of native animals. The introduced forms are *Equus,* the horse, and *Bubalus,* the water buffalo. One may see herds of wild horses on almost all the islands. Descendants of horses imported by the Portuguese in the eighteenth century, they are difficult to approach since their sight and hearing are excellent. These splendid animals, often uniformly chestnut color, are an unforgettable sight as they gallop, manes flying in the wind, across the island landscapes. Water buffalos, introduced more than ten centuries ago by Indian invaders, have completely abandoned their semi-aquatic habits and adapted perfectly to the dry and hilly terrains of the Lesser Sundas. They are lively animals and, despite their great weight —adult males are nearly a ton—can climb like goats.

How deer *(Cervus timorensis)* and wild boars *(Sus scrofa)* came to occupy most of the islands of Wallacea is a mystery. It is possible that Malay sailors transported them from island to island, but it is also possible that the animals came by themselves, for they are strong swimmers. Quite often, deer or boars colonize an island but disappear when conditions become unfavorable, as, for example, after a very dry period. However the animals reached the islands, they must have come from the Greater Sundas, for most of the eastern archipelagos were almost without animals in primitive times.

It is also very probable that civets *(Pardoxurus hermaphroditus)* and long-tailed macaques *(Macaca irus)* were introduced by man into the entire chain between Java and Timor. The Malays often make pets of both and take them to sea in thair raffia-sailed pirogues. In fact, except for a few bats and the giant rat of Flores *(Papagomys armandvillei),* the mammals now on the Lesser Sundas must be attributed to man's intervention.

The northern islands of Wallacea, Celebes and the Moluccas, are much richer in native animals, including a few endemic genera or species. A small forest ox, the anoa *(Anoa depressicornis)* lives on Celebes. Although most zoologists consider it a dwarf form of the water buffalo, it bears more of a resemblance to an antelope for it has small straight horns and a narrow, elongated head. It does not, moreover, behave like a buffalo and it lives on the most mountainous parts of the island, not in the low-lying swamps. Some zoologists have compared it with the tamarou *(Tamarau mindorensis)* of the Philippines, but the tamarou is truly a small buffalo, while the anoa is more like the Indian nilgai or some African forest antelopes.

Another animal peculiar to this region is the babirusa *(Babirussa babirussa)* of Celebes, Buru and the tiny Sula Islands. A very large wild boar, it stands high on its legs, has almost completely hairless skin, and looks like a tapir or a dwarf hippopotamus. The male has long, curved and hornlike tusks. Its appearance has probably earned it its Malayan name, for *babi* means pig and *rusa,* deer. Although classed

among the boars, it differs from them in that the females bear only one or two young at a time, while the rule for the boar family is six or seven. Endowed with extremely sharp hearing and a keen sense of smell, it is a very timid forest animal, quite difficult to trap. Except for a few large males, it leads a family life, feeding on bulbs, roots, fruits and larvae, most of which it gets, like all relatives of the boar, by digging in the ground. As for the tusks of the male, it has been suggested that they protect the animal while it is digging, but they are more probably a secondary sexual characteristic like the lion's mane or the comb and spurs of the cock.

Celebes, the richest island in native mammals, also has a squirrel *(Hyosciurus),* a civet *(Macrogalidia)* and two native monkeys. One of the monkeys, the Moor macaque *(Macaca maura),* which lives in the south of the island, is a very large monkey that differs from those on the Malay Archipelago in that it lacks a tail and has a thick coat of long black or brown hair. The second primate peculiar to Celebes is the cynopithecus or black ape *(Cynopithecus niger).* Although it has nothing in common with African baboons, its long muzzle and general appearance immediately bring them to mind and have earned it the scientific name of cynopithecus, meaning "dog-monkey." Peculiar to Celebes, it has been introduced to Batjan in the northern Moluccas, where all the monkeys descend from a single pair given to the local rajah during the nineteenth century.

The islands all abound in native species or subspecies of rodents, reptiles, amphibians and insects. Almost each one has its own bird-wing *(Ornithoptera),* giant iridescent butterflies, some of which are very expensive collector's items. Gigantism seems to occur quite often among the insects of the region. One of the largest coleoptera in the world, a longicorn *(Macrotoma heros)* with a six-inch-long body, can be found on Ambon. Its larvae live in rotting wood, are the size of Vienna sausages and are considered a delicacy by the natives. These tidbits are so sickeningly sweet that when our hosts offered them to us we always had difficulty in eating more than one or two out of sheer politeness. Still another of the coleoptera of the island is *Euchirus longimanus,* with a two-inch body but front legs at least twice that length. It ressembles a huge, very clumsy spider.

A collector may be lucky enough on Ambon and in New Guinea to trap a large lizard whose back and tail have a crest like the dorsal fin of the flying fish. This is the water lizard *(Hydrosaurus amboinensis),* sometimes called "water iguana" although it has nothing in common with the South American lizard of that name. The water lizard may be more than three feet long and ordinarily rests on trunks or branches of big trees overhanging water. At the slightest alert, it drops noisily from heights that may exceed forty feet and disappears under the water. It surfaces far away only when all danger seems to have passed.

Right above: The Komodo dragon is a true living fossil. About 1,500 individuals live on Komodo and the neighboring islets of Rintja and Padar. (Pierre Pittet)   Right: Gekko lineatus is a small nocturnal gekko found on the Moluccas. During the day, it takes refuges in the heart of Metroxylon *or sago palms.   Far right: The spotted cuscus* (Phalanger maculatus), *found in the Moluccas, is a phalanger, a tree-dwelling marsupial with nocturnal habits. (Both, Pierre Pfeffer)*

A gray heron (Ardea cinerea) *crosses the muddy beach of Flores at low tide. The isle of Rintja is visible in the offing. (Georges Bourdelon)*

DRAGON ISLANDS

The most astonishing reptile in tropical Asia and perhaps in the world, the Komodo dragon, lives on the west coast of Flores and three tiny neighboring islets, Komodo, Rintja and Padar. The last survivor of the giant reptiles of the Secondary Era, it is still the unchallenged giant of the lizard world for it may reach a length of more than ten feet and a weight of nearly 350 pounds.

Oddly enough, although so many insignificant creatures have been known to science for centuries, this monster was not officially discovered until 1912. Rumors of an island inhabited by ferocious dragons had been circulated by Malay fishermen for a long time, but these were not taken seriously until a pioneer Dutch aviator landed on Komodo accidentally and found himself surrounded by several gigantic saurians. Upon his return to Java he had great difficulty in getting scientists to believe his report. Finally a Dutch lieutenant went to Komodo and, to the astonishment of the world of zoology, brought back the remains of two giant lizards of an absolutely unknown species. It was named the Komodo varan or dragon *(Varanus komodoensis)*.

No sooner was it discovered than the species was nearly exterminated, for the Dutch East Indies were then the main source of reptile skins. Chinese hunters betook themselves to the islands and, just as a beginning, killed a hundred giant lizards. Luckily for the Komodo dragon, its skin proved without value for it contains countless small bony plaques that make tanning impossible. Resourceful Chinese merchants next launched dragon's tail oil as a sovereign remedy for burns, but the Sultan of Bima, overlord of the islands, intervened and stopped the massacre of these survivors of prehistory.

Very little was known about this monitor lizard until 1956 when we were able to spend nearly five months on these islands. Its anatomy had been studied between the two wars by the great German herpetologist Robert Mertens, but almost everything else about it was a mystery: its way of life, feeding habits, method of reproduction and even the number of living specimens. It is now estimated that about fifteen hundred remain, divided between the west coast of Flores and the isles of Komodo and Rintja.

The Komodo dragon is purely carnivorous and all one need do is kill a deer, boar or buffalo to have the giant reptiles rush in from all sides to attack the cadaver. The spectacle is fascinating and inevitably makes one think of a film reconstruction of prehistoric monsters devouring their prey. Arched on their strong legs armed with sharp claws, the animals tear off huge mouthfuls of the animal, gulping them down in one swallow and panting hard after each mouthful. The strength of their jaws and saw-edged teeth is unbelievable. They can tear out a piece of buffalo hide without effort or rip out the thorax of a deer or boar, cutting through ribs like a giant can-opener. We watched a large male swallow the cadaver of a large macaque, then the thigh and shoulder of a deer and several pounds of the deer's flesh. The animal's belly was soon so horribly swollen that we feared it would burst. Another dragon swallowed the four legs of a buffalo, hoofs and all, while a third took a deer's head in its mouth but could not swallow it because the antlers were too wide.

The Komodo dragon thus plays here the same part as do the hyena or jackal of other regions. It is, however, not satisfied with eating only dead flesh and, when occasion offers, will take medium- or large-sized prey, although it stops short of adult buffaloes or wild horses. The mimicry of these reptiles is so good that often we nearly stumbled over one in the tall grass; a monkey, deer or middle-sized boar would have easily been captured and slain. The monitor is remarkably strong: we saw one drag an adult deer more than 250 feet in ten minutes. Monitors probably also take advantage of the dark to approach sleeping prey for we were once awakened by one of the monsters wandering among us as we lay in our sleeping bags.

The Komodo dragon is actually more peacable than it looks.

It displays no aggressive tendencies toward man and the only fatal accident we heard of involved a Komodo islander who tried to take away a doe killed by a monitor. The lizard bit him so badly that he died two hours later. In captivity the lizards become quite tame and can be safely petted by their keepers.

The origin of the dragon and its survival in this one place on the globe remains a mystery. Perhaps it came originally from Australia where the remains of a lizard twenty-three feet long and much like the Komodo dragon have been found. It is possible that until the beginning of the Quaternary Era this lizard inhabited the entire mountain range later broken up into the Lesser Sunda Islands by the rising of the sea level. This topographical change would have separated the lizards, but why they survived in one part of the archipelago and disappeared elsewhere is unclear. They may have disappeared as a result of unfavorable conditions, or even because of competition with other species, most particularly the common Malayan monitor *(Varanus salvator)*. This monitor lizard is found all over the islands except on Komodo and Rintja. It is smaller, more active, can take a greater variety of foods, climbs and swims with ease and can therefore adapt more readily to different habitats than the heavy Komodo dragon.

THE CUSCUSES

The proximity of Australia is also evident on most of the islands in the form of marsupials of the genus *Phalanger.* These animals, called cuscuses, are the size of a cat but resemble small baby bears. They have thick, woolly fur, pointed muzzles, and great bulging eyes with vertically slit pupils indicating nocturnal habits. Their long tails are worm-like, quite pink and almost entirely hairless. The prehensile tail and sturdy legs, ending in four toes having curved claws and an opposable thumb tipped with a nail, show clearly that cuscuses are tree-dwellers.

When on the ground they are very awkward, but they are excellent climbers and move through trees with an agility out of all proportion to their heaviness. But they cannot jump even short distances and if cornered on the end of a branch simply hesitate till they are forced to tumble off. In moving from one branch to another, cuscuses hang by the end of the tightly rolled tail and swing back and forth trying to grasp another limb with their "hands."

Generally solitary forest animals, cuscuses are strict vegetarians, their basic diet consisting of leaves of the large trees of the genus *Pterocarpus,* to which they sometimes add fruit. They sleep during the day in the hollows of trees or in the hammocks formed by interlaced vines. A strong odor of musk, heaviest in adult males, frequently reveals their presence. When they move about, phalangers always follow the same route, and native hunters take advantage of this by setting wire snares along their paths. Hunters can sometimes lure them by uttering a succession of nasal groans resembling the battle cries of the males. I followed a native of Ambon who excelled in this art and once saw two large males come simultaneously from opposite directions.

The young, as in all marsupials, are born in an embryonic stage. The little one is no more than an inch long, but it already has strong limbs with well-developed claws. It crawls toward the maternal pouch, perhaps guided by the female. During the first week it grows very rapidly and at two or three months begins to come out of the pouch to nibble a few leaves, although nursing seems to continue for at least two months more. The four mammary glands of the female lead into the pouch where the nursling grasps the elongated end of one of the teats in a depression of its tongue, and remains suspended on it.

Several species of cuscuses have been distinguished. The most common is *Phalanger orientalis,* which inhabits Timor, Celebes and all the islands eastward as far as the Solomons. The females have golden-brown fur, while the males, especially in the southern Moluccas, are often entirely white. Since this is a hereditary characteristic occurring only in males, it is a strange case of albinism linked to sex. In the Moluccas and in New Guinea there is also a spotted cuscus *(Phalanger maculatus)* with piebald, black and white fur. A large-sized species *(Phalanger ursinus)* lives in Celebes; it has dark brown or black fur mixed with white, rougher in texture than that of other cuscuses. Still other brown or spotted species inhabit the same island and the northern Moluccas.

Index

ARCTIC OCEAN

TUNDRA

SIBERIAN

Yenisey R.

URAL MTS.

Irku

TIEN SHAN RANGE

TAKLA MAKAN DESERT

ALTA

ARAL
SEA

Syr Dar'ya R.

CASPIAN SEA

Amu Dar'ya R.

PAMIRS
KARAKORAMS

HINDU KUSH

PLATEA

HIMA

PLATEAU OF IRAN

Delhi

SYRIAN
DESERT

Indus R.

PERSIAN GULF

Karachi

ARABIAN DESERTS

ASIA

**THE BELTS
OF VEGETATION**

Tundra

Taiga

Steppe

Cold Desert

Montane Zone

Hot Desert

Mixed Forest

Monsoon Plain

Monsoon Forest

Equatorial Rain Forest

RED SEA

EMPTY
QUARTER

ARABIAN SEA

DECCAN
PLATEAU

WESTERN GHATS

INDIAN OCEAN

THE AUTHOR

Dr. Pierre Pfeffer, Asian specialist on the staff of the Muséum National d'Histoire Naturelle in Paris, is a naturalist, author and explorer. Five years in Russia, a year in the heart of Borneo, and expeditions in Central Asia, China, India, Indochina, Malaysia and Indonesia, along with a command of half a dozen languages, equip him with first-hand knowledge of the ecology of Asia. His academic training at the Sorbonne includes degrees in zoology, botany, geology and biology.

Dr. Pfeffer has written several authoritative books and many articles, and he is also known for his films and broadcasts. His *Bivouacs in Borneo* and *To the Dragon's Islands* are the stories of his expeditions among the Dyaks of Borneo and the giant lizards of Komodo.

ENGRAVED AND PRINTED BY CONZETT & HUBER OF ZURICH—DESIGNED BY ULRICH RUCHTI